TACKLING
HEALTH
INEQUALITIES

TACKLING HEALTH INEQUALITIES

Lessons from International Experiences

edited by

Dennis Raphael

CANADIAN SCHOLARS' PRESS INC.
TORONTO

Tackling Health Inequalities: Lessons from International Experiences
Edited by Dennis Raphael

First published in 2012 by
Canadian Scholars' Press Inc.
425 Adelaide Street West, Suite 200
Toronto, Ontario
M5V 3C1

www.cspi.org

Canadian Scholars' Press Inc. gratefully acknowledges financial support for our publishing activities from the Government of Canada through the Canada Book Fund (CBF).

Library and Archives Canada Cataloguing in Publication

Tackling health inequalities : lessons from international experiences / edited by Dennis Raphael.

Includes bibliographical references and index. Issued also in electronic formats.
ISBN 978-1-55130-412-0

1. Health services accessibility—Case studies. 2. Medical policy—Political aspects—Case studies. 3. Social medicine—Case studies. 4. Equality—Health aspects—Case studies. I. Raphael, Dennis

RA418.T33 2012   362.1   C2012-905317-1

Text design by Brad Horning
Cover design by Aldo Fierro
Cover images: Ints Vikmanis © Shutterstock

Printed and bound in Canada by Webcom

Canadä

MIX
Paper from
responsible sources
FSC® C004071

Table of Contents

Foreword

Straight Talk about Health Equity

Like many of the authors in this outstanding volume, I draw significant influence from 19th-century revolutionary socialism. Long before the 2008 credit crash, the inequalities described by Engels and others displayed obvious relevance to contemporary global health politics (Bambra et al., 2005; Labonte et al., 2009). Marx's (1875, 1978) vision of equity—"from each according to his ability, to each according to his needs"—remains the best we have. The understanding of what we now call the social determinants of health was crystal clear in William Morris's 1884 political speech "How we live and how we might live" (Morris, 1884, 1979):

> [A]t least I know this, that if a man is overworked in any degree he cannot enjoy the sort of health I am speaking of; nor can he if he is continually chained to one dull round of mechanical work, with no hope at the other end of it; nor if he lives in continual sordid anxiety for his livelihood, nor if he is ill housed, nor if he is deprived of all enjoyment of the natural beauty of the world, nor if he has no amusement to quicken the flow of his spirits from time to time: all these things, which touch more or less directly on his bodily condition, are born of the claim I make to live in good health ...

It is not uncommon for health equity commentators to acknowledge, tokenistically, the relevance of historical health revolutionaries like Friedrich Engels or Rudolf Virchow while failing to acknowledge any such activities in the present or recent past. Witness the relative silence about the contributions of Salvador Allende and of Latin American social medicine in the "economic north." The same could be said of Paulo Freire—though, as is also often the case, "sanitized" versions of his popular education methodology appear from time to time in northern settings. This dilution and absorption into mainstream culture of popular and potentially threatening ideas is of course how global capitalism defends and sustains itself—what Gramsci described as hegemony.

The most important fact about health inequalities, a fact rarely, if ever, acknowledged in health policy discourse, is their inevitability in capitalist societies within which they form a systematic and intentional product. Indeed many—including, amusingly, recent US governments of all colours—talk of "eliminating" health inequalities: a non sequitur if ever I heard one. Inequality between those who labour and those who profit remains the foundation on which capitalism is built and without which it would be unsustainable; this inequality constitutes in turn the root cause of most health inequalities.

It really is quite simple: health inequality results from social, economic, gender, racial, and other forms of inequality, and these in turn are all forms of power inequality. But the reason that no one has yet written *The Social Epidemiology of Power* is because researchers, funders, policy-makers, and politicians are more comfortable with visible and immediate causes of inequality than with addressing its root causes, which we increasingly understand to be the sole means of achieving lasting change (Phelan et al., 2004; Scott-Samuel, 2011).

Health and other forms of inequality are a systematic outcome of the political, economic, and social relations of capitalism. With a few exceptions, the psychosocial characteristics of successful capitalist entrepreneurs and politicians—toughness, competitiveness, excessive risk-taking, emotional illiteracy—are those which also characterize the globally dominant (hege-monic, patriarchal) form of masculinity (Scott-Samuel et al., 2009). There is thus a symbi-otic relationship between patriarchy and capitalism, which helps sustain them both (Oakley, 2002). The power inequalities central to both, and also to racial inequality, form the focus of feminist intersectionality scholarship (Weber, 2006), though they have yet to become the focus of mainstream health inequalities research.

There are obvious problems in developing fundamental solutions. Political expediency will always dominate—for example, in the case of the World Health Organization's impressive headline recommendation about challenging the inequitable distribution of power, money, and resources in their commission on "Social Determinants of Health" (WHO, 2008), which was unsupported by any discussion in the report about the nature and causes of power inequalities. The same was true of the report's identification of "bad politics" as a key determinant of health inequality.

It is hard for those in neoliberal capitalist societies to look beyond the lure of social demo-cratic capitalist solutions to the inequalities they experience. Social democracies may in turn be complacent about their relatively good fortune (in global terms). This demonstrates the importance of explicit acknowledgement in policy discourse of the concept of "acceptable inequalities," i.e. what kinds and levels of inequality a society is content to live with or prepared to accept, and the need to debate and define what this means in any given society.

A further difficulty arises in trying to address the "determinants of patriarchy." These clearly include virtually all the world's major religions, with their masculine-pronoun gods and male leaders, their hierarchies and their patriarchal structures and practices. While it can be credibly argued that institutionalized religion plays a key role in a substantial proportion of the world's avoidable suffering, it retains its popularity for reasons beyond the scope of this Foreword. Another institution which plays a key role in the social reproduction of patriarchy and of structural (and interpersonal) violence is militarism—an equally hard nut to crack. Inequal-ity, including health inequality, is not about to leave the global stage. But the knowledge and argumentation gathered in this impressive book are in the vanguard of the challenge.

Alex Scott-Samuel
Director, EQUAL (Equity in Health Research and Development Unit)
and Senior Clinical Lecturer in Public Health,
Department of Public Health and Policy, University of Liverpool
April 2012

References

Bambra, C., Fox, D., & Scott-Samuel, A. (2005). Towards a politics of health. *Health Promotion International, 20,* 187–193.

Labonté, R., Schrecker, T., Packer, C., & Runnels, V. (2009). *Globalization and health: Pathways, evidence, and policy.* New York: Routledge.

Marx, K. (1875, 1978). *Critique of the Gotha programme.* Moscow: Progress Publishers.

Morris, W. (1884, 1979). How we live and how we might live. In A.L. Morton (Ed.), *Political writings of William Morris.* London: Lawrence and Wishart.

Oakley, A. (2002). *Gender on planet earth.* Cambridge, UK: Polity Press.

Phelan, J.C., Link, B.G., Diez-Roux, A., Kawachi, I., & Levin B. (2004). Fundamental causes of social inequalities in mortality: A test of the theory. *Journal of Health and Social Behavior, 45,* 265–285.

Scott-Samuel A., Stanistreet D., & Crawshaw P. (2009). Hegemonic masculinity, structural violence, and health inequalities. *Critical Public Health, 19,* 287–292.

Scott-Samuel, A. (2011). Further evidence that effective interventions on health inequalities must tackle the root causes. *British Medical Journal Rapid Response.* Available at: http://tinyurl.com/7j7wx7c.

Weber, L. (2006). Reconstructing the landscape of health disparities research: Promoting dialogue and collaboration between feminist intersectional and biomedical paradigms. In A.J. Schulz, & L. Mullings (Eds.), *Gender, race, class, and health: Intersectional approaches.* San Francisco: Jossey Bass.

World Health Organization. (2008). *Closing the gap in a generation: Health equity through action on the social determinants of health.* Final report of the commission on social determinants of health. Geneva: World Health Organization.

Preface

In his 1845 volume *The Condition of the Working Class in England*, Friedrich Engels decried how working-class residents of Manchester were sicker and died earlier than their well-off neighbours. Engels saw these inequalities in health as resulting from the economic system's relentless attempt to squeeze profits out of the labour of workers. Engels did not hesitate to point out the consequences of these processes—"Society places hundreds of proletarians in such a position that they inevitably meet a too early and an unnatural death"—nor did he hesitate to direct moral culpability to those responsible for these states of affairs—"I have further to prove that society knows how injurious such conditions are to the health and the life of the workers, and yet does nothing to improve these conditions."

Engels also identified the processes—foreshadowing work by Michaela Benzeval and colleagues by 150 years—by which differing living conditions created health inequalities between Manchester's working class and Manchester's business owners and managers.

The first process was the working-class experience of material deprivation.

> They are given damp dwellings, cellar dens that are not waterproof from below or garrets that leak from above. Their houses are so built that the clammy air cannot escape. They are supplied bad, tattered, or rotten clothing, adulterated and indigestible food.

The second process was the working-class experience of psychological stress that resulted from these adverse living circumstances.

> They are exposed to the most exciting changes of mental condition, the most violent vibrations between hope and fear; they are hunted like game, and not permitted to attain peace of mind and quiet enjoyment of life.

The third process was the working class adopting unhealthy behaviours as a means of coping with deprivation and stress.

> They are deprived of all enjoyments except that of sexual indulgence and drunkenness, are worked every day to the point of complete exhaustion of their mental and physical energies, and are thus constantly spurred on to the maddest excess in the only two enjoyments at their command.

There have certainly been improvements since 1845 in the health of citizens of wealthy developed nations such as Canada. This is a result of the steady improvements in living conditions. There have also been advances in our understanding of the factors that shape health. Yet, in many ways Engels's indictment of society's willingness to accept health inequalities seems as relevant as ever. In the Canada of 2012, health inequalities continue to exist and these are not of minor magnitude. At age 25 years the poorest one-fifth of Canadian men can expect to die 7.4 years earlier than the wealthiest one-fifth of Canadian men. For Canadian women, the difference between poor and rich is 4.5 years. Health inequalities are seen among adults in incidence of cardiovascular disease and adult-onset diabetes, and for children, childhood asthma and injuries, among many other afflictions. For both adults and children these diseases and injuries are two to four times more likely among poor Canadians than wealthy ones. Health inequalities between Canada's Aboriginal and non-Aboriginal populations are of similar magnitude: Aboriginal peoples live from five to 14 years shorter lives and infant mortality rates—that is children dying before their first year—are 1.5 to four times greater than the overall Canadian rate.

But health inequalities are not limited to differences between rich and poor. Health inequalities are seen right across the socio-economic spectrum. Wealthy Canadians are healthier, live longer, and are less likely to experience chronic disease and injuries than middle-class Canadians. Middle-class Canadians are healthier, live longer, and are less likely to experience chronic disease and injuries than poor Canadians. And health inequalities are also seen between urban and rural Canadians, and between Canadian men and women.

Engels's analysis of the causes of these health inequalities is also relevant to the Canada of 2012. Health inequalities among Canadians are driven by differences in material advantage or disadvantage, the experience of psychological well-being or stress, and differences in adoption of health-threatening behaviours, all of which are closely related to the degree of advantage or disadvantage. How much variation is there in these living circumstances that create health inequalities among Canadians?

According to the Organisation for Economic Co-operation and Development, in today's Canada 15 percent of children experience the material and social deprivation associated with living in poverty. The Canadian Association of Food Banks reports that in March 2011 851,000 Canadians (of a total population of 34 million) visited a food bank, a number that vastly underestimates the number of Canadians experiencing food insecurity estimated by Health Canada at 1.92 million, of which 228,500 are children. Of these 1.92 million Canadians, 546,100 adults and 60,000 children experience "severe food insecurity." These same people—and an increasing number of not-poor middle-class Canadians—experience increasing day-to-day worry as to how they are going to make ends meet.

How do Canadian governmental authorities respond to these health inequalities and the conditions that create them? Engels, were he alive today, would not be surprised to see governmental authorities whose public policies create the living conditions that spawn health inequalities chastising vulnerable Canadians for making "unhealthy lifestyle choices." Rather than address the fundamental causes of poor health, governmental authorities—aided in many cases by health authorities and disease associations—prefer to blame at-risk Canadians for not exercising, eating "unhealthy" food, and using tobacco and alcohol. They do so even though these factors' health-threatening effects pale in comparison to the increasing economic and social insecurity being experienced by Canadians. This neglect is especially compelling with regard to the material and social deprivation experienced by the many Canadians living in poverty or near-poverty.

This volume examines whether these health inequalities and the conditions that spawn them are inevitable. Through examination of the differing experiences of seven wealthy developed nations, *Tackling Health Inequalities: Lessons from International Experiences* shows they are not inevitable. Not only have some nations identified the presence of health inequalities as cause for concern, they have exerted considerable governmental activity in tackling them. Unfortunately, Canada is not one of these nations. Why is this so and what can be learned about the experiences of other nations in tackling health inequalities?

The first chapter of *Tackling Health Inequalities: Lessons from International Experiences* provides an overview of why tackling health inequalities in wealthy developed nations such as Canada is important. It considers a variety of explanations of how health inequalities come about and suggests that the sources of health inequalities are to be found in a nation's economic and political systems and how they distribute economic, political, and social resources among the population.

Chapters 2 to 8 provide descriptions of the health inequalities scene in Canada and six other wealthy developed nations. The nations have been chosen on the basis that each has recognized— at least in their policy documents and statements—the importance of tackling health inequalities. But these nations differ profoundly in actually tackling them and achieving results.

In each chapter the authors first provide an overall national description that includes the nation's political organization and structure. They then provide an overview of how health inequalities have been conceptualized by governing authorities in national policy statements and documents. The state of research on health inequalities in each nation is described and evidence concerning the extent of health inequalities and their causes is provided. Finally, this situation is placed within the broader context of how each nation's public policies create, maintain, or tackle health inequalities.

Australia and the United Kingdom have achieved recognition for their activities, but their success in tackling health inequalities has been modest. In North America, the picture is rather bleak. The US has just begun to highlight the issue of health inequalities, but governmental authorities have done little to tackle them. Health inequalities in the US are among the highest of wealthy developed nations and, in many cases, they are increasing. Unlike the US, Canadian policy documents have long recognized the importance of tackling health inequalities. But like the US, the issue of health inequalities has not been placed on the public policy agenda and there is evidence that like the US, some health inequalities in Canada are increasing.

In Finland, Norway, and Sweden, not only do governmental authorities recognize in their policy documents and statements the importance of tackling health inequalities, but they have achieved notable success in implementing public policy that aims to do so. It appears that these differences among these nations are embedded within their general public policy approaches to provision of economic and social security to their citizens.

Canada, Australia, the UK, and the US are said to be "liberal" welfare states that are less committed to providing income and social security to their citizens. In these societies the economic marketplace is said to be the dominant institution that shapes distribution of resources among the population. The state plays a relatively minor role in regulating this distribution.

In contrast, Sweden, Norway, and Finland are "social democratic" welfare states that show greater commitments to providing income and social security. In these societies the state—in the form of elected governments—is the dominant institution that regulates the distribution of resources among the population. These general approaches to governance are directly shaped by the politics of each nation. It may be that greater willingness to tackle health inequalities is the result of a nation being governed by social democratic parties of the left. The greater the influence of social democratic parties, so the argument goes, the more likely governing authorities will tackle health inequalities. The lesser the influence, the less likely governing authorities will tackle health inequalities. In each nation's case study, evidence is provided to allow assessment of this argument.

Chapter 9 identifies the key themes that emerge across these national case studies and places them within a political economy framework that considers how power relationships and differing influences of various sectors (i.e., labour, business, and civil society) shape public policy-making related to tackling health inequalities. It aims to answer a number of important questions: How do political and economic structures and processes play out in the willingness of a nation's governing authorities to tackle health inequalities? What are the implications of these political and economic structures and processes for placing the issue of tackling health inequalities on the public policy agenda? What are the barriers and supports to tackling health inequalities in Canada and elsewhere?

Chapter 10 takes these findings and identifies how tackling health inequalities can be maintained as a public policy priority for nations already tackling them and moved onto the public policy agenda of the nations that neglect them. This involves presentation of various theories of public policy change and analysis of the role of political and social movements, and how each form of the welfare state—liberal and social democratic—either facilitates or hinders these movements' ability to influence public policy that tackles health inequalities. What do we know about how public policy is made? What are the implications of this for tackling health inequalities? What are the actions that members of a society can take to move this agenda forward?

Tackling health inequalities is ultimately a moral issue that says much about a society's values and commitments to its citizens. Failure to tackle health inequalities represents societal acceptance of unnecessary and unfair suffering and pain among its citizens. Governing authorities of nations tackling health inequalities must be encouraged to continue these efforts. Governing authorities of nations that do not tackle health inequalities must be called to account for this neglect.

Such accounting will take place when an aroused citizenry—made aware of their governing authorities' indifference to the unnecessary suffering associated with excess disease and injuries among their citizens—demands an end to this neglect. This volume therefore aims to understand how governing authorities come to either tackle or ignore existing health inequalities and the conditions that create them. It also aims to encourage governing authorities that are tackling health inequalities to continue these efforts. Most importantly, it aims to encourage efforts by citizens in Canada—and elsewhere where such efforts are lacking—to build the political and social movements that will compel governmental authorities to tackle the health inequalities that haunt our societies.

Dennis Raphael
April 2012

Chapter 1

The Importance of
Tackling Health Inequalities

Dennis Raphael

Most OECD countries have endorsed the reduction of inequalities in health status and the principle of adequate or equal access to health care based on need as major policy objectives.

—Organisation for Economic Co-operation and Development, 2009

Introduction

Tackling health inequalities has become an important public policy focus among many governing authorities around the world (World Health Organization, 2008). Health inequalities are observed differences in health outcomes among individuals, groups, communities, or jurisdictions, including nations (Kawachi, Subramanian & Almeida-Filho, 2002). These inequalities include differences in life expectancy, death rates from various diseases and injuries, and incidence of these diseases and injuries. The best means of tackling health inequalities is to raise the level of health of those experiencing adverse health outcomes so that it is closer to those with the best health outcomes (Dahlgren & Whitehead, 2006; Whitehead & Dahlgren, 2006).

The practical justification for tackling health inequalities is to diminish the suffering associated with unnecessary disease and injury experienced by individuals, members of specific groups, entire communities, and jurisdictions, including nations. The moral justification for tackling health inequalities is based on ethics-based commitments to human rights, human health, and human dignity contained in international agreements such as the United Nations Universal Declaration of Human Rights, the International Covenant on Economic, Social, and Cultural Rights, and, specifically in the case of Canada, the Canadian Charter of Rights and Freedoms (Rioux, 2010).

While some health inequalities are not very amenable to governmental action as they result from genetic dispositions, aging, freely chosen recreational choices, and sometimes just plain bad luck, most are the result of individuals, specific groups of individuals, communities, and residents of jurisdictions, including nations, living in circumstances that not only fail to support health but actually threaten it (Whitehead, 1985).[1] In many cases, these individuals, groups, and residents of jurisdictions have little or no immediate control over whether or not they experience these health-threatening circumstances. Yet, in a good number of cases these adverse living circumstances are amenable to action by governmental authorities such that the health inequalities that result from inaction are preventable (World Health Organization, 2008). The problem is that frequently these authorities, despite their expressions of commitments to providing human rights, human health, and human dignity, choose not to improve these adverse living circumstances. These preventable health inequalities are the focus of this volume.

Canada has been seen as a world leader in developing concepts such as health promotion and population health that are concerned with tackling health inequalities and the circumstances that create them (Hancock, 2011; Restrepo, 1996). The Public Health Agency of Canada states:

Box 1.1
Defining Health Inequalities and Health Inequities

In this volume the term "health inequalities" is used rather than "health inequities" as the former phrase is most commonly used. In reality, most health inequalities—especially the ones of concern in this volume—are avoidable and therefore unfair, essentially making the terms "health inequalities" and "health inequities" interchangeable. Kawachi et al. (2002) provide the following definitions of each.

Health inequality is the generic term used to designate differences, variations, and disparities in the health achievements and risk factors of individuals and groups ... a descriptive term that need not imply moral judgment.

Health inequity refers to those inequalities in health that are deemed to be unfair or stemming from some form of injustice.... On one account, most of the health inequalities across social groups (such as class and race) are unjust because they reflect an unfair distribution of the underlying social determinants of health (for example, access to educational opportunities, safe jobs, health care, and the social bases of self respect).

The conditions that need to be met for regarding health inequalities as fair are, in fact, extremely stringent. Thus, many genetic differences, exposure to different childhood conditions, differences in most health behaviours, as well as most environmental exposures are unfair.

Source: I. Kawachi, S.V. Subramanian & N. Almeida-Filho (2002), A glossary for health inequalities, *Journal of Epidemiology and Community Health*, 56(9), 647–652.

Population health is an approach to health that aims to improve the health of the entire population and to reduce health inequities [inequalities] among population groups. In order to reach these objectives, it looks at and acts upon the broad range of factors and conditions that have a strong influence on our health. (Public Health Agency of Canada, 2001)

Canada's contributions to understanding and outlining means of tackling health inequalities are celebrated and applied in many jurisdictions around the world. These contributions include identifying the sources of health inequalities, ameliorating their consequences for individuals, and developing public policy that would reduce their occurrence (O'Neill, Pederson, Dupere & Rootman, 2007). But Canada has been identified as a laggard in implementing public policy that addresses its own health inequalities (Senate Subcommittee on Population Health, 2008). In contrast, other wealthy developed nations—most of which are not as rich as Canada—have systematically taken up the task of tackling health inequalities. The purpose of this volume is to analyze these experiences and identify lessons for Canada—and other nations—on how to tackle existing health inequalities.

This chapter begins with an overview of the nature of health inequalities and how these are defined and measured. It then provides an introduction to health inequalities in Canada and the various means by which the causes of these health inequalities can be conceptualized. These conceptualizations are important as they shape our thinking of how health inequalities come about and how to tackle them. The chapter concludes with an examination of the moral imperatives involved in identifying and tackling health inequalities in Canada and elsewhere.

Defining Health Inequalities

Health inequalities are differences in health outcomes among individuals, specific groups, communities, and jurisdictions, including nations (Kawachi et al., 2002). Among individuals, health inequalities are apparent at all stages of the life course from birth until old age (Graham, 2007). Among Canadian children, health inequalities exist for infant mortality rates, low birth-weight rates, asthma, functional health, incidence of injuries, and numerous other indicators of physical, mental, and social health (Raphael, 2010b). Among Canadian adults, health inequalities exist in life expectancy and premature years of life lost prior to age 75. These adult health inequalities are a result of varying incidence and mortality from a wide range of diseases and afflictions that include cardiovascular disease, adult-onset diabetes, depression, respiratory disease, suicide, and many cancers, among others (Wilkins, 2007; Wilkins, Berthelot & Ng, 2002).

Some of these health inequalities among individuals are "natural" in the sense that they result from biological characteristics such as a genetically determined disease like Huntington's chorea, or from a choice to engage in a high-risk recreational activity such as automobile racing, aging, or just plain bad luck (Whitehead, 1985). But the overwhelming proportion of health inequalities—encompassing those between specific groups, communities, and jurisdictions (which include nations)—are not natural and result from exposures to adverse living circumstances that threaten health (Public Health Agency of Canada, 2007). Since most of these health inequalities are preventable through governmental action, the failure to address them therefore makes their presence unfair and unjust.

Inequalities also occur in health between specific groups of individuals, and these inequalities result from particular groups being more likely to experience adverse living circumstances. And since these groups cluster in particular locations, inequalities in health are seen among various communities and jurisdictions, including nations. Importantly, however, there are also specific aspects of jurisdictions themselves—that is, the characteristics and environments of communities, regions, and even nations—that either support or threaten health, thereby creating health inequalities.

Sources of Health Inequalities

The issue of tackling health inequalities requires identifying and working to address differences in living circumstances or exposures that create these health inequalities. These circumstances have come to be called the social determinants of health and include income and wealth, employment and working circumstances, housing and food security, and health and social services, among others (Mikkonen & Raphael, 2010). These social determinants of health are not themselves health outcomes, but they are rather good predictors of the incidence of all the afflictions for which health inequalities have been identified. The fact that some individuals are exposed to social determinants that enhance health while others are exposed to health-threatening ones had led to examination of how these social determinants of health are distributed among populations (Graham, 2007).

The extent of inequality among a population in income and wealth, education, employment and working circumstances, housing and food security, and access to health and social services is responsible for many health inequalities. The concern with inequality in the distribution of these social determinants of health has led to focus on the public policies that shape these distributions (Raphael, 2010a). Analysis is also necessary of the economic and political forces that underlie these public policies. Rather than simply examine the health effects of the social determinants of health, inquiry becomes focused on the social determinants of health inequalities, the public policies that spawn them, and the societal forces that shape these health-enhancing or health-threatening public policies.

If these social determinants of health and their distribution are amenable to control by governing authorities, and if decisions are being made not to improve their quality, these health

---

Box 1.2
World Health Organization Statement on the Sources of Health Inequalities

"These inequities in health, avoidable health inequalities, arise because of the circumstances in which people grow, live, work, and age, and the systems put in place to deal with illness. The conditions in which people live and die are, in turn, shaped by political, social, and economic forces."

Source: World Health Organization, *Closing the Gap in a Generation: Health Equity through Action on the Social Determinants of Health* (Geneva: World Health Organization, 2008), 1.

inequalities are therefore avoidable. The failure to address these health inequality-producing issues is therefore unfair and unjust. These health inequalities become, in essence, health inequities. Most health inequalities—especially those between groups, communities, and jurisdictions, including nations—are really health inequities as they result from governmental authorities' unfair and unjust failure to address their fundamental causes.

Identifying Health Inequalities

Two tasks must be undertaken prior to identifying and then tackling health inequalities. The first is to formulate the bases upon which health inequalities are defined (Braveman & Gruskin, 2003). The second is to formulate the causes of these health inequalities (Bartley, 2003). As noted, these health inequalities exist at the individual, group, community, and jurisdictional, including national, levels. But on what basis of comparison is a health inequality identified? Inquiry is not made into whether health inequalities exist between people with blue eyes versus brown eyes, nor do we look for health inequalities between people who play board games versus those who engage in solitary play. Inquiry is undertaken to identify health inequalities between individuals, groups, and residents of jurisdictions who differ on what are judged to be important dimensions of their identities or situations.

One especially useful concept that identifies some of the dimensions upon which individual and group health inequalities exist is that of social location(s): "An individual's social locations consists of her ascribed social identities (gender, race, sexual orientation, ethnicity, caste, kinship status, etc.) and social roles and relationships (occupation, political party membership, etc.)" (Anderson, 2011). As it turns out, health inequalities are present among people who differ in these and other social locations such as social class and disability status. This is the case since people who differ on these dimensions experience very different life circumstances. These life circumstances lead to differing exposures to the social determinants of health and raise two important questions: Why do these individuals experience such different life circumstances? How do these life circumstances become translated into health inequalities?

The same kinds of questions can be asked when health inequalities between communities are looked at. What are the important dimensions upon which communities differ that result in health inequalities? At the very minimum, communities consist of different numbers of people of varying social locations. Health outcomes of working-class communities are worse than health outcomes of middle-class communities. Middle-class communities fare worse than wealthy communities (Tremblay, Ross & Berthelot, 2002). In Canada, communities with more members of racial minorities show worse health outcomes than communities with more individuals of European descent. Rural areas have worse health outcomes than urban ones (Canadian Population Health Initiative, 2006). Communities with higher numbers of Aboriginal peoples show worse outcomes than communities where their numbers are lower (Smylie, 2009).

There are also specific structural characteristics of communities such as presence or absence of parks, employment opportunities, affordable housing, polluting industries, public transportation, or even responsive elected officials that can translate into health inequalities (Raphael et al., 2001). Health inequalities among communities therefore may represent either the differing prevalence of individuals of differing social locations, differences in the characteristics of these communities, or both.

Jurisdictional Determinants of Health Inequalities

Finally, jurisdictions (i.e., cities, regions, nations) also differ in their aggregate health outcomes (Organisation for Economic Co-operation and Development, 2011a). At this level of analysis it is usually more common—though not universal—to look to differences in public policy approaches toward the social determinants of health as the sources of these health inequalities than might be the case for health inequalities among individuals, groups, and communities. Does a jurisdiction's public policy approach toward income distribution, employment security and working circumstances, availability of housing, and quality of health and social services account for the health inequalities that exist (Navarro & Shi, 2002)? Can these differences in public policy be traced to differing ideological approaches that reflect the influence of governing political parties (Bryant, 2010)?

But public policy also plays a key role in explaining health inequalities identified at the individual, group, and community levels. Individual differences in health outcomes that result from differing social locations do so because existing public policy leads these individuals to experience differing life circumstances (Raphael, 2011c). For example, receiving less income by itself should not guarantee differing life circumstances that result in adverse health outcomes. But since public policy in most wealthy developed nations requires that health-maintaining or health-promoting resources be purchased, findings that income is first related to differing life circumstances and then related to differing health outcomes should not be surprising. Similarly, a higher level of education by itself may not determine health outcomes, but rather can serve as a pathway to higher paying and more secure employment, thereby leading to experiencing social determinants of health that support health.

Inequalities in health among communities reflect the fact that public policy is such that both the social locations of individuals within communities and the structural aspects of these same communities lead community members to experience differing life circumstances. Again, there is nothing that guarantees that some communities should be more or less health supporting than others. Community characteristics and their effects upon health are strongly related to public policy, which shapes the distribution of the social determinants of health among individuals, groups, and the communities in which they live.

It seems reasonable, therefore, to argue that it is at the jurisdictional level that the role public policy plays in producing health inequalities should be most apparent. But even then, explanations are frequently offered that jurisdictional differences in health outcomes result from individuals in these jurisdictions making different behavioural choices about what they eat, their extent of physical activity, or their decisions to smoke tobacco, drink alcohol, or take drugs rather than the public policies these jurisdictions enact that shape the distribution of the social determinants of health. The emphasis, for example, on the Mediterranean diet as the cause of better health outcomes among residents of some nations rather than the experience of specific social determinants of health driven by public policy is an example of this kind of explanation.

Therefore, it must not be forgotten that at whatever level health inequalities are explored, social locations and community characteristics are embedded within a jurisdiction's approach to governance and distribution of economic and social resources. The focus upon how jurisdictions' public policy approaches—and the economic and political imperatives that shape these approaches—both influence the occurrence and response to health inequalities that exist between individuals, groups, and communities, including nations, is a key feature of this volume.

Another key feature of this book is the assumption that failure to address these health inequality-producing issues is unfair and unjust. These health inequalities are, in essence, health inequities. Most health inequalities between individuals of differing social locations or groups, communities, and jurisdictions, including nations, are really health inequities as they result from governmental authorities' unwillingness to address their fundamental causes. They therefore speak to whether a society is committed to the provision of human rights and human dignity to their members.

The Extent of Health Inequalities in Wealthy Developed Nations

A wide range of health inequalities are seen in every wealthy developed nation. But their extent and magnitude differ among nations, as do governmental responses to their presence (Raphael & Bryant, 2010). To illustrate the kinds of health inequalities that form the focus of this volume, a few examples of health inequalities among Canadian children and adults of differing incomes are provided. This is followed by cases of health inequalities among Canadian communities. Instances of health inequalities between Canada and some other wealthy developed nations complete this overview. Further discussion of individual and community health inequalities is included in the Canadian case study. Examples of health inequalities in other wealthy developed nations are in each nation's case study.

Income-Related Health Inequalities among Children in Canada

Infant mortality and low birth-weight rates differ among Canadian children as a function of income (Raphael, 2010b). These indicators are very important as the rate of children dying before the age of one year is a very sensitive indicator of a population's health. Low birth-weight rates are important as such children come to experience a wide range of health issues over their entire lifespan.

Figure 1.1 shows the most recent data available from urban areas in Canada. The data indicate that the lower the average income of a neighbourhood, the higher the infant mortality and low birth-weight rates. The infant mortality rate is 60 percent higher in the poorest 20 percent of Canadian urban areas than in the richest 20 percent of urban areas. The low birth-weight rate is 43 percent higher in the poorest income quintile of areas than in the richest quintile of areas. The Canadian case study provides additional examples of health inequalities among children in Canada.

Income-Related Health Inequalities among Adults in Canada

Life expectancy differs widely among individuals living in urban neighbourhoods of varying average incomes. Figure 1.2 shows that how long Canadians live is strongly related to the average income of their neighbourhood (Wilkins, 2007). Men living in the poorest 20 percent of urban neighbourhoods live almost four and a half years less than those in the wealthiest 20 percent. The corresponding figure for women is almost two years.

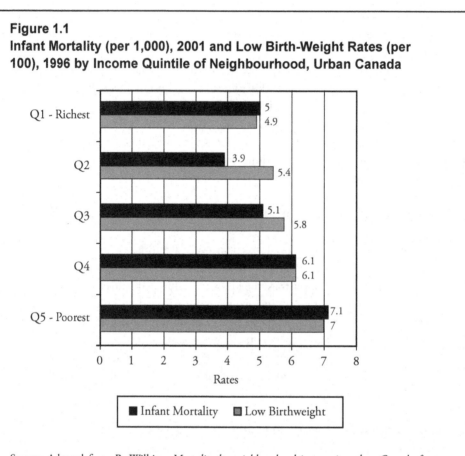

Figure 1.1
Infant Mortality (per 1,000), 2001 and Low Birth-Weight Rates (per 100), 1996 by Income Quintile of Neighbourhood, Urban Canada

Source: Adapted from R. Wilkins, *Mortality by neighbourhood income in urban Canada from 1971 to 2001* (Ottawa: Statistics Canada, Health Analysis and Measurement Group, 2007).

Community-Related Health Inequalities in Canada

Canadians who live in rural areas have more adverse health outcomes than residents of urban areas (Canadian Population Health Initiative, 2006). Canadians in very rural areas show 12 percent higher overall mortality rates than urban residents, and much of this has to do with their poorer socio-economic conditions, lower educational attainment, and, to some extent, less healthy behaviours. Rural life expectancy is 2.8 years lower for men (no difference for women) and these overall higher mortality rates reflect in large part greater prevalence and mortality from circulatory diseases, injuries, and suicide.

Jurisdictional-Related Health Inequalities: Canada versus Other Wealthy Developed Nations

Infant mortality and low birth-weight rates differ among wealthy developed member nations of the Organisation for Economic Co-operation and Development (Organisation for Economic Co-operation and Development, 2011a). Figure 1.3 shows that three of the nations detailed in

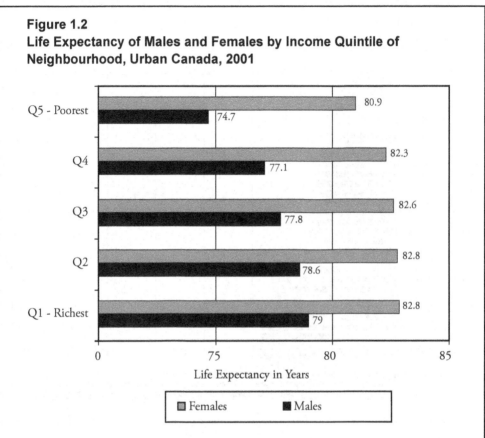

Figure 1.2
Life Expectancy of Males and Females by Income Quintile of Neighbourhood, Urban Canada, 2001

Source: R. Wilkins, *Mortality by neighbourhood income in urban Canada from 1971 to 2001* (Ottawa: Statistics Canada, Health Analysis and Measurement Group, 2007), HAMG Seminar, and special compilations.

this volume—Finland, Norway, and Sweden—show rather low infant mortality rates. In contrast, three others—Australia, the UK, and the US—show higher rates. Canada is placed with these higher-rate nations. Figure 1.4 shows similar data for low birth-weight rates (Organisation for Economic Co-operation and Development, 2011a). Finland, Norway, and Sweden show low rates, the US and the UK higher rates. The rates for Australia and Canada are mid-range.

What are the sources of these jurisdictional differences? They appear to be related to public policies that provide a more equitable distribution of the social determinants of health (Innocenti Research Centre, 2005). And these public policy approaches are themselves related to political and economic forces that shape the operation of their political and economic systems. The nations studied in this volume represent two distinct approaches to governance that reflect such jurisdictional differences: the social democratic and the liberal (Esping-Andersen, 1990; Saint-Arnaud & Bernard, 2003). Social democratic nations make significant efforts to ensure that the social determinants of health are distributed equitably among the population.

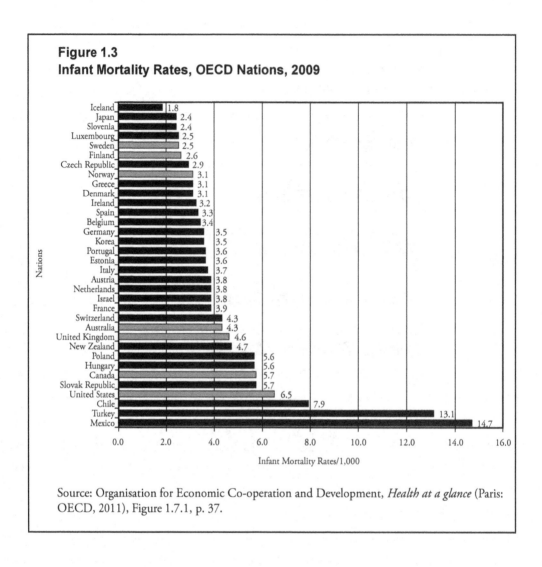

Figure 1.3
Infant Mortality Rates, OECD Nations, 2009

Source: Organisation for Economic Co-operation and Development, *Health at a glance* (Paris: OECD, 2011), Figure 1.7.1, p. 37.

The liberal nations make rather less effort to do so. Canada is firmly placed within the liberal camp of wealthy developed nations. As will be seen, this approach is associated with rather less favourable health outcomes than is the case for the social democratic nations (see Box 1.3).

Explaining Health Inequalities

How can the presence of health inequalities be explained? It is the position taken in this volume—and amply supported by accumulated evidence—that health inequalities are primarily a result of exposures to varying quality living and working circumstances, which have come to be known as the social determinants of health. Wealthy, high-income individuals, for example, enjoy the best health because their living and working circumstances are better than those experienced by other Canadians. These circumstances affect individuals' health through pathways associated with material advantage versus deprivation, a psychosocial sense of control

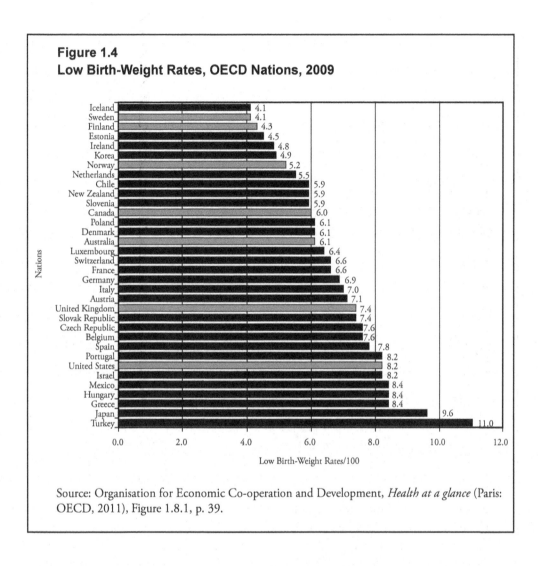

Figure 1.4
Low Birth-Weight Rates, OECD Nations, 2009

Source: Organisation for Economic Co-operation and Development, *Health at a glance* (Paris: OECD, 2011), Figure 1.8.1, p. 39.

versus lack of control, experience of low versus high stress, and adoption of adaptive versus maladaptive coping behaviours (Benzeval, Judge & Whitehead, 1995). These differences in living and working circumstances and their manifestation in health inequalities occur all the way from the top to the bottom of the socio-economic ladder in wealthy developed nations.

But while examination and identification of the links between these social determinants of health and health outcomes are important, it is also important to examine their distribution and how these distributions come about. In some jurisdictions, their distribution is much more equitable than in others. In the Scandinavian nations, for example, the distribution of income is much more equitable than is the case in wealthy developed English-language nations (Organisation for Economic Co-operation and Development, 2011b). It would be expected that the extent of their health inequalities would be less as well. Therefore, in addition to examining the social determinants of health, this volume also concerns itself with the distribution of these social determinants of health and how these unequal distributions come about.

Box 1.3
Distinctive Features of Social Democratic and Liberal Welfare States

Social Democratic

The social democratic welfare states (e.g., Finland, Sweden, and Norway) emphasize universal welfare rights and provide generous benefits and entitlements. Their political and social history is one of political dominance by social democratic parties of the left, a result of political organization of initially industrial workers and farmers, and later the middle class. Through universal provision of a range of benefits, these regimes have been able to secure the loyalties of a significant proportion of the population.

Liberal

Liberal welfare states (e.g., Australia, Canada, the UK and the US) provide modest benefits and the state usually steps in with assistance only when the market fails to meet citizens' most basic needs. Their political and social history is one of dominance by business interests that has led the population to give its loyalty to the economic system rather than the state as a means of providing economic and social security. These liberal welfare states are the least developed in terms of provision of citizen economic and social security.

Source: D. Raphael (2011), The political economy of health promotion: Part 2, national provision of the prerequisites of health, *Health Promotion International*, doi: 10.1093/heapro/dar058.

In the chapters that follow evidence will be provided of how these distributions are shaped by public policy-making in a wide range of areas that influence income and income distribution (e.g., taxation and benefits), employment and working circumstances (e.g., unionization and labour legislation), housing and food policy, and provision of health and social services. Even further, this volume concerns itself with the political and economic forces that shape public policy-making related to the social determinants of health. There is ample evidence that suggests the value of such an analysis.

Nevertheless, despite the accumulating evidence that it is exposures to differing quality of living and working circumstances or the social determinants of health that are the primary sources of health inequalities and that their distribution results from public policy-making, these insights have not led to concerted action in Canada to address existing health inequalities and their sources (Raphael, 2009). The volume also aims to identify some of the reasons why this is the case. One important reason that can be presented now is that Canadian policymakers have been provided with various "explanations" for health inequalities that may allow them to dodge primary responsibility for this state of affairs.

The Canadian public has also been provided with rather limited explanations of these phenomena such that they have come to have little understanding of both the existence and the sources of health inequalities (Raphael, 2011b). A brief overview of these various explanations will serve as an orientation for the material that follows. The variety of potential explanations also help illuminate some of the difficulties facing those who wish to tackle health inequalities.

Differing Explanations for the Presence of Health Inequalities

To my mind there are at least seven different explanations for the presence of health inequalities in common usage. These explanations offer accounts for the existence of health inequalities among individuals, specific groups, and communities in Canada as well as jurisdictions, including nations. More importantly, they suggest specific means of tackling these health inequalities. But the key issue is to what extent some of these explanations may be more useful than others. What exactly does this mean?

It is important to be clear in what ways some explanations are more useful than others in understanding the sources of health inequalities and the means of tackling them. One way of judging these is the extent to which each explanation helps explain how Canada and other nations have: (a) come to achieve their current level of health inequalities, and (b) provide means of tackling these health inequalities. Table 1.1 summarizes these different approaches. In the sections that follow, examples are provided of how each approach plays out in research, public education, and public policy activity related to explaining and then tackling health inequalities.

Approach 1: Genetic Differences and Biological Dispositions Create Health Inequalities

Here it is believed that the cause of health inequalities can best be understood as reflecting the influence of genes and biological processes. Health inequalities result from individuals, specific groups, and residents of jurisdictions, including nations, possessing differing genes and biological dispositions toward the development of disease (Mackenbach, 2005). The primary expression of this belief is biomedical research that maps the human genome and the body's biochemical processes. Since inequalities in health are seen as resulting from differences in genetics and biological dispositions to disease among individuals, specific groups, communities, and even nations' inhabitants, such research will come to explain and provide means of tackling these health inequalities.

The genetic and biological explanation for health inequalities is frequently the default explanation advanced by the biomedical community and is usually enthusiastically taken up by the mainstream media. Examples of this approach are seen in attempts to explain the greater incidence of type 2 diabetes among Aboriginal peoples around the world (McDermott, 1998), cardiovascular disease among black people in the US (Krieger, 2003), and kidney disease among non-European peoples (Shoham et al., 2008), among many others. In this view, health inequalities result from racial differences in biological makeup (Lee, Mountain & Koenig, 2001).

There is little evidence to support this explanation. There is greater heterogeneity within particular racial groups in genetic makeup than there is between racial groups (Braun, 2002). More specifically, there are very few diseases that are caused by the operation of a single or even multiple genes—Huntington's chorea comes to mind—and even when such disease-causing genes are

Table 1.1
Differing Explanations for the Presence of Health Inequalities

Health Inequalities Interpretation	Key Concept for Addressing Health Inequalities	Primary Approach for Addressing Health Inequalities	Practical Implications of the Approach
1. Health inequalities result from genetic differences and biological dispositions.	Health inequalities can be reduced by identifying the genes and processes causing disease.	Carry out more and better biomedical research.	Medicalization of health inequalities and endorsement of the societal status quo.
2. Health inequalities result from differences in access and quality of health and social services.	Health inequalities can be reduced by strengthening health care and social services.	Create more and better health care services in hospitals, clinics, and social service agencies.	Focus limited to promoting the health of those already experiencing health inequalities.
3. Health inequalities result from differences in important modifiable medical and behavioural risk factors.	Health inequalities can be reduced by encouraging people to make "healthy choices" and adopt "healthy lifestyles."	Develop and evaluate healthy living and behaviour modification programs and protocols.	Healthy lifestyle programming that ignores the material basis of health inequalities can widen existing health inequalities.
4. Health inequalities result from differences in material living conditions.	Health inequalities can be reduced by improving material living conditions.	Conduct research and disseminate results of how differences in living conditions create health inequalities.	Assumption that governmental authorities are receptive to and will act upon research findings.
5. Health inequalities result from differences in material living conditions shaped by public policy.	Health inequalities can be reduced by advocating for healthy public policy that reduces disadvantage.	Analyze how public policy decisions impact health (i.e., health impact analysis).	Assumption that governments will create public policy on the basis of its effects upon health.
6. Health inequalities result from differences in material living conditions that are shaped by economic and political structures and their justifying ideologies.	Health inequalities can be reduced by influencing the societal structures that create and justify health inequalities.	Analysis of how the political economy of a nation creates inequalities identifies avenues for social and political action.	Requirement that reducing health inequalities requires building social and political movements that will shape public policy.
7. Health inequalities result from the power and influence of those who create and benefit from health inequalities.	Health inequalities can be reduced by increasing the power and influence of those who experience these inequalities.	Critical analysis empowers the majority to gain understanding of and increase their influence and power.	Requirement that these social and political movements recognize and shift imbalances of power within society.

found, they usually provide only a small clue as to whether an individual will get a disease (Davey Smith et al., 2005). These discoveries certainly will not influence the incidence of the great proportion of health inequalities, especially the main killers of cancers, heart disease, and respiratory disease. They provide little insights into the profound health inequalities among specific groups, communities, and residents of differing jurisdictions, including nations.

The tendency to focus on genetics and biological explanations for the existence of health inequalities is widespread and persistent even in light of numerous critiques that not only identify the flaws in such arguments but the real dangers of this tendency. These explanations provide implicit justification of the inequitable and health-threatening living circumstances that many experience. Moreover, by attributing adverse health outcomes among specific groups, communities, and residents of jurisdictions to genetic and other biomedical dispositions, this approach ignores the adverse living circumstances many people experience and the public policies that create these adverse circumstances (Braun, 2002; Nazroo, 1998).

This approach also facilitates the medicalization of all aspects of health and illness. Its narrow focus on individuals and their bodies excludes consideration of living circumstances and the public policy decisions that shape these circumstances. It provides status and influence to the medical profession and biomedical researchers and makes action based on our increasing understandings of the sources of health inequalities more difficult. Ultimately, it endorses the political and economic status quo (Seedhouse, 2003).

Approach 2: Health Inequalities Result from Inequalities in Access to and Quality of Health Care Services

In this approach, health inequalities among individuals, communities, and jurisdictions, including nations, result from the organization and delivery of health care and social services. Individuals of different social locations who reside in different communities and jurisdictions may have less access to necessary services or these services may be of less than optimal quality (Schoen & Doty, 2004). This is a particularly relevant issue in the US, where many millions of Americans are without health insurance. It is less of an issue in most other wealthy developed nations where health care services are more or less provided on a universal basis. There are, however, inequalities in access to health care in Canada and other nations. In Canada, much of these inequalities result from the health care system not covering costs associated with drugs, rehabilitation services, and home care services, which put lower-income individuals at risk (Raphael, 2011a). There are also profound geographic inequalities in access to health care services (McGibbon, 2009).

For example in Canada, analyses that controlled for a wide range of factors, such as age, education, minority status, and residential location, revealed that below-average–income Canadians—as compared to above-average–income Canadians—were 50 percent less likely to see a specialist when needed, 50 percent more likely to find it difficult to get care on weekends or evenings, and 40 percent more likely to wait five days or more for an appointment with a physician (Schoen & Doty, 2004). More importantly, lower-income Canadians were three times more likely to not fill a prescription due to cost, three times more likely to have a medical problem but be unable to see a doctor due to cost, and 60 percent more likely to not get a needed test or treatment.

But this is not just an issue among lower-income Canadians. Average-income Canadians—as compared to above-average–income Canadians—were almost twice as likely to not get a prescription filled, and were twice as likely to have problems paying medical bills. Similar issues are seen across a range of wealthy developed nations.

An appropriate policy approach would be to reduce barriers to care and improve the quality of these services (McGibbon, 2009). These activities are important, but access to health care and quality of services are not the primary causes of health inequalities in Canada and most developed nations. If research and policy activity are limited to these issues, there may be neglect of the social determinants of health and how their inequitable distribution results in health inequalities. It can reinforce already dominant public policy approaches toward health care, obscuring the role that living circumstances play in creating health inequalities.

Approach 3: Health Inequalities Result from Differences in Modifiable Medical and Behavioural Risk Factors

Here, differences in "modifiable" individual risk factors are frequently seen as the source of health inequalities. These individual risk factors include what Sarah Nettleton calls the "holy trinity of risk": tobacco use, lack of physical activity, and diet (Nettleton, 1997). The emphasis on healthy choices in Canadian health approaches illustrates this approach, which argues that if Canadians only made healthier behavioural choices, the incidence of various deadly diseases would be significantly reduced. As one telling example, for decades Canadians have been led to believe through messaging, such as the "Healthy Swede," that the reason Swedes live longer and healthier lives than Canadians was because of Swedes' commitment to physical activity (ParticipAction, 2011).

Canadians have been made well aware of the "holy trinity of risk" (Nettleton, 1997). In fact, a national survey found that Canadians have overwhelmingly learned and internalized these messages (Canadian Population Health Initiative, 2004). Disturbingly, this same study found that Canadians have virtually no knowledge of how their health is profoundly shaped by their living circumstances or social determinants of health.

While there is little doubt that behaviours such as tobacco use, lack of physical activity, and inadequate diets contribute to adverse health outcomes among individuals of differing social locations, communities, and jurisdictions, their contribution is relatively minor compared to the broader issues subsumed within the term "social determinants of health" (Raphael et al., 2003; Raphael & Farrell, 2002). In addition, these behavioural risk factors are embedded within people's living circumstances such that exposures to adverse social determinants of health are clearly implicated as an important source of these risk behaviours (Jarvis & Wardle, 2003). The Canadian public's profound lack of awareness of the social determinants of health limits public pressure on authorities to shift their ways of thinking about health and illness.

Unlike Approach 2, which stresses provision and improvement of important health services, this approach has many negative aspects. First, medical and behavioural risk factors account for relatively little of the health inequalities that exist in Canada and elsewhere. Second, it assumes that individuals are capable of "making healthy lifestyle choices" such that those who fail to do so are responsible for their own adverse health outcomes (Labonte & Penfold, 1981). Third, programs show rather little evidence of effectiveness among the most vulnerable and may increase health inequalities as "healthy living" messaging is more likely to be taken up by the already advantaged (Jarvis & Wardle, 2003).

Approach 4: Health Inequalities and Differences in Material Living Circumstances

In this approach living circumstances are seen to operate through material, psychological, and behavioural pathways to "get under the skin" to shape health (Brunner & Marmot, 2006). In this framework, differences in objective living circumstances explain the presence of health inequalities. Benzeval and colleagues argue that there are three key mechanisms that link living circumstances to health inequalities: (1) differing experience of material living circumstances; (2) differing experience of psychosocial stress that result from experiencing these different living circumstances; and (3) differing take-up of health-supporting or health-threatening behaviours associated with these varying living circumstances (Benzeval et al., 1995). All of these mechanisms reflect experience with concrete living circumstances.

The key aspect of this view is that individuals, specific groups, communities, and residents of jurisdictions, including nations, experience differing exposures to positive and negative living circumstances throughout their lives. These different exposures accumulate to produce adult health outcomes (Shaw, Dorling, Gordon & Davey Smith, 1999). The experience of material advantage or disadvantage also determines the extent of stress experienced (part 2 of the Benzeval thesis) and the take-up of either health-supporting or health-threatening behaviours (part 3 of the Benzeval thesis).

Social locations in a society, such as class, gender, and race, are powerful predictors of health in Canada as these are important indicators of material advantage or disadvantage over the lifespan (Raphael, 2011d). These material circumstances of life include childhood advantage or deprivation related to quality of nourishment and housing, and adult issues of employment or unemployment, occupational quality and hazards, and access to resources such as health and social services, among others (Shaw, Dorling, Gordon & Davey Smith, 1999). At the individual level, material circumstances of life determine health by influencing the quality of individual development, family life and interaction, and community environments (Brooks-Gunn, Duncan & Britto, 1998).

And the quality of material life circumstances—in a finely stepped pattern from poverty through to tremendous wealth—are associated with the likelihood of physical problems (infections, malnutrition, chronic disease, and injuries), developmental problems (delayed or impaired cognitive, personality, and social development), educational problems (learning disabilities, poor learning, early school leaving), and social problems (socialization, preparation for work, and family life) (Raphael, 2010c).

These differences in living circumstances then go on to contribute to group differences as those of particular social locations experience advantage or disadvantage in the aggregate. These differences are multiplied at the community level as these aggregate differences in living circumstances may be influenced by additional factors associated with the characteristics of particular neighbourhoods. That is, particular communities with greater proportions of disadvantaged individuals may also suffer from weak physical and social infrastructure (e.g., lack of employment opportunities, inadequate public transit, air and water pollution, or crime and unsafe areas). These advantages or disadvantages can be compounded at the jurisdictional level where these aggregations of health threats become associated with health inequalities among jurisdictions, even including national differences in the extent of health inequalities.

This approach is at the heart of social determinants of health-related research activity. Connections are made between adverse living circumstances and analysis is made of the processes by which these living circumstances and health outcomes are linked. Health inequalities are a result of social inequalities. However, unless this analysis is taken further to identify how these social inequalities come about, activity may result in sterile statements about the findings of research with little public policy action resulting from these analyses.

Approach 5: Health Inequalities Result from Differences in Material Living Circumstances Shaped by Public Policy

This approach recognizes the important role that material living circumstances play in producing health inequalities, but then goes on to consider how these circumstances are shaped by public policy decisions made by governing authorities. The importance of public policy in creating health inequalities is becoming increasingly apparent, but remains relatively unaddressed among Canadian health researchers. In many ways this approach states the obvious: *The distribution of economic and social resources that influence health and is responsible for creating health inequalities results from public policy decisions made by governing authorities.* This is most obvious when examining the key drivers of health inequalities: the differences among individuals, groups, communities, and residents of jurisdictions, including nations, in access to the social determinants of health.

The World Health Organization states this conclusion rather more strongly: "This unequal distribution of health-damaging experiences is not in any sense a 'natural' phenomenon but is the result of a toxic combination of poor social policies and programmes, unfair economic arrangements, and bad politics" (World Health Organization, 2008). According to this approach, the presence of health inequalities is shaped by access to material resources such as income, housing, food, and educational and employment opportunities, among others. These resources are related to parents' employment security, wages, and the quality of their working circumstances and availability of quality, regulated child care, all of which are shaped by public policy decisions (Raphael, 2010b).

There is a rather striking unwillingness among many health researchers and workers to explicitly outline the public policy antecedents of health inequalities (Raphael, Curry-Stevens & Bryant, 2008). Kirkpatrick and McIntyre (2009) comment on this tendency with regard to the Chief Public Health Officer of Canada's (CPHO) report on health inequalities in Canada (Butler-Jones, 2009):

> The CPHO report's failure to emphasize the essential role of government action is reinforced by the examples used to illustrate "successful interventions that … may serve to reduce Canada's health inequalities and improve quality of life for all Canadians" (p. 1). In fact, the interventions highlighted tend to be community-based programs that are unable to address the structural determinants of health inequalities. (Kirkpatrick & McIntyre, 2009, 94)

It may be that health researchers and workers trained within the assumptions of so-called "objective" science are sensitive to the accusation that such analyses are "political." It is more likely that there is a perception that such analyses—likely as they are to be critical of current governmental public policy approaches—may threaten research and program funding, weaken regard by professional colleagues, and ultimately threaten career prospects. The profound lack of training in public policy analysis among most health-related researchers and workers also cannot be disregarded.

Hardly a day goes by without a public policy issue arising at either the municipal/regional, provincial, or federal level in Canada that has health inequalities implications: minimum wages, social assistance rates, recreation fees, labour laws, public transportation, education, child care, and just about every other social determinant of health. Considering what is known about these issues, how then can we explain the last three decades of government policy-making in Canada, which has worsened the unequal distribution of resources, resulting in health inequalities, as well as the lack of any significant analysis of the impact of these public policies by health promoters, their agencies, and institutions upon health?

Approach 6: Health Inequalities Result from Economic and Political Structures and Their Justifying Ideologies

One of the reasons for putting together this volume is the belief that how jurisdictions approach the issue of tackling health inequalities is shaped by their economic and political organization. Governing authorities make decisions on the basis of existing economic and political structures of influence and power (Brooks & Miljan, 2003). Policy-making can be made in the interests of those with the most influence and power or in the interests of all. These decisions are then justified on the basis of particular ideologies and positions, such as what is good for particular interest groups is good for society. This analysis goes far in explaining why Canada—which is seen as a leader in creating health promotion and population concepts that have been applied in the service of tackling health inequalities elsewhere—has always been somewhat of a laggard in addressing health inequalities. Public policy is not being made in the interests of the majority of Canadians but rather for those with more influence and power. In Canada, this is the business and corporate sectors whose interests are aligned with the wealthy in society.

These economic and political approaches to creating public policy that either create or reduce health inequalities will differ from one jurisdiction to another. As will be seen in the following chapters, Sweden, Norway, and Finland have placed the reduction of health inequalities high on their public policy agenda with accompanying public policy activity; nations such as Australia, Canada, the UK, and the US rather less so (Raphael & Bryant, 2010). Research and governmental activity are embedded within these differing economic and political structures.

In this analysis Canada, Australia, the UK, and the US have a set of historical traditions and economic and political structures that represent a form of the welfare state identified as "liberal." Finland, Norway, and Sweden's traditions and structures lead to a form of the welfare state identified as "social democratic." Two Canadian sociologists provide a graphic that suggests how differences in political and economic structures and processes (political economy) are related to the issue of identifying and tackling health inequalities (Saint-Arnaud & Bernard, 2003).

Identifying and tackling health inequalities requires a societal commitment to providing citizens with an equitable distribution of economic and social resources. In wealthy developed

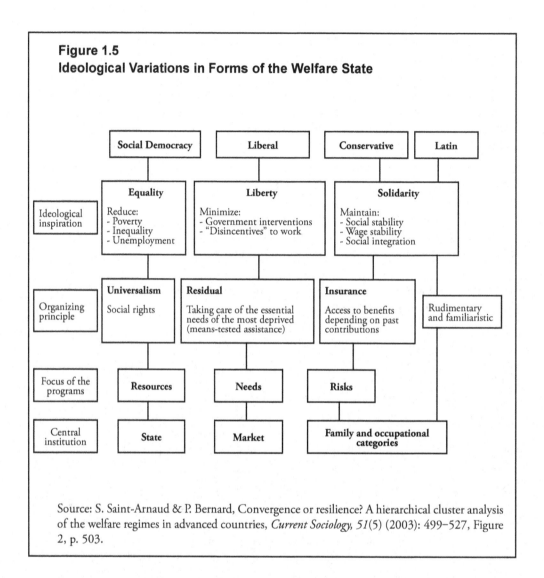

Figure 1.5
Ideological Variations in Forms of the Welfare State

Source: S. Saint-Arnaud & P. Bernard, Convergence or resilience? A hierarchical cluster analysis of the welfare regimes in advanced countries, *Current Sociology, 51*(5) (2003): 499–527, Figure 2, p. 503.

nations, this requires governmental intervention in the operation of the market economy. There is no wealthy developed society in which the economic system by itself provides an equitable distribution of economic and social resources. What is required to achieve an equitable distribution of resources is managing the economic system through regulations on labour practices, governmental provision of resources in a range of domains, and assuring that the interests of differing sectors of society are balanced.

The liberal and social democratic welfare states offer differing visions of society. As shown in Figure 1.5, the dominant inspiration of the liberal welfare state is to minimize governmental intervention in the operation of its central institution—the market. It should not be surprising that Canada and its liberal partners have been identified as failing to address issues of health inequalities through public policy that creates more equitable distribution of economic and social resources. It should also not be surprising that Canadian public policy-makers are averse to tackling health inequalities.

In contrast, the social democratic welfare state has as its main ideological inspiration the reduction of inequality. It also has the state as its main institution, which creates public policy on the basis of universalism and social rights. Available evidence suggests that such an approach is especially effective in reducing social inequalities and promoting health, with no adverse effects upon the operation of their market economies (Conference Board of Canada, 2009; Innocenti Research Centre, 2007; Raphael, 2010d). The distinction between these two forms of the welfare state should guide readings of the material in this volume.[2]

Approach 7: Health Inequalities Result from Activities of Those Who Create and Benefit from Health Inequalities

This final explanation for the existence of health inequalities identifies the individuals and groups in Canada and other nations who, through their undue influence upon governments, create and benefit from health inequalities and the situations that create them. These individuals and groups have lobbied for and successfully shifted the tax structures to favour the corporate sector and the wealthy. They have also called for reductions in public expenditures that reduce inequalities, controlling the wages and employment benefits of working people, and relaxing labour standards and protections (Chernomas & Hudson, 2009; Langille, 2009; McBride & Shields, 1997; McQuaig, 1987, 1993; Scarth, 2004).

In Canada, these public policy changes have led to striking increases in income and wealth among the already wealthy, but have also led to increasing income and wealth inequalities, stagnating incomes for most Canadians, and increased incidence of housing and food insecurity (Jackson, 2000; Kerstetter, 2002; Lee, 2007). As a result, Canada has come to have one of the most undeveloped welfare states—with attendant health inequalities—among wealthy developed nations (Raphael, 2007).

Who exactly are these influences and how can they be resisted? In Canada, Langille (2009) identifies business associations, such as the Canadian Bankers Association and the Canadian Chamber of Commerce; think tanks, such as the C.D. Howe Institute and the Fraser Institute; citizen institutions, such as the Canadian Taxpayers Federation and the National Citizens Coalition; and lobbyists, such as Earnscliffe and Hill and Knowlton, as important advocates for public policies that have been shown to create the conditions that result in health inequalities.

In the UK, Scambler developed a Greedy Bastards Hypothesis (GBH) in which he identifies members of a "core capitalist-executive/power elite" whose ever-adaptive behaviours are responsible for the UK's "persisting—even widening—health inequalities" (Scambler, 2002, 103). In this analysis, growing health inequalities are the largely unintended outcomes, according to Scambler, of this elites' influence upon public policy-making in the pursuit of corporate profits. Navarro is less forgiving. He states: "It is not inequalities that kill, but those who benefit from the inequalities that kill" (Navarro, 2009, 15).

In this final approach there is explicit recognition of the individuals, groups, and classes whose influence result in health inequalities-creating public policy. These individuals and groups who—through their undue influence upon governments—create and benefit from health inequalities are identified. These individuals and groups lobby for shifting the tax structures to favour the corporate sector and the wealthy, reducing public expenditures, controlling wages and employment benefits, and relaxing labour standards and protections. These are all factors that create health inequalities.

The Moral Imperative of Tackling Health Inequalities

Why tackle health inequalities? Usually researchers and advocates answer this question on empirical grounds by showing how the majority of health inequalities are avoidable and taking such action would reduce human misery. These arguments include economic arguments concerning the extra costs to society of the presence of health inequalities and the adverse living conditions that create them.

But perhaps a more compelling argument is that Canada is obliged to tackle health inequalities as health is a basic human right enshrined in numerous international covenants to which Canada is committed (Office of the United Nations High Commissioner for Human Rights & World Health Organization, 2008). Even more relevant to the Canadian scene is that the Canadian Charter of Rights and Freedoms—the law of the land—guarantees Canadians "security of the person." The following sections focus on the argument that health is a human right.

Health as a Human Right

A human rights approach places the issue of health, health inequalities, and the sources of health inequalities within a larger framework of human rights principles (Rioux, 2010). The United Nations Population Fund (UNFPA), whose mission is to "promote the right of every woman, man and child to enjoy a life of health and equal opportunity," outlines these human rights principles that inform their work (United Nations Population Fund, 2011):

Universality and inalienability: Human rights are *universal* and *inalienable*. *All people everywhere* in the world are entitled to them.

Indivisibility: Human rights are *indivisible*. Whether they relate to civil, cultural, economic, political or social issues, human rights are inherent to the dignity of every human person. Consequently, all human rights have equal status, and cannot be positioned in a hierarchical order.

Interdependence and interrelatedness: Human rights are *interdependent* and *interrelated*. Each one contributes to the realization of a person's human dignity through the satisfaction of his or her developmental, physical, psychological, and spiritual needs.

Equality and non-discrimination: All individuals are equal as human beings and by virtue of the inherent dignity of each human person. No one, therefore, should suffer discrimination on the basis of race, colour, ethnicity, gender, age, language, sexual orientation, religion, political, or other opinion ... or other status as established by human rights standards.

Participation and inclusion: All people have the right to participate in and access information relating to the decision-making processes that affect their lives and well-being.

Accountability and rule of law: States and other duty-bearers are answerable for the observance of human rights. In this regard, they have to comply with the legal norms and standards enshrined in international human rights instruments.

These principles serve as the basis for numerous international agreements to which Canada is a signatory. In relation to health and the presence of health inequalities, the principles manifest in two broad sets of commitments: commitments to provide health care and commitments to provide the conditions necessary for health. Canada's Health Care Act addresses Canada's commitment to health care. Canada's failure to provide the conditions necessary for health, which results in health inequalities, is, however, particularly problematic. This failure is morally reprehensible as public policy decisions create unnecessary misery and suffering among Canadians.

Canada's Commitments to Health as a Human Right

Canada is signatory to numerous international covenants that guarantee the right to health. These agreements contain universal commitments to all citizens, and others have commitments that are relevant to particular groups of citizens. The World Health Organization (2002) classifies these commitments as constituting three spheres. The first sphere is Human Rights Violations Resulting in Ill Health, which focuses on issues of harmful traditional practices, torture, slavery, and violence against women and children. The second sphere, Reducing Vulnerability to Ill Health through Human Rights—which most directly addresses the issue of health inequalities in wealthy developed nations such as Canada—focuses on the right to health, the right to education, the right to food and nutrition, and freedom from discrimination. The third, also very relevant, Promotion or Violation of Human Rights through Health Development, is concerned with the right to participation, freedom from discrimination, the right to information, and the right to privacy. Box 1.4 provides some of the international covenants to which Canada is signatory that are relevant to tackling health inequalities (see Rioux, 2010, for additional ones).

As a signatory to these conventions, Canada is required to periodically report to United Nations committees on their adherence to these agreements. These international authorities have consistently responded to Canada's reports with criticism and rebukes (Poverty and Human Rights Centre, 2007). The issues regularly identified include:

- Canada's failure to address poverty
- Canada's failure to improve standards of living and human rights of Aboriginal peoples
- continuing levels of women's inequality
- failures in human rights enforcement
- failure to take responsibility for human rights treaty obligations
- failure to monitor compliance and enforcement

The report concludes that: "Canada is developing a reputation for making legislative, policy, and budgetary choices at home that are diminishing the human rights of its residents" (Poverty and Human Rights Centre, 2007, 8). Why this is the case will become clearer as Canada's approach to tackling health inequalities is examined in relation to activities of the other wealthy developed nations profiled in this volume.

Box 1.4
Particularly Relevant Excerpts from International Conventions on the
Right to Health to which Canada Is a Signatory

Universal Declaration of Human Rights (1948)
Article 25 (1): "Everyone has a right to a standard of living adequate for the health of himself and his family, including food, clothing, housing and medical care and necessary social services and the right to security in the event of unemployment, sickness, disability, widowhood, old age or other lack of livelihood in circumstances beyond his control."

International Covenant on Economic, Social, and Cultural Rights (1966)
Article 12 (1): States parties recognize "the rights of everyone to the enjoyment of the highest attainable standard of physical and mental health."
Article 12 (2): Illustrates the breadth of areas that needed to be addressed and other human rights that have to be addressed "to achieve the full realization of this right."

The Convention on the Elimination of All Forms of Discrimination
against Women (1979)
Article 11 (1): "States Parties shall take all appropriate measures to eliminate discrimination against women in the field of employment in order to ensure, on a basis of equality of men and women, the same rights, in particular:
(b) The right to the same employment opportunities, including the application of the same criteria for selection in matters of employment;
(d) The right to equal remuneration, including benefits, and to equal treatment in respect of work of equal value, as well as equality of treatment in the evaluation of the quality of work;
(e) The right to social security, particularly in cases of retirement, unemployment, sickness, invalidity and old age and other incapacity to work, as well as the right to paid leave."

Convention on the Rights of the Child (1989)
Article 24 (1): "States Parties recognize the right of the child to the enjoyment of the highest attainable standard of health and to facilities for the treatment of illness and rehabilitation of health. States Parties shall strive to ensure that no child is deprived of his or her right of access to such health care services."

Convention on the Rights of Persons with Disabilities (2006)
Article 25: "States Parties recognize that persons with disabilities have the right to the enjoyment of the highest attainable standard of health without discrimination on the basis of disability. States Parties shall take all appropriate measures to ensure access for persons with disabilities to health services that are gender-sensitive, including health-related rehabilitation."

Declaration on the Rights of Indigenous People (2007)

Article 21(1): "Indigenous peoples have the right, without discrimination, to the improvement of their economic and social conditions, including, inter alia, in the areas of education, employment, vocational training and retraining, housing, sanitation, health, and social security."

Article 21(2): "States shall take effective measures and, where appropriate, special measures to ensure continuing improvement of their economic and social conditions. Particular attention shall be paid to the rights and special needs of indigenous elders, women, youth, children, and persons with disabilities."

Source: Adapted from Office of the United Nations High Commissioner for Human Rights & World Health Organization (2008), *The Right to Health*, Fact Sheet no. 31, retrieved from: www.ohchr.org/Documents/Publications/Factsheet31.pdf.

Distinguishing between Relative and Absolute Health Inequalities

An important methodological distinction has to be made between what are termed relative health inequalities and absolute health inequalities. *Relative* health inequalities are the extent of inequalities identified on the basis of differences among groups within a jurisdiction in relation to the scores of the best performing group. They are usually expressed in terms of a percentage or a risk ratio. If the healthiest group in a jurisdiction has a 5/100 rate of a disease and the worse performing group has a 10/100 rate of the disease, then the worse group is said to have a 100 percent worse rate with a risk ratio of 2.0. For this same group, the *absolute* health inequality is the difference between their concrete rate (10/100) and the rate of the healthiest group (5/100), which is, in this case, 5/100. Box 1.5 shows why both measures need to be examined when considering the extent of health inequalities within a nation.

Conclusion

This volume takes a critical political economy approach by which the extent of health inequalities—and the actions taken to address these health inequalities—is shaped by public policies embedded within the economic, political, and social structures of the society. One such framework that is useful—mindful of the unique historical and contemporary aspects of each nation—is that of differing forms of their welfare state.

The social democratic welfare states are distinguished by their strong commitments to state provision of citizen economic and social security, while the liberal welfare states generally rely upon the economic marketplace to distribute economic and social resources. The UK, the US, Canada, and Australia are all considered to be liberal welfare states, while Finland, Sweden, and Norway are considered social democratic welfare states. Members of each group share similarities in terms of their provision of citizen resources and how they approach the issue of health

Box 1.5
Relative versus Absolute Differences in Health Inequalities between Income Quintiles among Nations Low, Medium, and High in Infant Mortality Rate

Nation	Q1	Q2	Q3	Q4	Q5	Mean	RR[1] Q5/Q1	AD[2] Q5–Q1
Low	2.0	2.5	3.0	3.5	4.0	3.0/1,000	2.0	2.0
Medium	3.75	4.40	5.0	5.6	6.25	5.0/1,000	1.67	2.5
High	5.0	6.0	7.0	8.0	9.0	7.0/1,000	1.8	4.0

1 RR is the ratio between the richest and poorest quintiles' infant mortality rates.
2 AD is the absolute difference in infant mortality rates between the richest and poorest quintiles.

The table above illustrates the need to consider both relative and absolute differences in health outcomes when examining the extent of health inequalities in a nation. In the example of the low infant mortality nation, the mean rate is 3.0/1,000. The relative difference between the wealthiest 20 percent (Q1) of families and the poorest 20 percent (Q5) of families is 2.0: the poorest have twice the rate as the wealthiest. The absolute difference between these quintiles is 2.0/1,000.

Among the nation with the highest infant mortality rate of 7.0/1,000, the relative difference between Q1 and Q5 appears to be lower, with the poorest quintile (Q5) having 1.8 times the infant mortality rate of the richest (Q1). However, among this high infant mortality nation the absolute difference in rates between Q1 and Q5 is 4.0/1,000, twice the absolute difference between Q1 and Q5 of the low infant mortality nation. Finally, the medium infant mortality nation shows the lowest relative difference between Q1 and Q5 and a mid-range absolute difference between Q1 and Q5. If one compares the worse-off group, Q5, in the low infant mortality nation to the other nations, it can be seen that this group does rather well in such comparisons.

inequalities. But each nation has specific political and economic histories and contemporary institutions that should lead to differences in these approaches.

In the chapters to follow, analyses of these similarities and differences will highlight the supports and barriers to tackling health inequalities. The goal is to identify the most effective means of tackling the health inequalities that cause so much unnecessary suffering in Canada and elsewhere. In order to do so, we must come to understand the economic, political, and social structures that shape the distribution of resources among the members of a society and the powerful forces that maintain these societal structures. By gaining such understandings, we can identify means of strengthening societal structures that reduce health inequalities and weakening those that create health inequalities.

Notes

1. These exposures include both favourable experiences that support health and adverse experiences that threaten it. For ease of presentation, the focus is on adverse experiences that threaten health, but health-enhancing experiences are also important in understanding the sources of health inequalities and the means of tackling them.
2. The Conservative and Latin welfare states offer third and fourth approaches that fall somewhere in the middle of these two. See Saint-Arnaud & Bernard (2003) for an examination of these welfare states.

Critical Thinking Questions

1. If you had thought about differences in health among people you know, what factors do you think would be behind these differences?
2. Which of the different explanations provided for the existence of health inequalities is most consistent with what you have been taught in your classes or read in the media? How has your thinking changed since reading this chapter?
3. Who do you think is responsible for providing people with the best possible living circumstances for health? How did you come to this view?
4. What might be some of the reasons why governments will not address health inequalities? How could these reasons for not acting be justified?

Recommended Readings

Bartley, M. (2003). *Health inequality: An introduction to concepts, theories, and methods.* Cambridge: Polity Press.
  Large differences in life expectancy exist between the most privileged and the most disadvantaged social groups in industrial societies. This book assists in understanding the four most widely accepted theories of what lies behind inequalities in health: the behavioural, psychosocial, material, and life-course approaches.

Graham, H. (2007). *Unequal lives: Health and socioeconomic inequalities.* New York: Open University Press.
  Unequal Lives provides an evidence-based introduction to social and health inequalities. It brings together research from social epidemiology, sociology, and social policy to guide the reader to an understanding of why people's lives and people's health remain so unequal, even in rich societies where there is more than enough for all.

Kawachi, I., Subramanian, S.V., & Almeida-Filho, N. (2002). A glossary for health inequalities. *Journal of Epidemiology and Community Health, 56*(9), 647–652.
  The authors not only provide some excellent definitions of health inequalities and related concepts, but they also provide an overview and some answers to eight key questions pertinent to health inequalities, their causes, and means of addressing them.

Whitehead, M. (1985). *The concepts and principles of equity and health.* Copenhagen: WHO Regional Office for Europe. Retrieved from: http://salud.ciee.flacso.org.ar/flacso/optativas/equity_and_health.pdf.
  This classic report examines the concepts and principles of equity as understood in the context of

the World Health Organization's Health for All policy. It sets out to examine how some of the health inequalities observed in populations are inevitable and others are unnecessary and unfair.

Recommended Websites

Innocenti Research Centre (IRC): www.unicef-icdc.org/
IRC works to strengthen the capacity of UNICEF and its co-operating institutions to respond to the evolving needs of children and to develop a new global ethic for children. It promotes the effective implementation of the Convention on the Rights of the Child in both developing and developed countries, thereby reaffirming the universality of children's rights and UNICEF's mandate. The IRC produces numerous reports about health inequalities in children and the public policies that create them.

Learn about the Social Determinants of Health and Social Inequities in Health: http://tinyurl.com/6xquhjs
The Sudbury and District Health Unit in Ontario, Canada, has emerged as a leader in communicating to the public about the determinants of health and the determinants of health inequalities. Look at their video, *Let's Start a Conversation about Health … and Not Talk about Health Care at All*, to get a quick introduction to what tackling health inequalities is all about.

United Nations Human Rights: http://www.ohchr.org/en/issues/Pages/WhatareHumanRights.aspx
The Office of the United Nations High Commissioner for Human Rights (OHCHR) represents the world's commitment to universal ideals of human dignity. It has a unique mandate from the international community to promote and protect all human rights and is part of the United Nations Secretariat, with their headquarters in Geneva.

Unnatural Causes: Is Inequality Making Us Sick?: www.unnaturalcauses.org/
California Newsreel provided a documentary series that would serve as the basis for establishing a new public health in the US and elsewhere. The website provides details about the documentary as well as numerous resources to build awareness of, and support for, a broader approach to addressing poverty and its health effects. The contrasts between the American and Swedish situations are especially useful.

References

Anderson, E. (2011). *Feminist epistemology and philosophy of science*. Retrieved from: http://plato.stanford.edu/archives/spr2011/entries/feminism-epistemology/.

Bartley, M. (2003). *Understanding health inequalities*. Oxford: Polity Press.

Benzeval, M., Judge, K., & Whitehead, M. (1995). *Tackling inequalities in health: An agenda for action*. London: Kings Fund.

Braun, L. (2002). Race, ethnicity, and health: Can genetics explain disparities? *Perspectives in Biology and Medicine, 45*(2), 159–174.

Braveman, P., & Gruskin, S. (2003). Defining equity in health. *Journal of Epidemiology and Community Health, 57*, 254–258.

Brooks, S., & Miljan, L. (2003). Theories of public policy. In S. Brooks & L. Miljan (Eds.), *Public Policy in Canada: An Introduction* (pp. 22–49). Toronto: Oxford University Press.

Brooks-Gunn, J., Duncan, G.J., & Britto, P.R. (1998). Are SES gradients for children similar to those for adults? Achievement and health of children in the United States. In D.P. Keating & C. Hertzman (Eds.), *Developmental health and the wealth of nations: Social, biological, and educational dynamics* (pp. 94–124). New York: Guilford Press.

Brunner, E., & Marmot, M. (2006). Social organization, stress, and health. In M. Marmot & R.G. Wilkinson (Eds.), *Social determinants of health* (2nd ed., pp. 6–30). Oxford: Oxford University Press.

Bryant, T. (2010). Politics, public policy, and health inequalities. In T. Bryant, D. Raphael & M. Rioux (Eds.), *Staying alive: Critical perspectives on health, illness, and health care* (2nd ed., pp. 239–265). Toronto: Canadian Scholars' Press Inc.

Butler-Jones, D. (2009). *Report on the state of public health in Canada 2008: Addressing health inequalities*. Ottawa: Public Health Agency of Canada.

Canadian Population Health Initiative. (2004). *Select highlights on public views of the determinants of health*. Ottawa: CPHI.

Canadian Population Health Initiative. (2006). *How healthy are rural Canadians? An assessment of their health status and health determinants*. Ottawa: Canadian Population Health Initiative.

Chernomas, R., & Hudson, I. (2009). Social murder: The long-term effects of conservative economic policy. *International Journal of Health Services, 39*(1), 107–121.

Conference Board of Canada. (2009). *How Canada performs: A report card on Canada*. Ottawa: Conference Board of Canada.

Dahlgren, G., & Whitehead, M. (2006). *Levelling up (Part 2): A discussion paper on European strategies for tackling social inequities in health*. Copenhagen: WHO Regional Office for Europe.

Davey Smith, G., Ebrahim, S., Lewis, S., Hansell, A.L., Palmer, L.J., & Burton, P.R. (2005). Genetic epidemiology and public health: Hope, hype, and future prospects. *The Lancet, 366*(9495), 1484–1498.

Esping-Andersen, G. (1990). *The three worlds of welfare capitalism*. Princeton: Princeton University Press.

Graham, H. (2007). *Unequal lives: Health and socioeconomic inequalities*. New York: Open University Press.

Hancock, T. (2011). Health promotion in Canada: 25 years of unfulfilled promise. *Health Promotion International, 26*(Suppl. 2), ii263–ii267.

Innocenti Research Centre. (2005). *Child poverty in rich nations, 2005: Report card no. 6*. Florence: Innocenti Research Centre.

Innocenti Research Centre. (2007). *An overview of child well-being in rich countries: A comprehensive assessment of the lives and well-being of children and adolescents in the economically advanced nations*. Florence: Innocenti Research Centre.

Jackson, A. (2000, February 15). Taxes, growth, and inequality. Behind the numbers: Economic facts. *Figures and Analysis, 2*, 4.

Jarvis, M.J., & Wardle, J. (2003). Social patterning of individual health behaviours: The case of cigarette smoking. In M.G. Marmot & R.G. Wilkinson (Eds.), *Social determinants of health* (2nd ed., pp. 224–237). Oxford: Oxford University Press.

Kawachi, I., Subramanian, S.V., & Almeida-Filho, N. (2002). A glossary for health inequalities. *Journal of Epidemiology and Community Health, 56*(9), 647–652.

Kerstetter, S. (2002). *Rags and riches: Wealth inequality in Canada*. Ottawa: Canadian Centre for Policy Alternatives.

Kirkpatrick, S.I., & McIntyre, L. (2009). The chief public health officer's report on health inequalities: What are the implications for public health practitioners and researchers? *Canadian Journal of Public Health, 100*(2), 93–95.

Krieger, N. (2003). Does racism harm health? Did child abuse exist before 1962? On explicit questions, critical science, and current controversies: An ecosocial perspective. *American Journal of Public Health, 93*(2), 194–199.

Labonte, R., & Penfold, S. (1981). Canadian perspectives in health promotion: A critique. *Health Education, 19*, 4–9.

Langille, D. (2009). Follow the money: How business and politics shape our health. In D. Raphael (Ed.), *Social determinants of health: Canadian perspectives* (2nd ed., pp. 305–317). Toronto: Canadian Scholars' Press Inc.

Lee, M. (2007). *Eroding tax fairness: Tax incidence in Canada, 1998 to 2005*. Ottawa: Canadian Centre for Policy Alternatives.

Lee, S.S., Mountain, J., & Koenig, B. (2001). The meanings of race in the new genomics: Implications for health disparities research. *Yale Journal of Health Policy, Law and Ethics, 1*, 33–75.

Mackenbach, J.P. (2005). Genetics and health inequalities: Hypotheses and controversies. *Journal of Epidemiology and Community Health, 59*(4), 268–273.

McBride, S., & Shields, J. (1997). *Dismantling a nation: The transition to corporate rule in Canada.* Halifax: Fernwood Publishing.

McDermott, R. (1998). Ethics, epidemiology, and the thrifty gene: Biological determinism as a health hazard. *Social Science & Medicine, 47*(9), 1189–1195.

McGibbon, E. (2009). Health and health care: A human rights perspective. In D. Raphael (Ed.), *Social determinants of health: Canadian perspectives* (2nd ed., pp. 318–335). Toronto: Canadian Scholars' Press Inc.

McQuaig, L. (1987). *Behind closed doors: How the rich won control of Canada's tax system—and ended up richer.* Toronto: Viking.

McQuaig, L. (1993). *The wealthy banker's wife: The assault of equality in Canada.* Toronto: Penguin.

Mikkonen, J., & Raphael, D. (2010). *Social determinants of health: The Canadian facts.* Retrieved from: http://thecanadianfact.org.

Navarro, V. (2009). What we mean by social determinants of health. *Global Health Promotion, 16*(1), 5–16.

Navarro, V., & Shi, L. (2002). The political context of social inequalities and health. In V. Navarro (Ed.), *The political economy of social inequalities: Consequences for health and quality of life* (pp. 403–418). Amityville: Baywood.

Nazroo, J.Y. (1998). Genetic, cultural or socio-economic vulnerability? Explaining ethnic inequalities in health. *Sociology of Health & Illness, 20*(5), 710–730.

Nettleton, S. (1997). Surveillance, health promotion, and the formation of a risk identity. In M. Sidell, L. Jones, J. Katz & A. Peberdy (Eds.), *Debates and dilemmas in promoting health* (pp. 314–324). London: Open University Press.

Office of the United Nations High Commissioner for Human Rights & World Health Organization. (2008). *The right to health*, Fact Sheet no. 31. Retrieved from: http://www.ohchr.org/Documents/Publications/Factsheet31.pdf.

O'Neill, M., Pederson, A., Dupere, S., & Rootman, I. (Eds.). (2007). *Health promotion in Canada: Critical perspectives.* Toronto: Canadian Scholars' Press Inc.

Organisation for Economic Co-operation and Development. (2009). *Health update—the newsletter on health-related activities at the OECD.* Retrieved from: http://www.oecd.org/dataoecd/63/18/43305158.pdf.

Organisation for Economic Co-operation and Development. (2011a). *Health at a glance: OECD indicators 2011 edition.* Paris: Organisation for Economic Co-operation and Development.

Organisation for Economic Co-operation and Development. (2011b). *Society at a glance 2011, OECD social indicators.* Paris: Organisation for Economic Co-operation and Development.

ParticipAction. (2011). *The early years: The 60-year-old Swede.* Retrieved from: http://www.usask.ca/archives/participaction/english/motivate/swede.html.

Poverty and Human Rights Centre. (2007). *Human rights treaty implementation: The consensus on Canada.* Retrieved from: http://www2.ohchr.org/english/bodies/cedaw/docs/ngos/PHRC_Canada42.pdf.

Public Health Agency of Canada. (2001). *What is the population health approach?* Retrieved from: http://www.phac-aspc.gc.ca/ph-sp/approach-approche/index-eng.php.

Public Health Agency of Canada. (2007). *Canada's response to WHO Commission on social determinants of health.* Retrieved from: http://www.phac-aspc.gc.ca/sdh-dss/bg-eng.php.

Raphael, D. (2007). Canadian public policy and poverty in international perspective. In D. Raphael (Ed.), *Poverty and policy in Canada: Implications for health and quality of life* (pp. 335–364). Toronto: Canadian Scholars' Press Inc.

Raphael, D. (2009). Escaping from the Phantom zone: Social determinants of health, public health units, and public policy in Canada. *Health Promotion International, 24*(2), 193–198.

Raphael, D. (2010a). *About Canada: Health and illness.* Winnipeg: Fernwood Publishing.

Raphael, D. (2010b). The health of Canada's children. Part I: Canadian children's health in comparative perspective. *Paediatrics and Child Health, 15*(1), 23–29.

Raphael, D. (2010c). The health of Canada's children. Part II: Health mechanisms and pathways. *Paediatrics and Child Health, 15*(2), 71–76.

Raphael, D. (2010d). The health of Canada's children. Part III: Public policy and the social determinants of children's health. *Paediatrics and Child Health, 15*(3), 143–149.

Raphael, D. (2011a). Interactions with the health and service sector. In D. Raphael (Ed.), *Poverty in Canada: Implications for health and quality of life* (2nd ed., pp. 186–219). Toronto: Canadian Scholars' Press Inc.

Raphael, D. (2011b). Mainstream media and the social determinants of health in Canada: Is it time to call it a day? *Health Promotion International, 26*(2), 220–229.

Raphael, D. (2011c). *Poverty in Canada: Implications for health and quality of life* (2nd ed.). Toronto: Canadian Scholars' Press Inc.

Raphael, D. (2011d). Who is poor in Canada? In D. Raphael (Ed.), *Poverty in Canada: Implications for health and quality of life* (2nd ed., pp. 62–89). Toronto: Canadian Scholars' Press Inc.

Raphael, D., Anstice, S., Raine, K., McGannon, K., Rizvi, S., & Yu, V. (2003). The social determinants of the incidence and management of type 2 diabetes mellitus: Are we prepared to rethink our questions and redirect our research activities? *Leadership in Health Services, 16*, 10–20.

Raphael, D., & Bryant, T. (2010). The political economy of public health: Public health concerns in Canada, the US, UK, Norway, and Sweden. In T. Bryant, D. Raphael & M. Rioux (Eds.), *Staying alive: Critical perspectives on health, illness, and health care* (2nd ed., pp. 371–394). Toronto: Canadian Scholars' Press Inc.

Raphael, D., Curry-Stevens, A., & Bryant, T. (2008). Barriers to addressing the social determinants of health: Insights from the Canadian experience. *Health Policy, 88*, 222–235.

Raphael, D., & Farrell, E.S. (2002). Beyond medicine and lifestyle: Addressing the societal determinants of cardiovascular disease in North America. *Leadership in Health Services, 15*, 1–5.

Raphael, D., Renwick, R., Brown, I., Steinmetz, B., Sehdev, H., & Phillips, S. (2001). Making the links between community structure and individual well-being. Community quality of life in Riverdale, Toronto, Canada. *Health and Place, 7*(3), 17–34.

Restrepo, H.E. (1996). Introduction. In Pan American Health Organization (Ed.), *Health promotion: An anthology* (pp. ix–xi). Washington: Pan American Health Organization.

Rioux, M. (2010). The right to health: Human rights approaches to health. In D. Raphael, T. Bryant & M. Rioux (Eds.), *Staying alive: Critical perspectives on health, illness, and health care* (2nd ed., pp. 93–120). Toronto: Canadian Scholars' Press Inc.

Saint-Arnaud, S., & Bernard, P. (2003). Convergence or resilience? A hierarchical cluster analysis of the welfare regimes in advanced countries. *Current Sociology, 51*(5), 499–527.

Scambler, G. (2002). *Health and social change: A critical theory*. Buckingham: Open University Press.

Scarth, T. (Ed.). (2004). *Hell and high water: An assessment of Paul Martin's record and implications for the future*. Ottawa: Canadian Centre for Policy Alternatives.

Schoen, C., & Doty, M.M. (2004). Inequities in access to medical care in five countries: Findings from the 2001 Commonwealth Fund international health policy study. *Health Policy, 67*, 309–322.

Seedhouse, D. (2003). *Health: The foundations of achievement*. New York: John Wiley & Sons.

Senate Subcommittee on Population Health. (2008). *A healthy, productive Canada: A determinant of health approach*. Ottawa: Government of Canada.

Shaw, M., Dorling, D., Gordon, D., & Davey Smith, G. (1999). *The widening gap: Health inequalities and policy in Britain*. Bristol: The Policy Press.

Shoham, D.A., Vupputuri, S., Kaufman, J.S., Kshirsagar, A.V., Diez Roux, A.V., Coresh, J., et al. (2008). Kidney disease and the cumulative burden of life course socioeconomic conditions: The atherosclerosis risk in communities (ARIC) study. *Social Science & Medicine, 67*(8), 1311–1320.

Smylie, J. (2009). The health of Aboriginal peoples. In D. Raphael (Ed.), *Social determinants of health: Canadian perspectives* (2nd ed., pp. 280–304). Toronto: Canadian Scholars' Press Inc.

Tremblay, S., Ross, N.A., & Berthelot, J.-M. (2002). Regional socio-economic context and health. *Health Reports, 13*(Suppl.), 1–12.

United Nations Population Fund. (2011). *Human rights principles.* Retrieved from: http://www.unfpa.org/rights/principles.htm.

Whitehead, M. (1985). *The concepts and principles of equity and health.* Copenhagen: WHO Regional Office for Europe.

Whitehead, M., & Dahlgren, G. (2006). *Concepts and principles for tackling social inequities in health: Levelling up Part 1.* Copenhagen: WHO Regional Office for Europe.

Wilkins, R. (2007). *Mortality by neighbourhood income in urban Canada from 1971 to 2001.* Ottawa: Statistics Canada, Health Analysis and Measurement Group.

Wilkins, R., Berthelot, J.-M., & Ng, E. (2002). Trends in mortality by neighbourhood income in urban Canada from 1971 to 1996. *Health reports (Stats Can), 13*(Suppl.), 1–28.

World Health Organization. (2002). *Health and human rights.* Geneva: World Health Organization.

World Health Organization. (2008). *Closing the gap in a generation: Health equity through action on the social determinants of health.* Geneva: World Health Organization.

Chapter 2

American Experiences

Stephen Bezruchka

If they can get you asking the wrong questions, they don't have to worry about answers.

—Thomas Pynchon, 1973

Introduction

This chapter will show that health inequalities in the United States as a nation are the worst of all wealthy developed countries: Americans die younger and suffer worse health than people in over 30 other nations. The situation is not improving despite enormous expenditures on medical services, with the US paying close to half of the world's health care bill. The reasons for these health inequalities relate to the political economy of the nation, rooted in its founding history and overlaid with recent changes wrought by neo-liberalism. Sixty years ago the nation was one of the world's healthiest, but as a consequence of political choices that have increased the wealth of a few, everyone's health has suffered. The US provides many lessons for other countries that want to avoid this health catastrophe.

National Description and Political Organization and Structure

It is impossible to understand a country without seeing how it varies from others. Those who know only one country know no country.

—Seymour Lipset, 1996

United States Political History

The United States of America was founded in 1776 with a Declaration of Independence espousing the right to life, liberty, and the pursuit of happiness. The statement at its time was revolutionary, as were its founders. Its subsequent history, however, is one of expansionism—termed "Manifest Destiny" in the 1800s—as the country sought to exert control over the Americas. The US was one of the last nations to declare slavery illegal because of the comparative advantage of this labour for its cotton production. With the end of slavery after the Civil War, the sanctioned reparations of "forty acres and a mule" were never carried out and legacies remain today. Increasingly, the nation became a big innovator and a stronghold of capitalist enterprise. President Coolidge stated it succinctly: "The business of America is business." Federal economic policies stressed protectionism from outside competition and massive government subsidies of industry.

The founding fathers designed a system with a deliberately weak central government. A federal government came into being with separation of powers into the executive, judiciary, and legislative branches. The legislative branch had two houses, one (the House of Representatives) with seats apportioned on the basis of population, the other (the Senate) with seats apportioned equally to states regardless of size. Both operate under a first-past-the-post system whereby the candidate with the largest number of votes wins the seat. This arrangement has made it difficult to get legislation enacted without significant compromises that cater to various interests. In recent years these compromises responding to special interests have been through earmarks, specific provisions responding to powerful lobby and constituent forces. There were few state-owned industries and those that did exist have been privatized. Governments at all levels within the country, from the federal to the state to the county, do not have the power of those in other industrialized nations (Kingdon, 1999).

The Aboriginal population was decimated through imported diseases and violence. Besides the various Indian wars, some jurisdictions paid bounties for killing American Indians that varied depending on whether it was a man, woman, child, or chief. There were various attempts to eradicate the Native cultures. Treaties were signed with various tribes, but not honoured in many cases. Today they comprise less than 1 percent of the population.

There were periods of substantial immigration from Europe, and through diligence, hard work, and some luck, the so-called American Dream was perpetuated, encouraging immigrants to believe that it was possible to escape aristocracies in Europe and attain a modicum of wealth in the US. People looked to solve their problems at the local level. The myth of equality of opportunity helped foster support for limited government. Legislation such as the New Deal in the 1930s, in which major laws substantially benefited ordinary people during the Great Depression, was an aberration of these ideals. The country has the smallest public sector of any democracy with relatively few direct government services. Tax rates are similarly small in comparison to other nations.

The country is very litigious, with a higher concentration of lawyers than any other nation. There is less governmental regulation of industry and society than in other nations. Instead of government regulations, the dominant belief is that anyone who has been harmed has the right to bring suit and seek redress as a private individual matter. An important system of social regulation in the US is a strong tort system, which potentially allows everyone to "have their day in court."

Spending on national defence has been a prominent way for the American public to fund government expenditure for other purposes. For example, the development of the modern commercial airliner was done mostly through the military, which developed bombers that were modified for passenger use. Military might and economic wealth allowed the country to become very powerful, and after the collapse of the Soviet Union, the US remained the only superpower. The population has grown to 310 million, and the economy has transformed from manufacturing into service, together with a huge increase in the financial sector.

The political system of the US differs from that of most wealthy nations. Political parties in the US are weaker than parliamentary parties in many other democracies as party affiliation does not guarantee the direction of one's vote. Individuals have to raise their own funds to run their campaigns for election. Today there are two political parties that tend to be similar in their support for small government and tax cuts while supporting big business, resulting in substantial government expenditures that benefit the corporate sector. In recent years massive big business lobbies have had great influence over policies. The nation has both the greatest concentration of wealth as well as the most poverty of any wealthy developed nation. Voting rates in this nominal democracy are among the lowest in the world, with those who are young and poor tending to not exercise their franchise. The political left in the US is well to the right of what most other countries would consider the political centre.

Before the Great Depression, the richest 1 percent held nearly half of the country's wealth. Over the next four decades the wealth share of the richest 1 percent in the country dropped, reaching its nadir around 1975, when it represented less than a quarter of all US wealth. By means of various welfare cutbacks and tax cuts favouring the wealthy, inequality has since soared to record levels (Duménil & Lèvy, 2004). The made-in-America economic crisis that began in 2008 was the result of bold efforts by the very rich to further enrich themselves. This crisis has affected most of the world and especially the US, yet people in the US remain remarkably complacent. In the Saint-Arnaud and Bernard typology (see Chapter 1), liberty predominates in the US and solidarity has eroded, resulting in a huge polarization in living standards.

At its founding, much power was delegated to states, but funding mechanisms are often controlled at the federal level. US states have the power to tax and spend and are responsible for education, contribution to the development and maintenance of roads, and much regulatory policy. Sources of revenue generation at the state level vary widely across the country, as do most other state functions. This heterogeneity results in greater resistance to national initiatives than in most other rich countries. The political system at the state level increases localism and contributes to the weakness of national parties.

Political cultures among the US states vary widely. Elazar grouped them into three categories: (1) individualistic (a marketplace where government interventions are limited to those who put the majority party into power); (2) traditionalistic (the government's role preserves existing order); and (3) moralistic (the government achieves "good community" through positive action) (Kunitz, McKee et al., 2010). While this grouping is not static, it can guide understanding of considerable state variation in political policies and resulting inequalities.

Class issues have never loomed large in US history, in contrast to Europe with its feudal past. Feudalism was never a part of US history. The French Revolution was fundamentally different than the American Revolution, since the US had no internal aristocracy to fight. Without the growth of class consciousness in the US, there has been less pressure for government programs to redress economic imbalances. Even US radical movements in the 1960s stressed decentralization and community control in contrast to those in Europe, which supported centrism. Civil rights legislation in the 1960s was a major milestone. Since then labour rights have been severely eroded and public welfare support is among the lowest of any rich nation.

US Health Policy

The US remains the only wealthy developed country without universal access to medical services. Major, centralized health initiatives in the country have been rare, although various efforts have been directed toward increasing access to health care. The enactment of Medicare in 1966—which had the federal government paying for hospital care for those aged 65 and over—was an attempt to reform the provision of medical care. Medicaid is a federally supported state program targeted at poor people, and its terms vary widely among states. Even with the passage of the Patient Protection and Affordable Care Act (PPACA) in 2010, substantial numbers still lack access to health care. Strong political forces in the country attempt to weaken or eliminate even that legislation.

At the federal level, the Department of Health and Human Services (HHS) is the principal agency for "protecting the health of all Americans." It includes 10 regional offices and a number of institutions, including the Centers for Disease Control and Prevention (CDC), and the National Institutes of Health. The position of Surgeon General is largely symbolic. The department has issued Healthy People reports, beginning through the Office of the Surgeon General in 1979 and followed by Healthy People 1990, 2000, and 2010. But only the first report offered comparisons of US mortality rates with other nations. Healthy People 2000 set out to reduce health disparities among Americans, while Healthy People 2010 aimed to eliminate them. These reports offered national targets related to mortality rates, health disparities, behaviour changes, and disease prevalence, but only a tiny fraction of targets have ever been met.

Health disparities came to prominence in 1985 with the publication of the HHS Heckler report on black and minority health. Since then the disparities focus has remained along this racial and ethnic perspective. The Office of Minority Health is housed in the US HHS and has a National Partnership for Action to End Health Disparities.

Healthy People 2020 is web-based, with four broad goals relating to longer lives; health equity (meaning improving the health of all groups); creating healthy social and physical environments; and improving quality of life, healthy development, and healthy behaviours across all life stages. There is one very small section on international comparisons for life expectancy.

In Healthy People 2020 the determinants of health, which can influence an individual's or population's health, are described as "Powerful, complex relationships exist between health and biology, genetics, and individual behaviour, and between health and health services, socioeconomic status, the physical environment, discrimination, racism, literacy levels, and legislative policies." Healthy People 2020 defines a health disparity as

> a particular type of health difference that is closely linked with social, economic, and/or environmental disadvantage. Health disparities adversely affect groups of people who have systematically experienced greater obstacles to health based on their racial or ethnic group; religion; socioeconomic status; gender; age; mental health; cognitive, sensory, or physical disability; sexual orientation or gender identity; geographic location; or other characteristics historically linked to discrimination or exclusion.

The Institute of Medicine's 2003 report, *The Future of the Public's Health in the 21st Century*, contained a chapter on population health and mentioned the country's poor health status, but most of the document did not carry these ideas forward to consider actions (Institute of Medicine, 2003). Another IOM report considered the racial disparities in medical treatment (Smedley, Stith et al., 2003).

Efforts at reducing health inequities from the US state level vary tremendously at the level of state departments of health and with public health departments that operate at the county and city level. They are tasked with carrying out the goals of Healthy People 2020 while budgets are being slashed. The next section looks further at US policy documents relating to health inequalities.

US Policy Documents and Statements on Health Inequalities

There are few federal policy documents that have described the relatively poor health status of people in the US, and none that have caught the public's attention. Part of the difficulty in promoting public interest about these issues is related to the predominance of commercial enterprises and other non-governmental organizations in service provision. Some, such as health care insurance and pharmaceutical companies, have managed to profit handsomely over the last few decades. This is likely to continue in the future from national health care policies such as the PPACA.

The US Congress issued a report in 1993 pointing out the poor health status of people in the US compared to other nations (United States Congress, Office of Technology Assessment, 1993). The Centers for Disease Control and Prevention produces annual reports titled *Health United States*, which have tables listing infant mortality rates and life expectancy at birth and age 65 for the US and selected countries, with trends and rankings from 1960 onwards. Public attention has not been drawn to this material, however.

One recent governmental report has acknowledged the health inequalities within the US. In a January 14, 2011 supplement to the CDC's *Morbidity and Mortality Weekly Report*, an entire issue was devoted to a report on US health disparities and inequalities (Frieden, 2011). It included language stating a commitment to socio-economic justice, noting that health disparities are differences in health outcomes between groups that reflect social inequalities (see quotation below). A section on education and income in the US reflected issues rarely raised by its federal agencies. There were other sections on housing and air quality, as well as documentation of mortality stratified by race.

> Health disparities are differences in health outcomes and their determinants between segments of the population, as defined by social, demographic, environmental, and geographic attributes. Health inequalities, which is sometimes used interchangeably with the term health disparities, is more often used in the scientific and economic literature to refer to summary measures of population health associated with individual- or group-specific attributes (e.g., income, education, or race/ethnicity). Health inequities are a subset of health inequalities that are modifiable, associated with social disadvantage, and considered ethically unfair. (Truman, Smith et al., 2011, 3)

A key finding from the CDC study is that inverse educational and poverty gradients in mortality in the US have not shown any improvement between 2005 and 2009 (Beckles &

Truman, 2011). Other studies have shown that educational gradients, where the less well educated have worse health outcomes, are not explained by behavioural risk factors among the less
educated (Cutler, Lange et al., 2010).

A variety of action plans have been issued by public agencies to "reduce racial and ethnic
health disparities," with the actions outlined having a strong focus on individual risk factors
and medical care. There has been fragmentation over action at the national, state, and local
levels to deal with health inequities. Efforts are almost always focused on modifying individual
health-related behaviours, since health promotion as a concept in the US tends to focus on
four modifiable behavioural issues (physical activity, poor nutrition, tobacco use, and excessive
alcohol consumption) that are considered to be responsible for much of the early death due to
chronic diseases (CDC, 2011).

Research on Health Inequalities in the US

Research on health inequalities is done mostly through academic departments with some
efforts in that area conducted by the CDC. The studies contain very little material implicating
the political forces in the country in the production of health and ill health. What follows is
a compilation of the most recent material on health inequities within the US, beginning with
the declining relative health status of the US compared to other nations.

Health Inequalities Comparing the US to Other Nations

Although in the early 1950s the US could claim to have some of the best health outcomes in
the world, by 2010 at least 30 other countries have better health outcomes (Bezruchka, 2012).
For life expectancy the gap is so large that eradicating either heart disease or cancer as a cause
of death would not enable the nation to rank at the top. An estimate of the body count that
has resulted from the US not being the healthiest country for each year of the last century is 66
million (Muszynska & Rau, 2009). That is, if the US had the same health status as the country
with the highest life expectancy in each year of the last century, there would be 66 million more
people alive in 2000. That this toll represents 60 Holocausts defies comprehension—an example
of structural violence that kills far more people than the behavioural variety (Gilligan, 1999).

A recent study examining the health status of counties in the US found that considering
life expectancy for both men and women, the nation ranked 37th in 2007, meaning that 36
nations had longer life expectancy (Kulkarni, Levin-Rector et al., 2011). There are essentially
no mortality measures of health where it ranks much better. This study calculated a time series
of average life expectancy of the 10 lowest mortality countries each year from 1950 to 2010.
This was termed the international "life expectancy frontier." The researchers asked how many
calendar years behind the frontier a nation might be. For men, the US is 13 years behind and
for women, 16. This is comparable to saying that the top 10 nations have an innovative, highly
useful product that is in great demand and makes life much better, but it won't be available in
the US for roughly another 15 years. If this were an iPad, we wouldn't tolerate it, but because
it is the more abstract concept of our health, it seems to be accepted. A part of that apparent
acceptance, however, lies in a lack of awareness among most Americans of how unhealthy
people are in the US compared to other nations.

Being so far behind this health frontier may be the most egregious health inequity: people in the richest and most powerful country in world history that pays half of the world's health care bill die much younger than in many other countries. But because of the profound individual health production focus in the US, health inequalities or inequities are not concepts understood by most Americans. They tend to believe that health outcomes are under individual control, and discount the concept that societal unfairness may be behind many poor health outcomes.

Child health, as well as adult mortality, is also relatively poor in the US. The child mortality rate *ranking* for the US in 1970 was better than in 2010 (Rajaratnam, Marcus et al., 2010b). Although the rate improved over time, it did not drop as fast as in many other nations. But child mortality is not responsible for the relatively low average life expectancy; the probability of an American youth age 15 living to age 60 is lower in the US than in over 40 other nations. A 15-year-old boy in Peru has a better chance of reaching age 60 than a boy in the US. Similar results hold for a girl in Sri Lanka compared to an American girl. US health status is that of a middle-income country or worse. While the ranking among nations since 1970 has improved for boys by 2010, it has not for girls (Rajaratnam, Marcus et al., 2010b). The gap in health between the US and western Europe is the result of slow health improvements in the near-elderly (e.g., age 50 and beyond) Americans compared to western Europeans (Michaud, Goldman et al., 2011).

Women in the US in particular have been victims of health inequities. This is demonstrated below for US counties, but is also apparent for the nation as a whole, especially at older ages. Remaining years of life at age 50 (e_{50}) demonstrate that women begin falling further behind in comparison to other nations around 1980 (Glei, Meslé et al., 2010; see Figure 2.1). Another analysis from 1980 to 2006 comparing the US to other rich nations shows the same striking decline in the ranking of life expectancy at age 50 for women, although the decline was less for men (Wilmoth, Boe et al., 2010).

To consider these health inequalities among countries at older ages, standard deviation trends for life expectancy at age 50 can be found for much of the last 100 years using the best available data sources. Again, the inequalities within the US counties surpass those within Canada, France, Germany, and Japan (Wilmoth, Boe et al., 2010). Table 2.1 lists health neighbours for the US, namely countries just above and just below the US, in various mortality measures of health (Hogan, Foreman et al., 2010; Rajaratnam, Marcus et al., 2010a,b). The health status of people within the US is that of a middle-income country and far below what might be appropriate for the richest and most powerful country in world history.

Some studies compare health in the US with neighbouring Canada or Cuba. Cuba's health is on par with the US, while Canada's is much better (Cooper, Kennelly et al., 2006; Siddiqi & Hertzman, 2007; Willson, 2009; Feeny, Kaplan et al., 2010). The effect of race on health depends on whether the US or Canada is considered, with Canada having attenuated inequities (Siddiqi & Nguyen, 2010). White Americans have poorer health than all Canadians, with political differences being important reasons (Kunitz & Pesis-Katz, 2005). These included Canada's universal welfare programs in contrast to those in the US, which were much less redistributive.

The relatively poor health status of the US depends not only on what that nation does that impacts its health, but on what other nations do (Bezruchka, 2001). National governments

Figure 2.1
Life Expectancy Trends for Women at Age 50 (e^{50}) for Selected
Countries from 1955 to 2008

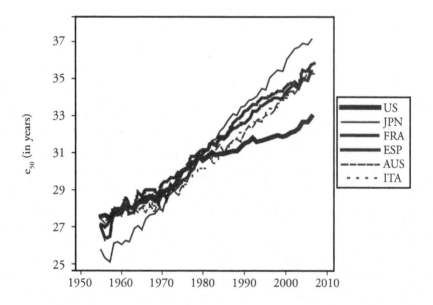

Source: D.A. Glei, F. Meslé et al., Diverging trends in life expectancy at age 50: A look at causes of
death, In E.M. Crimmins, S.H. Preston & B. Cohen (Eds.), *International Differences In Mortality
at Older Ages: Dimensions and Sources* (Washington: National Academies Press, 2010, 22).

tend not to set benchmarks for health in comparison to other nations. Australia is the only
country to do so recently in an effort to surpass Japan as the healthiest nation (National Preventative Health Taskforce, 2010).

Many other studies demonstrate similar findings: No matter what health outcome measure
is used for a country, the United States' ranking continues to fall further behind (Bezruchka,
2012). There is little or no awareness among the US inhabitants of this situation. For example,
a third of medical students in one study thought the US was the world's healthiest nation
(Agrawal, Huebner et al., 2005). The author's personal experiences in speaking at conferences
of public health workers or health care reporters attest to this profound ignorance of US health
status in comparison to other nations.

Health Inequalities within the US

A variety of methods have been used to characterize health inequalities within the US. One
novel method partitioned the country into "eight Americas" based on geographical and racial

Table 2.1
The United States' Health Neighbours

	Life Expectancy at Birth	Years Left at Age 50	Maternal Mortality Ratio	45q15 Male (chances of living to 60 at age 15)	45q15 Female (chances of living to 60 at age 15)	Under-Five Mortality
Just ahead (healthier)	Denmark	Malta	Lithuania	Peru	Maldives	Slovakia
US (ties)	US	US	US Macedonia	US Algeria	US Armenia	US Macedonia
Just behind (less healthy)	Qatar	Korea	Latvia	Barbados	Poland	Lithuania
Compared to the best	4.9 years	3.3 years	4.3x	2x	2x	2.7x

characterizations with major differences in mortality trends from 1982 to 2001 (Murray, Kulkarni et al., 2006). One of the "Americas" comprised Native populations living in the West on or near reservations who had some of the worst mortality outcomes in the country. Some subpopulations of American Indians had life expectancies 33 years behind some of the highest in that study.

Research over the last few years has documented absolute health declines in a large percentage of US counties. Analysis from 1983 to 1999 showed substantial declines in contrast to the comparison period of 1961 to 1983 (Ezzati, Friedman et al., 2008).

Analysis of county mortality until 2007 documents an even graver picture (Kulkarni, Levin-Rector et al., 2011). "US racial/ethnic and geographic health disparities are vast" and "have been growing since 1983" (p. 1). These geographic health inequities are worth considering further as they illustrate the use of new measures that enhance comparability across nations. This study used the novel "years behind the international life expectancy frontier" approach, mentioned earlier, for the country as a whole. These calendar years (not life expectancy years) were calculated using a time series to indicate how many years ahead or behind the frontier a geographical unit was. For the county analysis, the 3,147 US counties were grouped into 2,357 clusters to reflect redistricting and small populations (and hence small numbers of deaths in some original counties). The calendar years behind the frontier were calculated for life expectancy in US county groups in 2000 and then for 2007 to observe trends. In what follows, county groups will be called counties.

In 2000, county life expectancy ranged from nine years ahead of the frontier to over 50 years behind for men and one year ahead to 45 years behind for women. In 2007, county life expectancy ranged from 15 years ahead to over 50 years behind for men and 16 years ahead to over 50 years behind for women. In other words, some counties could attain the health of the frontier in 50 years if present trends continued. The comparisons showed that men in 661 counties and women in 1,373 counties fell more than five years behind the international life expectancy frontier between 2000 and 2007. In 67 counties for men, and in 222 counties for women, they fell more than 10 years behind between 2000 and 2007. Only in 357 counties for men and in 168 counties for women were they fewer years behind in 2007 than in 2000. In all the others, health relative to the top 10 nations declined over this period.

Indeed, between 2000 and 2007 more than 85 percent of US counties fell further behind the international life expectancy frontier. In absolute terms, life expectancy has declined in close to a third of US counties for women (saee Figure 2.2). The remarkable shift to worse absolute health status for significant parts of the US is unprecedented in modern times, except for some countries of the former Soviet Union after its breakup and in high AIDS-prevalent nations in southern Africa.

Geographically across the US, the county life expectancy trends from 1987 to 2007 reveal striking inequalities for women and less prominent but still sobering ones for men. Declines in health in such a substantial portion of the nation are certainly worrisome (Institute for Health Metrics and Evaluation, 2011). Figures 2.3 and 2.4 display life expectancy changes by county in absolute years for both men and women from 1987 to 2007.

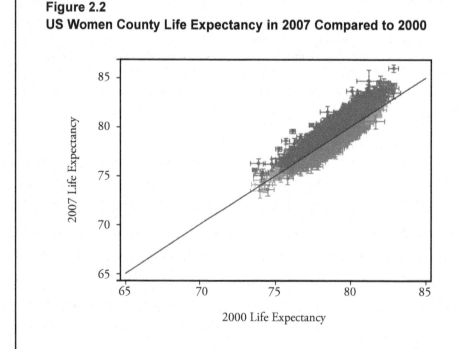

Figure 2.2
US Women County Life Expectancy in 2007 Compared to 2000

Source: S. Kulkarni, A. Levin-Rector et al., Falling behind: Life expectancy in US counties from 2000 to 2007 in an international context, *Population Health Metrics* 9(16) (2011): 8.

Figure 2.3
US County Female Life Expectancy Changes in Years from 1987 to 2007

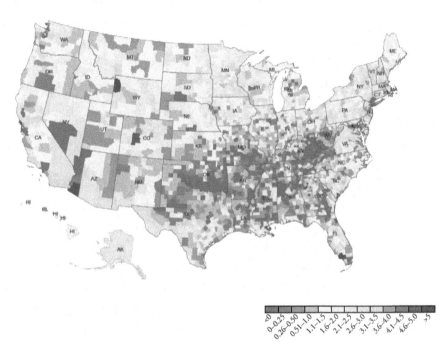

Source: Institute for Health Metrics and Evaluation (2011), Life expectancy in most US counties falls behind world's healthiest nations, retrieved from: http://www.healthmetricsandevaluation.org/news-events/news-release/life-expectancy-most-us-counties-falls-behind-worlds-healthiest-nations, figure 1.

When analysis was done for African Americans at the county level where there were sufficient numbers for reliable estimates, the expected worse health for African Americans was found. For black men, 65 percent of counties studied found life expectancies over 50 years behind, and for women this was found in 22 percent of counties. Considerable research has demonstrated racial or ethnic and other health inequalities for a variety of indicators that appear to be resistant to change (Bezruchka, 2010b). A vast number of Americans, distinctly identified by their socio-demographic characteristics and place of residence, have life expectancies that are similar to some low-income developing countries (Murray, Kulkarni et al., 2006). The patterns were similar for white and black, pointing out that the US health inequality situation is not simply due to racial inequities. It is too early to tell whether or not health for the nation as a whole will decline as predicted in the last decade (Olshansky, Passaro et al., 2005).

Analysis of mortality in geographical subunits in nations, comparable to US counties, allows some comparison of health inequities among them. This was done for the US, Canada, the United Kingdom, and Japan, making comparisons to the "frontier" countries. For Japanese

Figure 2.4
US County Male Life Expectancy Changes in Years from 1987 to 2007

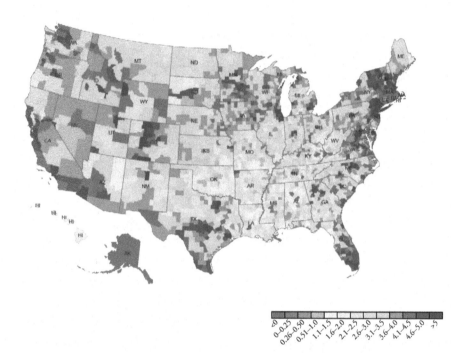

Source: Institute for Health Metrics and Evaluation (2011), Life expectancy in most US counties falls behind world's healthiest nations, retrieved from: http://www.healthmetricsandevaluation.org/news-events/news-release/life-expectancy-most-us-counties-falls-behind-worlds-healthiest-nations, figure 2.

women, 99 percent of the administrative levels had life expectancies above the international frontier countries, and for Japanese men, over 50 percent exceeded this marker (see Figures 2.5 and 2.6). The US has an insignificant number of counties with this distinction. The United Kingdom and Canada did better too. This comparison illustrates yet again that even the best health in the US is far below the average of other nations. The worst health outcomes in the US stand almost alone in this comparison, except for the Inuit in Canada's North, who appear to do even worse.

Racial and ethnic minority health inequities have long been reported in the US (Pappas, Queen et al., 1993). They begin early in life with preterm births and low birth weight. Not unexpectedly, preterm birth rates in the US are the highest for all rich nations (MacDorman & Mathews, 2009). For black non-Latinos, preterm births are almost one in five (Martin, 2011). Birth weights of African-born black women in the US are closer to those of whites than of US-born black women (David & Collins, 1997).

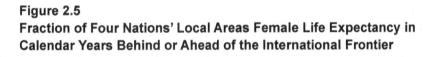

Figure 2.5
Fraction of Four Nations' Local Areas Female Life Expectancy in Calendar Years Behind or Ahead of the International Frontier

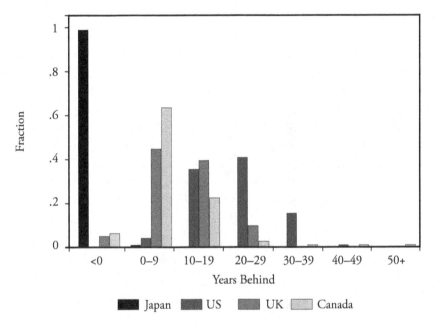

Source: S. Kulkarni, A. Levin-Rector et al., Falling behind: Life expectancy in US counties from 2000 to 2007 in an international context, *Population Health Metrics* 9(16) (2011): 5.

While there is no standard way of comparing health inequities across nations, some graphical depictions are illustrative. Use of the Gini coefficient for mortality shows large declines over the last few centuries, with the US lagging behind in recent decades (Peltzman, 2009). The standard deviation trends for age of death for people older than 10 years (S_{10}) across OECD countries show declines for most nations, but not the US, which remains higher than any other, as shown in Figure 2.7.

A dispersion measure of diversity in age at death equal to a weighted average of inter-individual differences in age at death ($e^\dagger$) has been proposed as a standard way of measuring health inequalities across nations (Shkolnikov, Andreev et al., 2011). This measure covers all ages, not just those older than 10 years. Plots of life expectancy versus $e^\dagger$ for rich nations show profoundly higher health inequalities for the US, as well as lower life expectancy for both sexes (see Figure 2.8). The ability to gauge both life expectancy and health inequality trends among nations presents striking findings for the US in relation to Japan, England and Wales, and Sweden.

A variety of studies have demonstrated US health disadvantage, considering chronic diseases and biomarkers in adults to be greater than those in Britain and Europe in comparison

Figure 2.6
Fraction of Four Nations' Local Areas Male Life Expectancy in
Calendar Years Behind or Ahead of the International Frontier

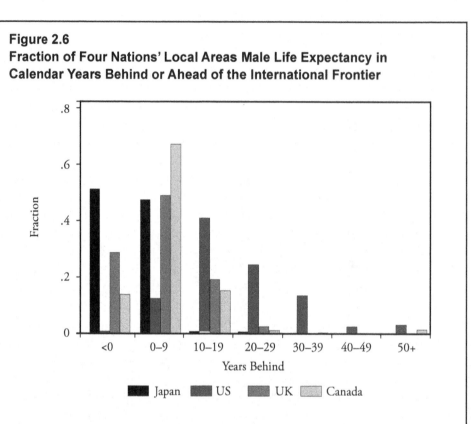

Source: S. Kulkarni, A. Levin-Rector et al. Falling behind: Life expectancy in US counties from 2000 to 2007 in an international context, *Population Health Metrics* 9(16) (2011): 5.

to other countries. This disadvantage begins at an early age before it could be impacted by personal behaviours (Banks, Marmot et al., 2006; Avendano, Glymour et al., 2009; Martinson, Teitler et al., 2011).

To summarize the health situation in the US metaphorically, consider a fast-flowing river that is full of human bodies catapulting downstream to their certain deaths. Along the bank is a monumental industry that propels lifelines out for the victims, who are then pulled ashore to be resuscitated. There are standards for this practice, guidelines to follow, and monitors who observe that quality is maintained, but no concern is voiced as to why all the people are coming downstream and require rescue. Over time the numbers increase substantially. After being rescued, many jump back into the torrent, which presents a continuing challenge for the industry situated further down the river.

Public Policy and Health Inequalities in the US

Health research is a large effort in the US, with the usual focus on health care services rather than the broader determinants of health. Most research looks at various inputs into medical

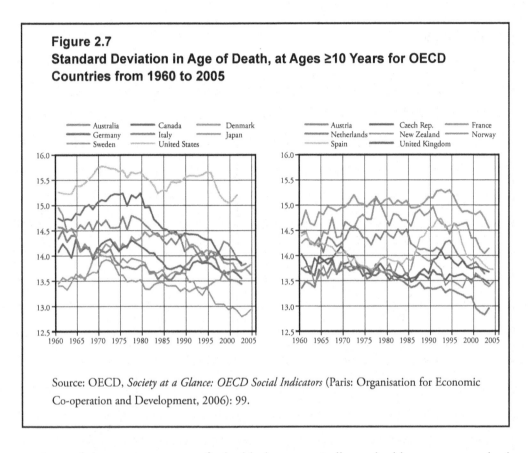

Figure 2.7
Standard Deviation in Age of Death, at Ages ≥10 Years for OECD
Countries from 1960 to 2005

Source: OECD, *Society at a Glance: OECD Social Indicators* (Paris: Organisation for Economic Co-operation and Development, 2006): 99.

services and the surrogate outputs for health that are typically not health outcomes at a level that can impact health inequities.

Health-Related Research from a Broader Policy Perspective

The concept embedded in the last paragraph of Geoffrey Rose's *Strategy of Preventive Medicine* is not considered in the US: "The primary determinants of disease are mainly economic and social, and therefore its remedies must also be economic and social. Medicine and politics cannot and should not be kept apart" (Rose, 1992, 129).

When one considers the economic and social aspects, one of the most pervasive findings in all current health research is the socio-economic gradient in health outcomes. This points to the observation that those lower down the socio-economic ladder tend to have worse outcomes (Adler, Boyce et al., 1994).

The last two decades have seen increasing exploration of and much insight into the gradient (Berkman & Kawachi, 2000). However, the approach that focuses on determinants of health of populations has made few inroads into public consciousness in the US, in contrast to Europe. The phrase "social determinants of health" is only now coming into the parlance of public health in the US. The concepts stress that societal or structural factors, especially related to socio-economic status, are more important in determining health outcomes than the provision of medical care and modifying personal health-related behaviours (Bezruchka, 2010a).

Figure 2.8
Trajectories of Life Expectancy at Birth (e_0) and Dispersion in Age of Death ($e^†$) (Inter-individual Differences in Age of Death or Average Life Expectancy Losses Attributable to Death) for England and Wales, Japan, Sweden, and the United States

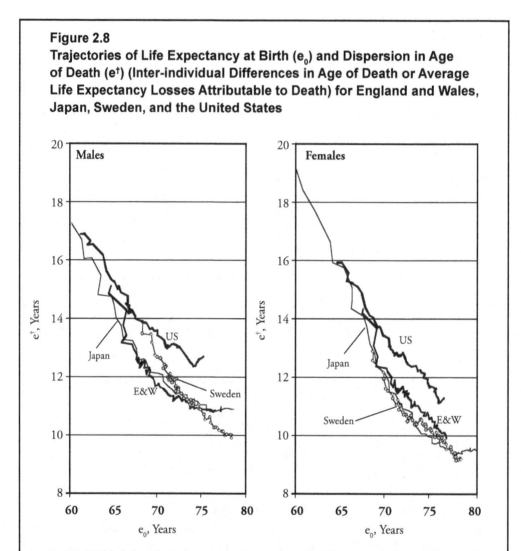

Source: V. Shkolnikov, E. Andreev et al., Losses of expected lifetime in the United States and other developed countries: Methods and empirical analyses, *Demography 48*(1) (2011): 211–239.

Developmental Origins of Health and Disease (DOHaD)

The DOHaD perspective demonstrates that a large proportion of adult health is programmed in the first 1,000 days of an individual's life, beginning with conception. Various stresses *in utero*, coupled with experience in the first few years of life after birth, forever affect health (Gluckman, Hanson et al., 2008; Gluckman, Beedle et al., 2009). Fetal nutrition, reflected by birth weight and gestational age, has an important impact on adult health (Paul, 2010). Maternal nutrition throughout a woman's lifespan before she becomes pregnant is critical for fetal, child, and adult health (Floud, Fogel et al., 2011). Socio-economic status and myriad environmental factors affect pregnancy outcomes.

Birth weight and rate of growth in childhood taken together predict chronic disease in adulthood (Barker, Osmond et al., 2005). Reactions that occur during pregnancy in response to adverse circumstances have the costly result of greater likelihood of later chronic, non-communicable diseases (Gluckman, Beedle et al., 2009). Across nations, differences in these early environments can profoundly influence a nation's health (Meza, Pourbohloul et al., 2010).

DOHaD posits that health is transmitted intergenerationally. US slavery, for example, and the stress experienced by slaves associated with deprivation, may explain the continuing low birth weight of contemporary African Americans (Jasienska, 2009), as positive changes in socioeconomic status in the US have not influenced low birth-weight rates among African American women (Colen, Geronimus et al., 2006). Fetal programming thus allows low birth weight to persist for women who were themselves born with low birth weight (Collins, Rankin et al., 2011; Hertzman & Boyce, 2010; Essex, Boyce et al., 2011; Godfrey, Sheppard et al., 2011).

Parenting of the very young is critical for health (Schore, 2005), with outcomes related to early life attachment (Ciechanowski, Russo et al., 2010). Inter-parental conflict has been shown to predict later lung function problems (Suglia, Ryan et al., 2009). Adverse childhood experiences impact later life, but good parenting may buffer their effects (Suglia, Enlow et al., 2009).

Societies with policies that recognize the importance of early life will have better health outcomes than those that neglect it. For example, national paid antenatal and paid parental leave policies impact health outcomes and reduce health inequities (Guendelman, Hubbard et al., 2009; Vrijkotte, van Der Wal et al., 2009; Heymann, Raub et al., 2011; Ruhm, 2000). Nations that spend more of their GDP on early life, (e.g., Sweden spends more public money on the first year of life than any subsequent year) enjoy better general health (OECD, 2007). Other social supports besides paid leave yield health benefits to children and the adults they become (Ray, Gornick et al., 2010).

Medical Care

The focus on health care services research in the US implies that medical care must be the critical factor influencing health and impact health inequalities. The role of medical care in producing health may be overstated in the US because not everyone in the nation has access to health care. While the terms "health" and "health care" are often considered synonymous, in fact there is little research evidence to demonstrate a substantial impact of medical care on population health outcomes for a society (Jamrozik & Hobbs, 2002; House, Schoeni et al., 2008). Certainly health care as presently organized in the US seems poorly suited to producing good health (Pritchard & Wallace, 2011).

Health care in the US is under the very profitable control of insurance companies. Their profits alone in 2005 were over $100 billion, and these profits are likely to increase substantially in the near future. At present, US health care costs represent about 18 percent of the GDP and almost half of the world's total. There appears to be no limit to the amount of medical care that Americans will pay for and consume, and costs are only slated to increase. Even with health care reform (PPACA), many millions of people will still lack access to medical services.

Increasing Inequality

Increasing inequality is considered a driver of health inequities just as it is for explaining differences in many outcomes for various other societal factors, such as teen pregnancies and youth violence (Wilkinson & Pickett, 2010). Many studies now attest to societal inequality being causally linked to worse health outcomes. Context, culture, threshold, and lag effects matter, but the concept that economic inequality is not healthy has gained considerable acceptance in Europe. There is little, if anything, about greater equality in society that is detrimental, but the concept, until recently, has been virtually unthinkable in the US.

One study found a third of all deaths in the US could be linked to the high income inequality present there when compared to the best outcomes to be found in Europe (Kondo, Sembajwe et al., 2009). To put this finding into perspective, it is equivalent to one September 11, 2001 tragedy (3,000 deaths) occurring every 30 hours continuously throughout every year. This depicts structural violence, in contrast to the 9/11 behavioural variety in which there was a discrete event, clearly a perpetrator, and greater visibility. With structural violence, deaths are continuous from the usual conditions that cause death, and there is no smoking gun (Gilligan, 1999).

Policies Driving Health Inequalities

A range of social policies are known to address many of the social and economic conditions known to affect health inequalities. In most cases, however, the US has not taken advantage of these opportunities to support the health and well-being of the population.

Labour Policy

Labour policy in the US has seen workers' wages remain flat, adjusted for inflation, since the 1970s while the incomes at the top have risen immensely. At the same time, productivity in the country has soared, but workers have not benefited commensurately (Cypher, 2011). Since 1973, labour unions have been decimated, with rates of unionization for the entire country going from 26.7 percent to 13.6 percent in 2009 and even more pronounced declines in the private sector, so there is now more than a 5:1 ratio of unionization between public and private (Economic Policy Institute, 2011; Bureau of Labor Statistics, 2011). A comparison of labour conditions, national competitiveness, and unemployment rates around the world finds the US at a great disadvantage in comparison to other rich nations (Heymann, 2009).

Family Policy

Family benefits in the US are among the lowest of all rich nations, with few cash or service transfers and only limited tax assistance (Raphael, 2007; OECD, 2008). The US stands alone among rich nations without paid antenatal or parental leave policies (Heymann, 2009; OECD, 2009a). UNICEF has compiled various reports ranking child well-being parameters in rich nations, and the US consistently stands among the worst-off nations in material, education, or health outcomes (UNICEF Innocenti Research Centre, 2010). There are remarkably few welfare programs targeted at families, especially in comparison to other rich nations (Raphael, 2010).

A work and family life transition with profound economic effects has occurred in the US. In 1970, a median two-parent, two-child family with one parent working outside the home had more disposable income after meeting necessary expenses than a similar family in 2000 in which both parents work outside the home (Warren & Tyagi, 2003).

A second demographic transition has taken place in the US. The first transition saw mortality and fertility declines and resulted in small families. In the 1970s patterns of delays in fertility and marriage, increases in single parenthood, and maternal employment outside the home arose. Higher-educated mothers delayed fertility, but those with less education did not. For less-educated mothers, employment opportunities are fewer, incomes are lower, single motherhood is the norm, and fathers are often absent. These results increase economic inequality for families and especially between richer and poorer children. The fathers of children of married mothers with low education spend less time with their children in contrast to the fathers of children of more educated mothers. Without government welfare support, child poverty increases dramatically and is transmitted intergenerationally. The US now has the most child poverty among rich nations for both single-parent and two-parent families (McLanahan, 2004).

The variety in current family structure has consequences for children's well-being, such as the developmental origins of adult disease, birth outcomes, and health (including mental health) in later life. The US has arguably the most mental illness of all nations, and much of this begins in childhood. The US also has the most psycho-pharmaceutical treatment, with increasing numbers of children on these drugs.

Women's Rights
The status of women holding political and executive business power in the US lags behind that in many nations (Hausmann, Tyson et al., 2010; United Nations, 2010). In those US states where women's status is measured by indices of political participation, economic autonomy, employment and earnings, and reproductive rights, their health is better than those living in states where they have lower status (Kawachi, Kennedy et al., 1999). Children fare worse where women have lower political, economic, and social status (Koenen, Lincoln et al., 2006). Women are now the majority in the workforce in the US, and their proportion is expected to increase rapidly in large part because they will work for lower wages, which cuts costs and increases profits for employers in a capitalist society. The remarkable lag in health outcomes for women shown earlier may well be due to the increasing demands on women in US society. Not only do they have to demonstrate excellence in mothering and homemaking, they now have to be successful in the workplace, be soccer moms, jocks, supermodels, and porn stars. By contrast, not as much, aside from earning a living, is expected from men.

Racism and Discrimination
With the election of an African-American president in the US, many feel that racism has been largely overcome, but evidence in health inequalities does not support that idea. The ethnic mix and heterogeneity of the US is often explained as the reason for its poor health status. However, many European countries and Canada have a much high percentage of a foreign-born population than the US, and the health of US immigrants tends to be better than the health of those born there. In the US, attempts are made to increase diversity in institutional settings; cultural competency trainings have become common, for example. But this perspective masks serious structural inequalities that are not only persistent for African Americans but increasing (Michaels, 2006). The African-American wealth inequities far surpass those related to income, are increasing, and

perpetuate greater inequality (Shapiro, 2004). The US meritocracy and the American Dream ideology haven't decreased health inequities among African Americans (Kwate & Meyer, 2010).

Social Assistance and Unemployment Policy

By most measures, the US is among the least generous of all rich nations in social assistance and public spending, especially for working-age people (OECD, 2011). This includes the lowest social assistance or welfare for the marginalized segments of the US, with attendant high poverty rates and the least unemployment benefits (OECD, 2009b). As with other measures, the low rates of social support are highly correlated with the relatively poor health status in the US.

Examining Political and Economic Forces behind These Public Policy Approaches

It is difficult to get a man to understand something when his salary depends upon his not understanding it.

—Upton Sinclair, 1935

The huge increase in inequality in the US to levels on par with those before the Great Depression have resulted from a variety of political policies based in neo-liberal ideology that invokes decreasing public support for the less well off, letting market mechanisms work without regulation in the belief that the rich will invest their much-increased wealth for the benefit of all through the trickle-down approach. The political power in the country is now vested in corporations that control the democratic process for their own benefit, in contrast to the situation in the 1960s, when organized labour made more contributions than business to political campaigns (Clawson, Neustadtl et al., 1998). The recent US Supreme Court's *Citizens United* decision is likely to further erode the democratic process in the country by allowing corporations to spend unlimited amounts on political advertising for election campaigns (Wiist, 2011).

The political forces that control the nation to enrich a few at the cost of everybody else are a modern example of cultural hegemony, a concept illustrated in the prison notebooks of Gramsci (Gramsci, 1973). These forces have produced a situation in which most people in the US have worse health than they might otherwise, given the comparisons with the health frontier mentioned earlier. They die from the usual illnesses and injuries. There is no outcry about the structural violence. It is as if there is an invisible, odourless, highly toxic lethal gas that envelops the oblivious nation, for business as usual is the norm. The key concept is business, as President Coolidge stated. There is a paradoxical focus on producing health in the nation beyond traditional medical care, as well as myriad other methods ranging from elixirs, supplements, spas, a huge self-help health industry, alternative treatments, health-enhancing exercises that defy description, to health-apps and who knows what the future may bring. This effort seems almost entirely a waste if it did not produce something besides huge profits.

Health Disparities Industry

Given the capitalist orientation of the US political system, it would be very surprising if a health disparities industry did not exist. A key feature of the profit-making approach is to define a problem and then set up an industry to capitalize on it. The US health disparities industry has a focus that has transformed from eliminating health disparities to reducing health disparities, which would result in a long-term need and almost unlimited "work" to address them (Shaw-Ridley & Ridley, 2010). The workforce of this industry includes health educators, health care providers, researchers, educators, administrators, consultants, policy-makers, mass media professionals, as well as consumers of prevention and health care services and the various students in pre-health and professional programs.

Profit centres of this industry include conferences, myriad continuing education offerings about health literacy, social marketing, health communication, and translation research, as well as setting up various research fellowships, teaching courses, offering degree and certificate programs, together with a flourishing publishing industry devoted to health disparities.

The Catch-22 of increasing health inequities, despite an industry tackling it, means that the well-intentioned stakeholders do not look at the root causes of health inequalities, but instead work on small issues that do not address the core concepts of population health. Upton Sinclair's quote above is key here: By not critically examining the paradigm through which work efforts proceed, there is continued employment for those involved. Shaw-Ridley and Ridley (2010) question the ethics of this industry and question a number of their practices. These include games of changing names, such as using community-based participatory research, as well as "illusionary collaborations and partnerships," including centres of excellence. Others they describe are "dysfunctional quality assurance and performance standards," an "anaemic response by agencies to fundamental causes," and "fragmentation of knowledge advancement." Some have more directly questioned the politics of health inequalities research in the US (Navarro, 2004). Exploratory discussions produce a variety of approaches (Krieger, Alegría et al., 2010).

Political Culture

There are major differences in the political cultures of the US compared to neighbouring Canada and western Europe that are rooted in history (Alesina & Glaeser, 2004). One reason offered for the widespread toleration of greater inequality in the US includes the lack of proportional representation, which makes it difficult for reform parties that might push for redistribution to take hold. The US has never been defeated militarily on its own territory, in contrast to Europe, where social democracies took hold after World War II (Navarro & Schmitt, 2005). The kind of class analysis of European Marxism was less likely to be applied in the US with its waves of immigration and melting-pot culture. European nations have relatively recent constitutions, in contrast to the United States Constitution, which was drafted by a minority of wealthy white men in 1787 and, among other effects, served to protect their wealth against expropriation. The US Supreme Court defends the rights of the wealthy. US racism concentrates poverty and prejudices against redistribution. Success in the US is considered a sign of goodness, reinforcing the moral failings of the poor (Alesina & Glaeser, 2004).

Compared to other nations, the US has the lowest proportion of the population who believe in the concept of the state taking care of the very poor in society; however, there are significant differences between the two major political parties (Pew Global, 2007).

Neo-liberal Restructuring and Welfare State Retrenchment
The neo-liberal effects on social welfare have been more pervasive in the US than in any other rich nation. A major result of many decades of restructuring, together with the decline of government welfare support for families, has been the rise of non-governmental organizations (NGOs), non-profit organizations that essentially depend on charitable giving or government grants for their existence. The dismantling of federal, state, and local government support has led to a greater role for these loosely organized external agencies.

The food bank situation in the US illustrates this process. Jobs used to be plentiful, and attaining sufficient food was not a problem for most people. In the 1970s there were relatively few destitute or homeless families in the US, and a few hundred missions throughout the nation helped feed them. In 1981 President Reagan cut the funding for low-cost housing and mental health services, which led to a dramatic increase in the numbers of homeless and destitute in the country, so the homeless became a daily observable fact of life. Statistics gathered by the federal government have found that perhaps one in 200 people has used a shelter in recent years (Wikipedia Homeless in the US). Now myriad NGOs provide various services for the homeless that include shelters and food banks. These institutions depend on individual generosity, including volunteer time, and their numbers have increased immensely so that by 2005, there were over 40,000 agencies providing food for various groups in the US. They have organized into networks so that, for example, members of Feeding America provide food for over 25 million Americans, or as many as one in 12.

Influence of Business and Corporate Sectors
The corporate sector in the US has enhanced its profitability in many ways that adversely impact economic inequalities in the nation. Corporations in the 1950s paid on average nearly a third of the federal tax bill, but now the figure is close to 6 percent. This has been brought about through a variety of mechanisms brokered by an extensive corporate lobbying industry in the nation's capital. In 1975 there were 3,400 registered lobbyists in Washington, DC, whereas by 2005 there were almost 10 times as many (Reich, 2007). This has allowed many legal ways of enhancing profits by moving production to poor countries, garnering government subsidies, decreasing tax burdens through a variety of mechanisms, and giving very high compensation to corporate executives by tying bonus pay to stock options.

The corporate sector has had a very strategic, immensely influential role in producing the health inequities in the US by increasing inequality. Because the public's view of health is grounded in individual responsibility rather than in a structural perspective, there is no appreciation of the links. This is remarkably similar to individuals' acceptance of their economic situations in the US that is divorced from any perception of political or corporate responsibility.

Recommendations for Future Activities
A key barrier to improving the health status of people in the US is that the understanding of what produces health in society is limited to personal health-related behaviours and to medical care (Lillie-Blanton, Brodie et al., 2000; Robert, Booske et al., 2008; Robert & Booske, 2011). This approach is taken by society at large, including most people involved in public health activities, those working in medical care, teachers, and the media. Creating a better

public understanding of social and economic determinants of health will be a critical but very challenging political step in addressing the relative health declines in the US (Gollust & Lantz, 2009; Gollust, Lantz et al., 2009).

If the goal is to improve US health to the level of, say, the frontier nations, the methods to do so do not require further research, but rather a commitment to act upon general guidelines. This is akin to John Snow removing the pump handle that was spreading disease during the cholera epidemic in the UK (Bezruchka, 2010a). The overarching aim would be to decrease economic inequality throughout the nation and to use the proceeds from that effort to foster a healthy early life environment for families. An important first step would be putting in place generous supports for antenatal and parental paid leave and community support for families and children, including those *in utero* and young infants. It would be important to identify other means of fostering caring and sharing relationships at all levels of society and monitoring progress toward those goals. The country could adopt a guaranteed annual income level for all families, particularly those with children, as was proposed by President Nixon in 1969 (Burke & Burke, 1974; Quadagno, 1990).

The impact of universal health care on decreasing health inequalities remains an open question. There is no reason why the US should remain the only rich nation without appropriate quality health care available for all.

The health disparities industry requires "*a genuine movement* to eliminate the fundamental causes of health disparities—beyond interventions and new programs that offer anaemic responses to a complex problem. The solutions at best may necessitate 'cultural confrontation' strategies—confronting political, social, economic, and education underpinnings of health disparities" (Shaw-Ridley & Ridley, 2010, 464).

The changes required to decrease health inequities in the US will occur only with broader awareness of what produces health in a nation. The education process for the nation needs to be multi-pronged and targeted at all levels, from preschool to post-graduate school. After the Russian launch of *Sputnik* in the late 1950s, the US realized its gap in science and math training and set a goal to increase its academic capability and to land a human on the Moon by the end of the following decade. The effort was successful in only 12 years, but the health challenge will take generations.

Mass media will be an important tool in the effort to bring about social transformation. The US media are controlled by a small number of corporate entities whose interests in enhancing profits do not cater to a population health agenda. Fostering critical thinking in education about the role of the media in US society could eventually lead to mechanisms to stem this power and direct it toward benefitting the well-being of citizens. With the advent of new media, including the Internet, there are many possibilities for broader education that could be spared the corporate domination of the print and broadcast modes. Legislation that fosters "net neutrality" would benefit the development of independent media that could engage the public in broader discussion of health (Nunziato, 2009).

The events of the economic crisis beginning in late 2007 and beyond were seen as an opportunity to rethink how the US economy functions and to build grassroots social and political movements. Instead, if anything, the grass has lost its roots and is withering. Whether the Occupy movement will revive the grass is unclear.

Conclusion

People in the US die much younger than those in many other countries. To date, most health-related efforts in the US have focused on increasing access to medical care and in changing personal health-related behaviours. This approach has not been successful in either improving the health of Americans in comparison to other nations, or in decreasing the health inequities within the country. At the heart of the reason why lies the political economic choices that structure the nature of caring and sharing relationships that produce health. To take on the neo-liberal enterprise that produces ill health in the US will require greater efforts than the Manhattan Project, undertaken when the US built the first nuclear weapon. At least as much is at stake now as when that effort was begun.

Critical Thinking Questions

1. Why is there so little awareness of the poor health status of the US in relation to other rich nations?
2. Is the health status of a nation compared to others a reasonable assessment of that country?
3. Why is there such a focus on the relatively less important factors affecting health inequalities that are related to personal behaviours and choices than on those related to societal political structures?
4. In the midst of the current global economic crisis, is there a political revolution going on that will change societal relationships all around the world and lead to a post-carbon economy with different priorities for people and the planet?

Recommended Readings

Understanding how the world works is necessary to make it better. Delving into such a big topic requires a guide. One of the best is Noam Chomsky, who has written an immense number of books and is the world's most cited living person. You could choose from a volume containing four works or an edited version of his ideas, or just about any other of his writings.

Chomsky, N., Barsamian, D., et al. (2011). *How the world works*. Berkeley: Soft Skull Press.
Chomsky, N., Mitchell, P.R., et al. (2002). *Understanding power: The indispensable Chomsky*. New York: New Press.
   The advantage of this volume is that the footnotes are available in a separate pdf online at http://www.understandingpower.com/AllChaps.pdf.

Gluckman, P.D., Beedle, A., et al. (2009). *Principles of evolutionary medicine*. Oxford/New York: Oxford University Press.
   A scientific revolution is taking place on understanding the origins of chronic diseases of aging, which are increasingly understood to be programmed in early life. These are difficult concepts for many to grasp and, like anything worthwhile, requires considerable work. This book frames the concepts in a broad perspective.

Each of these shows how the United States of America has a peculiar political system. These ideas are usually not discussed in American schools.

Kingdon, J.W. (1999). *America the unusual.* New York: Worth Publishers.

Lipset, S.M. (1996). *American exceptionalism: A double-edged sword.* New York: W.W. Norton.

Russell, J.W. (2011). *Double standard: Social policy in Europe and the United States.* Lanham: Rowman & Littlefield.

Wilkinson, R., & Pickett, K.E. (2010). *The spirit level: Why equality is better for everyone.* London: Penguin.
> The key source for understanding the structural factors affecting health of populations, this book has been a bestseller in Europe and has been translated into more than a dozen languages. It may be starting to have an impact on thinking in the US.

Recommended Websites

Equality Trust: http://www.equalitytrust.org.uk/
> The Equality Trust explores the effects of structural inequalities in society. It complements the Spirit Level recommended in the previous section and gives access to those who disagree with these ideas, together with responses.

Gapminder: http://www.gapminder.org/
> This website allows one to explore various data around the world relating to different indicators and see animations and trends over the last 100 years or more. It is a treasure trove.

Institute for Health Metrics and Evaluation: http://www.healthmetricsandevaluation.org/
> This website gives detailed health data customizable to the countries and indicators you wish to study and observe trends. You can see a variety of graphical and map displays. US county details are especially useful in understanding health inequalities there.

Population Health Forum: http://depts.washington.edu/eqhlth/
> This University of Washington website has material to help others present the concepts underlying the health of societies. There are many useful links, as well as broadcast talks by the author.

References

Adler, N.E., Boyce, T., et al. (1994). Socioeconomic status and health: The challenge of the gradient. *American Psychologist, 49*(1), 15–24.

Agrawal, J.R., Huebner, J., et al. (2005). Medical students' knowledge of the US health care system and their preferences for curricular change: A national survey. *Academic Medicine, 80*(5), 484–488.

Alesina, A. & Glaeser, E.L. (2004). *Fighting poverty in the US and Europe: A world of difference.* Oxford: Oxford University Press.

Avendano, M., Glymour, M.M., et al. (2009). Health disadvantage in US adults aged 50 to 74 years: A comparison of the health of rich and poor Americans with that of Europeans. *American Journal of Public Health, 99*(3), 540–548.

Banks, J., Marmot, M., et al. (2006). Disease and disadvantage in the United States and in England. *JAMA, 295*(17), 2037–2045.

Barker, D.J.P., Osmond, C., et al. (2005). Trajectories of growth among children who have coronary events as adults. *New England Journal of Medicine, 353*(17), 1802–1809.

Beckles, G.L. & Truman, B.I. (2011). Education and income—United States, 2005 and 2009. *MMWR, 60*(1), 13–17.

Berkman, L.F. & Kawachi, I. (Eds.). (2000). *Social epidemiology.* New York: Oxford University Press.

Bezruchka, S. (2001). Societal hierarchy and the health Olympics. *Canadian Medical Association Journal, 164*(12), 1701–1703.

Bezruchka, S. (2010a). Epidemiological approaches to population health. In T. Bryant, D. Raphael & M.H. Rioux (Eds.), *Staying alive: Critical perspectives on health, illness, and health care* (2nd ed., pp. 13–40). Toronto: Canadian Scholars' Press Inc.

Bezruchka, S. (2010b). Health equity in the USA. *Social Alternatives, 29*(3), 50–56.

Bezruchka, S.A. (2012). The hurrider I go the behinder I get: The deteriorating international ranking of US health status. *Annual Review of Public Health, 33*(1), 157–173.

Bureau of Labor Statistics. (2011). Union members summary. Retrieved from: http://www.bls.gov/news.release/union2.nr0.htm.

Burke, V.J., & Burke, V. (1974). *Nixon's good deed: Welfare reform.* New York: Columbia University Press.

CDC. (2011). *Chronic disease prevention and health promotion.* Retrieved from: http://www.cdc.gov/chronicdisease/overview/index.htm.

Ciechanowski, P., Russo, J., et al. (2010). Relationship styles and mortality in patients with diabetes. *Diabetes Care, 33*(3), 539–544.

Clawson, D., Neustadtl, A., et al. (1998). *Dollars and votes: How business campaign contributions subvert democracy.* Philadelphia: Temple University Press.

Colen, C.G., Geronimus, A.T., et al. (2006). Maternal upward socioeconomic mobility and black-white disparities in infant birthweight. *American Journal of Public Health, 96*(11), 2032–2039.

Collins, J.W., Jr., Rankin, K.M., et al. (2011). African American women's lifetime upward economic mobility and preterm birth: The effect of fetal programming. *American Journal of Public Health, 101*(4), 714–719.

Cooper, R.S., Kennelly, J.F., et al. (2006). Health in Cuba. *International Journal of Epidemiology, 35*(4), 817–824.

Cutler, D.M., Lange, F., et al. (2010). *Explaining the rise in educational gradients in mortality.* National Bureau of Economic Research Working Paper Series no. 15678. Cambridge MA: National Bureau of Economic Research.

Cypher, J.M. (2011). Nearly $2 trillion purloined from US workers in 2009. *Dollars & Sense.* Boston, Economic Affairs Bureau, Issue 295, 24–25.

David, R.J. & Collins, J.W. (1997). Differing birth weight among infants of US-born blacks, African-born blacks, and US-born whites. *New England Journal of Medicine, 337*(17), 1209–1214.

Duménil, G. & Lèvy, D. (2004). *Capital resurgent: Roots of the neoliberal revolution.* Cambridge: Harvard University Press.

Economic Policy Institute. (2011). *State of working America: Declining unionization.* Retrieved from: http://www.stateofworkingamerica.org/charts/view/204.

Essex, M.J., Boyce, T.W., et al. (2011). Epigenetic vestiges of early developmental adversity: Childhood stress exposure and DNA methylation in adolescence. *Child Development,* doi: 10.1111j1467-8624.2011.01641x.

Ezzati, M., Friedman, A.B., et al. (2008). The reversal of fortunes: Trends in county mortality and cross-county mortality disparities in the United States. *PLoS Medicine, 5*(4), e66.

Feeny, D., Kaplan, M.S., et al. (2010). Comparing population health in the United States and Canada. *Population Health Metrics, 8,* 8.

Floud, R., Fogel, R.W., et al. (2011). *The changing body health, nutrition, and human development in the Western world since 1700.* New York: Cambridge University Press.

Frieden, T.R. (2011). Foreword: CDC health disparities and inequalities report—United States, 2011. *MMWR, 60*(1), 1–2.

Gilligan, J. (1999). Structural violence. In R. Gottesman (Ed.), *Violence in America: An encyclopedia* (pp. 229–233). New York: Scribner.

Glei, D.A., Meslé, F., et al. (2010). Diverging trends in life expectancy at age 50: A look at causes of death. In E.M. Crimmins, S.H. Preston & B. Cohen (Eds.), *International differences in mortality at older ages: Dimensions and sources* (pp. 17–67).

Gluckman, P.D., Beedle, A., et al. (2009). *Principles of evolutionary medicine.* Oxford/New York: Oxford University Press.

Gluckman, P.D., Hanson, M.A., et al. (2008). Effect of *in utero* and early-life conditions on adult health and disease. *New England Journal of Medicine, 359*(1), 61–73.

Godfrey, K.M., Sheppard, A., et al. (2011). Epigenetic gene promoter methylation at birth is associated with child's later adiposity. *Diabetes, 60*(5), 1528–1534.

Gollust, S.E., & Lantz, P.M. (2009). Communicating population health: Print news media coverage of type 2 diabetes. *Social Science & Medicine, 69*(7), 1091–1098.

Gollust, S.E., Lantz, P.M., et al. (2009). The polarizing effect of news media messages about the social determinants of health. *American Journal of Public Health, 99*(12), 2160–2167.

Gramsci, A. (1973). *Letters from prison.* New York: Harper & Row.

Guendelman, S., Hubbard, A., et al. (2009). Maternity leave in the ninth month of pregnancy and birth outcomes among working women. *Women's Health Issues, 19*(1), 30–37.

Hausmann, R., Tyson, L.D., et al. (2010). *The global gender gap index 2010.* Geneva: World Economic Forum.

Hertzman, C. & Boyce, T. (2010). How experience gets under the skin to create gradients in developmental health. *Annual Review of Public Health, 31*(1), 329–347.

Heymann, J. (2009). *Raising the global floor: Dismantling the myth that we can't afford good working conditions for everyone.* Stanford: Stanford University Press.

Heymann, J., Raub, A., et al. (2011). Creating and using new data sources to analyze the relationship between social policy and global health: The case of maternal leave. *Public Health Reports, 126*(Suppl. 3), 127–134.

Hogan, M.C., Foreman, K.J., et al. (2010). Maternal mortality for 181 countries, 1980–2008: A systematic analysis of progress towards Millennium Development Goal 5. *The Lancet, 375*(9726), 1609–1623.

House, J.S., Schoeni, R.F., et al. (2008). The health effects of social and economic policy: The promise and challenge for research and policy. In R.F. Schoeni, J.S. House, G.A. Kaplan & H. Pollack (Eds.), *Making Americans healthier: Social and economic policy as health policy* (pp. 3–26). New York: Russell Sage Foundation.

Institute for Health Metrics and Evaluation. (2011). *Life expectancy in most US counties falls behind world's healthiest nations.* Retrieved from: http://www.healthmetricsandevaluation.org/news-events/news-release/life-expectancy-most-us-counties-falls-behind-worlds-healthiest-nations.

Institute of Medicine. (2003). *The future of the public's health in the 21st century.* Washington: National Academy Press.

Jamrozik, K., & Hobbs, M.S.T. (2002). Medical care and public health. In R. Detels, J. McEwen, R. Beaglehole & H. Tanaka (Eds.), *Oxford textbook of public health* (pp. 215–242). Oxford: Oxford University Press.

Jasienska, G. (2009). Low birth weight of contemporary African Americans: An intergenerational effect of slavery? *American Journal of Human Biology, 21*(1), 16–24.

Kawachi, I., Kennedy, B.P., et al. (1999). Women's status and the health of women and men: A view from the States. *Social Science & Medicine, 48*(1), 21–32.

Kingdon, J.W. (1999). *America the unusual.* New York: Worth Publishers.

Koenen, K.C., Lincoln, A., et al. (2006). Omen's status and child well-being: A state-level analysis. *Social Science & Medicine, 63*(12), 2999–3012.

Kondo, N., Sembajwe, G., et al. (2009). Income inequality, mortality, and self-rated health: Meta-analysis of multilevel studies. *British Medical Journal, 339*(Nov.): b4471, 1–12.

Krieger, N., Alegría, M., et al. (2010). Who, and what, causes health inequities? Reflections on emerging debates from an exploratory Latin American/North American workshop. *Journal of Epidemiology and Community Health, 64*(9), 747–749.

Kulkarni, S., Levin-Rector, A., et al. (2011). Falling behind: Life expectancy in US counties from 2000 to 2007 in an international context. *Population Health Metrics, 9*(16), 1–12.

Kunitz, S.J., McKee, M., et al. (2010). State political cultures and the mortality of African Americans and American Indians. *Health & Place, 16*(3), 558–566.

Kunitz, S.J., & Pesis-Katz, I. (2005). Mortality of white Americans, African Americans, and Canadians: The causes and consequences for health of welfare state institutions and policies. *Milbank Quarterly, 83*(1), 5–39.

Kwate, N.O.A., & Meyer, I.H. (2010). The myth of meritocracy and African American health. *American Journal of Public Health, 100*(10), 1831–1834.

Lillie-Blanton, M., Brodie, M., et al. (2000). Race, ethnicity, and the health care system: Public perceptions and experiences. *Medical Care Research Review, 57*(Suppl. 1), 218–235.

Lipset, S.M. (1996). *American exceptionalism: A double-edged sword.* New York: W.W. Norton.

MacDorman, M.F., & Mathews, T. (2009). *Behind international rankings of infant mortality: How the United States compares with Europe.* Hyattsville: National Center for Health Statistics.

Martin, J.A. (2011). Preterm births—United States, 2007. *MMWR, 60*(1), 78–79.

Martinson, M.L., Teitler, J.O., et al. (2011). Health across the life span in the United States and England. *American Journal of Epidemiology, 173*(8), 858–865.

McLanahan, S. (2004). Diverging destinies: How children are faring under the second demographic transition. *Demography, 41*(4), 604–627.

Meza, R., Pourbohloul, B., et al. (2010). Birth cohort patterns suggest that infant survival predicts adult mortality rates. *Journal of Developmental Origins of Health and Disease, 1*(03), 174–183.

Michaels, W.B. (2006). *Trouble with diversity: How we learned to love identity and ignore inequality.* New York: Metropolitan Henry Holt.

Michaud, P.-C., Goldman, D., et al. (2011). Differences in health between Americans and western Europeans: Effects on longevity and public finance. *Social Science & Medicine, 73*(2), 254–263.

Murray, C.J.L., Kulkarni, S.C., et al. (2006). Eight Americas: Investigating mortality disparities across races, counties, and race-counties in the United States. *PLoS Medicine, 3*(9), e260.

Muszynska, M.M., & Rau, R. (2009). Falling short of highest life expectancy: How many Americans might have been alive in the twentieth century? *Population and Development Review, 35*(3), 585–603.

National Preventative Health Taskforce. (2010). *Taking preventative action—a response to Australia: The healthiest country by 2020—The report of the National Preventative Health Taskforce.* Canberra: Commonwealth of Australia.

Navarro, V. (2004). The politics of health inequalities research in the United States. *International Journal of Health Services, 34*(1), 87–99.

Navarro, V., & Schmitt, J. (2005). Economic efficiency versus social equality? The US liberal model versus the European social model. *International Journal of Health Services, 35*(4), 613–630.

Nunziato, D.C. (2009). *Virtual freedom: Net neutrality and free speech in the Internet age.* Stanford: Stanford Law Books.

OECD. (2006). *Society at a glance: OECD social indicators.* Paris: Organisation for Economic Co-operation and Development.

OECD. (2007). *Health at a glance: OECD indicators 2007.* Paris: Organisation for Economic Co-operation and Development.

OECD. (2008). *Babies and bosses—balancing work and family life.* Paris: Organisation for Economic Co-operation and Development.

OECD. (2009a). *Doing better for children.* Paris: Organisation for Economic Co-operation and Development.

OECD. (2009b). *Society at a glance: OECD social indicators.* Paris: Organisation for Economic Co-operation and Development.

OECD. (2011). *Society at a glance: OECD social indicators.* Paris: Organisation for Economic Co-operation and Development.

Olshansky, S.J., Passaro, D.J., et al. (2005). A potential decline in life expectancy in the United States in the 21st century. *New England Journal of Medicine, 352*(11), 1138–1145.

Pappas, G., Queen, S., et al. (1993). The increasing disparity in mortality between socioeconomic groups in the United States, 1960 and 1986. *New England Journal of Medicine, 329*(2), 103–109.

Paul, A.M. (2010). *Origins: How the nine months before birth shape the rest of our lives.* New York: Free Press.

Peltzman, S. (2009). Mortality inequality. *Journal of Economic Perspectives, 23*(4), 175–190.

Pew Global. (2007). *World publics welcome global trade—but not immigration.* 47-nation Pew Global Attitudes Survey. Washington: The Pew Research Center.

Pritchard, C., & Wallace, M.S. (2011). Comparing the USA, UK, and 17 Western countries' efficiency and effectiveness in reducing mortality. *JRSM Short Reports, 2*(7), 1–10.

Pynchon, T. (1973). *Gravity's rainbow.* New York: Viking.

Quadagno, J. (1990). Race, class, and gender in the US welfare state: Nixon's failed family assistance plan. *American Sociological Review, 55*(1), 11–28.

Rajaratnam, J.K., Marcus, J.R., et al. (2010a). Neonatal, postneonatal, childhood, and under-5 mortality for 187 countries, 1970–2010: A systematic analysis of progress towards Millennium Development Goal 4. *The Lancet, 375*(9730), 1988–2008.

Rajaratnam, J.K., Marcus, J.R., et al. (2010b). Worldwide mortality in men and women aged 15–59 years from 1970 to 2010: A systematic analysis. *The Lancet, 375*(9727), 1704–1720.

Raphael, D. (2007). Public policies and the problematic USA population health profile. *Health Policy, 84*(1), 101–111.

Raphael, D. (2010). The health of Canada's children. Part III: Public policy and the social determinants of health. *Paediatrics and Child Health, 15*(3), 143–149.

Ray, R., Gornick, J.C., et al. (2010). Who cares? Assessing generosity and gender equality in parental leave policy designs in 21 countries. *Journal of European Social Policy, 20*(3), 196–216.

Reich, R.B. (2007). *Supercapitalism: The transformation of business, democracy, and everyday life.* New York: Alfred A. Knopf.

Robert, S.A., & Booske, B.C. (2011). US opinions on health determinants and social policy as health policy. *American Journal of Public Health, 101*(9), 1655–1663.

Robert, S.A., Booske, B.C., et al. (2008). Public views on determinants of health, interventions to improve health, and priorities for government. *WMJ, 107*(3), 124–130.

Ruhm, C.J. (2000). Parental leave and child health. *Journal of Health Economics, 19*(6), 931–960.

Schore, A.N. (2005). Attachment, affect regulation, and the developing right brain: Linking developmental neuroscience to pediatrics. *Pediatrics in Review, 26*(6), 204–217.

Shapiro, T.M. (2004). *The hidden cost of being African American: How wealth perpetuates inequality.* New York: Oxford University Press.

Shaw-Ridley, M., & Ridley, C.R. (2010). The health disparities industry: Is it an ethical conundrum? *Health Promotion Practice, 11*(4), 454–464.

Shkolnikov, V., Andreev, E., et al. (2011). Losses of expected lifetime in the United States and other developed countries: Methods and empirical analyses. *Demography, 48*(1), 211–239.

Siddiqi, A., & Hertzman, C. (2007). Towards an epidemiological understanding of the effects of long-term institutional changes on population health: A case study of Canada versus the USA. *Social Science & Medicine, 64*(3), 589–603.

Siddiqi, A., & Nguyen, Q.C. (2010). A cross-national comparative perspective on racial inequities in health: The USA versus Canada. *Journal of Epidemiology and Community Health, 64*(01), 29–35.

Sinclair, U. (1935). *I, candidate for governor: And how I got licked.* New York: Farrar & Rinehart, Inc.

Smedley, B.D., Stith, A.Y., et al. (2003). *Unequal treatment: Confronting racial and ethnic disparities in health care.* Washington: National Academy Press.

Suglia, S.F., Enlow, M.B., et al. (2009). Maternal intimate partner violence and increased asthma incidence in children: Buffering effects of supportive caregiving. *Archives Pediatric Adolescent Medicine, 163*(3), 244–250.

Truman, B.I., Smith, C.K., et al. (2011). Rationale for regular reporting on health disparities and inequalities—United States Supplements. *MMWR, 60*(1), 3–10.

UNICEF Innocenti Research Centre. (2010). *The children left behind: A league table of inequality in child well-being in the world's rich countries.* Innocenti Report Card no. 9, December. Florence: UNICEF.

United Nations. (2010). *The world's women 2010: Trends and statistics.* New York: United Nations.

United States Congress, Office of Technology Assessment. (1993). *International health statistics: What the numbers mean for the United States.* Washington: Office of Technology Assessment, United States Congress.

Vrijkotte, T.G.M., van Der Wal, M.F., et al. (2009). First-trimester working conditions and birthweight: A prospective cohort study. *American Journal of Public Health, 99*(8), 1409–1416.

Warren, E., & Tyagi, A.W. (2003). *The two-income trap: Why middle-class mothers and fathers are going broke.* New York: Basic Books.

Wiist, W. (2011). Citizens united, public health, and democracy: The Supreme Court ruling, its implications, and proposed action. *American Journal of Public Health*, AJPH.2010.300043.

Wilkinson, R., & Pickett, K.E. (2010). *The spirit level: Why equality is better for everyone.* London: Penguin.

Willson, A.E. (2009). "Fundamental causes" of health disparities: A comparative analysis of Canada and the United States. *International Sociology, 24*(1), 93–113.

Wilmoth, J., Boe, C., et al. (2010). Geographic differences in life expectancy at age 50 in the United States compared with other high-income countries. In E.M. Crimmins, S.H. Preston & B. Cohen (Eds.), *International differences in mortality at older ages: Dimensions and sources* (pp. 336–366). Washington: National Academies Press.

Chapter 3

Australian Experiences

Fran Baum, Matt Fisher, and Angela Lawless

Introduction

Australia is a nation of some 22.7 million people, and sits at the intersection between southeast Asia and the southwestern Pacific. It is around 7.6 million km^2 in area, consisting of the continental mainland, Tasmania, and many surrounding, smaller islands. Australia is a high-income country, with a gross national income per capita in the top 10 among OECD member countries (around US$36,900 in 2008). Annual average growth in GDP per capita in Australia from 1998 to 2008 was 4.6 percent, similar to the UK at 4.3 percent (Australian Bureau of Statistics, 2011b).

Australia's climate and geography place significant constraints on the pattern of human settlement. Sixty-five percent of the population live in one of the five major coastal cities, and 85 percent of the population are urban. Recent growth has been concentrated in the outer suburbs of Sydney, Melbourne, and Brisbane, and in clusters of regional development along the eastern coastline (Stilwell & Troy, 2000). Approximately 30 percent of Aboriginal peoples live in major urban centres (over 100,000), 42 percent in smaller urban centres, and the remainder in rural and remote areas (Memmott & Moran, 2001).

Australians have long prided themselves on being the country of a "fair go" in which all citizens have equal access to social, economic, and political rights. Yet historical and contemporary analysis shows that there are many Australians who have been excluded from the "fair go," most significantly Australia's Aboriginal and Torres Strait Islander peoples.[1] This chapter examines the extent of health inequalities in Australia and the ways in which issues of equity have played out in the Australian political system. It also examines the ways in which health equity has been a consideration in policy and the impact of social movements on public policy development related to health inequalities.

National Description and Political Organization and Structure

Australia has a stable, democratic system of government. It is a federation of six states (New South Wales, Queensland, South Australia, Tasmania, Victoria, and Western Australia) and two territories (Australian Capital Territory and Northern Territory). British colonization of Australia commenced in 1788, with six individual colonies established over the next 50 years. By the 1850s, each colony had achieved self-government in the form of a constitutional monarchy and partially democratic, Westminster-style Parliaments. The Australian Federation was formed in 1901, although states feared loss of sovereignty, and the smaller states feared political dominance by the larger states.

The Australian Constitution reflects this tension. Trade barriers were removed, while measures to protect states included a two-part legislature and a division of powers between Commonwealth and state governments (Parkin & Summers, 2010). Today, the Commonwealth government has most of the revenue-raising capacity while states are responsible for direct regulation and delivery of most public services, including education and health. Differences in ideology, political interest, or legislative structures can make federal and state relationships difficult. Australia also has 717 local governments.

Population Demographics

Australia's population of 22 million is currently growing by 1.4 percent annually, down from 2.2 percent in 2008. Fertility rate is below replacement level at 1.89 children per woman, and falling slightly. The median age of Australians is currently around 37 years and increasing. Between 1990 and 2010, the proportion of Australians aged 65 years and over increased from 11.1 percent to 13.6 percent. Aboriginal peoples make up about 2.5 percent of Australia's population, but are overrepresented in rates of low socio-economic status, ill health, poor housing, and incarceration. Thus, the health status of Aboriginal peoples is of particular significance to health inequalities in Australia.

Aboriginal peoples have lived in Australia for at least 40,000 years (Hiscock, 2008). Between 300,000 and 1 million Indigenous peoples (Trewin, 2002) lived across the continent and its islands at the time of British colonization (Memmott & Moran, 2001). These peoples had distinctive regional languages and cultures. The Aboriginal population declined sharply after colonization in response to introduced disease, repression, loss of land, and disruption of culture, and this decline continued until the early 20th century (Trewin, 2002).

Treatment of Aboriginal Peoples

As colonization progressed, Aboriginal peoples were increasingly moved off traditional lands onto specially established reserves (Memmott & Moran, 2001). This process of dispossession was justified by the doctrine of *terra nullius*, which defined Australian land as owned by no one (Jupp, 1998). The status of Aboriginal peoples as citizens was further eroded through paternalistic legislation in various forms (Peterson & Sanders, 1998), such that "by 1911 the Northern Territory and every State except Tasmania had 'protectionist legislation' giving the Chief Protector or Protection Board extensive power to control Indigenous people" (Human Rights and Equal Opportunities Commission, 1997, 23).

This included various measures to forcibly separate Aboriginal children from their families and culture, practices that continued well into the 20th century (Human Rights and Equal Opportunities Commission, 1997). Thus, some of the basic conditions for the continuing health divide between Aboriginal and non-Aboriginal Australians were established (Saggers & Gray, 1991).

The Australian government gained powers to legislate with respect to Aboriginal peoples in 1967 through a referendum that also enabled Aboriginal peoples who had previously been specifically excluded to be counted in population statistics—essential data to enable description of Aboriginal health status. In 1972 the conservative Coalition government replaced the discourse of assimilation with "integration," but there were no concessions on the important issue of land rights. Not until the election of the Whitlam Labor government at the end of 1972 was a policy of "self-determination" adopted and moves to legislate for Aboriginal land rights begun (Robbins & Summers, 2010). The notion of *terra nullius* was not overturned until 1992, when a landmark High Court judgment, known as the Mabo Judgment, was given.

Immigration and Multiculturalism
Australia remained determinedly British during the first century and a half of European settlement. Non-Europeans were effectively barred from immigration under the White Australia policy, citizenship rights were restricted to British subjects, and quotas or prohibitions on non-British immigration were employed. Small communities of other ethnicities were established, but these were exceptions to the rule. Non-British immigration opened up in 1947 in a postwar environment focused on nation-building and population growth (Jupp, 1998). The government recruited large numbers of "displaced persons" from camps in central Europe. Nevertheless, the White Australia policy saw Jews actively discouraged from immigrating, as well as Germans and Italians, and Asian refugees who had fled the Japanese were deported. The Displaced Persons program was completed by 1953, but had opened up the possibility of further migration programs.

In the 1950s and 1960s Australia looked to migrants for labour, and communities of southern European migrants began to develop in the major cities. By the mid-1970s immigrants came mainly from the poorest European countries (Jupp, 1998). Discriminatory immigration policies were finally abolished in 1973. Since then the mix of immigrant origins has changed considerably, with greater numbers from countries in Asia, the Middle East, and Africa. Current levels of migration to Australia are around 150,000 to 170,000 annually, accounting for approximately 60 percent of Australia's population growth (Department of Immigration and Citizenship, 2011a).

Contemporary Australia is highly ethnically diverse. Since 1945, 7 million people have migrated to Australia. Today, a quarter of Australia's 22 million people were born overseas, and 4 million speak a language other than English. Australians speak over 260 languages and identify with more than 270 ancestries (Department of Immigration and Citizenship, 2011b).

Form of Government and Political Parties
Nationally, Australia is governed by a Parliament with two chambers: the House of Representatives (single members represent a geographic division and are elected by a preferential voting system) and a Senate (12 senators represent each of the six states and are elected by a

system of proportional representation). The parliamentary system is based on the Westminster system, with government formed by the party that can command a majority in the House of Representatives. State and territory government structures and electoral methods vary. For example, Queensland has a unicameral Parliament, while all other states are bicameral. Generally, governments are formed (again) by the party able to command a majority within a lower house consisting of representatives of area electorates. Tasmania's House of Assembly elects five members per electorate by a proportional voting system. Other states use single-member electorates and preferential voting.

In the past 50 years the national government has been formed by two political groupings: the Australian Labor Party and a coalition between the Liberal Party and the National Party. The Australian Labor Party (ALP) arose through the trade union movement in the 1890s and first formed the government in 1904. From an initial socialist platform, the ALP has moved through phases of postwar nation-building, to social democratic reforms in the 1970s, to a form of liberal welfare model in the 1980s and 1990s (Saint-Arnaud & Bernard, 2003), combining neo-liberal market reforms and privatization with social democratic policies in education and health care, aged pensions, and welfare assistance for disadvantaged groups (Quiggin, 2001; Woodward, Parkin & Summers, 2010). It has had a strong commitment to Medicare, a national universal health insurance scheme funded by a progressive levy and general revenue.

The Liberal Party of Australia (Liberals) consolidated previous liberal-conservative forces in 1945, combining elements of *laissez-faire* economic liberalism with small *l* social liberal and social conservative values (Woodward et al., 2010). The Liberal Party governed in coalition for 23 years from 1949 to 1972, and for another seven years from 1975 to 1983. In 1996 it won government under John Howard in coalition with the socially conservative National Party, which has its roots in rural Australia. The party shifted significantly to the right, and over four terms of government it pursued socially conservative policies in industrial relations, education, Indigenous affairs, multiculturalism, drug policy, and asylum seekers (Woodward et al., 2010).

The ALP and Liberal-National Coalition have moved significantly to the right over the last several decades, and now adopt very similar policy orientations on a range of major issues (Quiggin, 2001). The progressive voice in Australian politics now comes in large part from the Australian Greens Party, which has gained significant ground in the federal Parliament and in 2011 held the balance of power in the Senate.

Key Public Policy Milestones Related to Citizen Support and Benefits, 1945–1990

The decades following World War II are often characterized as a period of nation-building in which Australian governments put into place the building blocks of a social democratic welfare state in areas such as education, health systems, and housing (Pusey, 1991). In general terms, policies progressively expanded access to goods and services in these areas through a mix of public and private provision.

Public expenditure on education expanded considerably in the 1960s and 1970s, facilitating rapid growth in participation in secondary and tertiary levels of education. Parity in school completion between males and females was also attained during this period. Around 65 percent of Australian students are educated in government schools, with a gradual shift of secondary students to private schools over the last 25 years (Wilkinson, Denniss & Macintosh,

2004). Secondary completion rates are generally high, but decrease progressively with degree of remoteness, from around 80 percent in major cities to around 30 percent in the most remote communities. The high school completion rates of Indigenous peoples remain around half those of non-Indigenous Australians (Australian Bureau of Statistics, 2008).

In the 1950s, the proportion of Australians going on to tertiary education from school was around 5 percent. By the end of the 1990s, this had increased to 30 percent, and taking into account mature entry, total participation in tertiary education was approximately 50 percent (Marginson, 1998). The Labor government abolished university fees in 1974 and increased higher education spending (Hughes, 1998). Fees were reintroduced in the 1980s, but they could be deferred and paid through the tax system when the student's income reached a certain level. Further deregulation in 2005–2006 allowed universities to apply higher fees.

A publicly subsidized private health insurance scheme was introduced by the Liberal government after the war. A universal public health insurance scheme was first introduced by the Labor government in 1972. This was dismantled following a change of government, and then reintroduced as Medicare when Labor returned to government in 1983. The universality of this scheme meant that it would help all Australians, particularly those who were disadvantaged, to gain access to hospital and GP services when sick (Duckett, 2007). Strong public support has seen Medicare retained despite continuing ideological opposition from conservative parties. The Howard coalition government reintroduced public subsidies and other legislative incentives to increase participation in private health insurance to considerable effect (Gray, 2010). Currently around 45 percent of Australians hold some level of private health insurance, ranging from 20 percent within the lowest income quintile to nearly 80 percent for the highest quintile (Australian Bureau of Statistics, 2006a).

In housing, Australia has traditionally favoured home ownership, followed by private rental, and then public housing. Since 1945, public housing programs have been funded under Commonwealth-State Housing Agreements, and served to house immigrant workers in newly developing industry sectors. The proportion of occupied dwellings held by public housing authorities has been in decline since 1990 (Stilwell & Troy, 2000). Public housing is now increasingly targeted toward those most in need. Australian governments have funded rent assistance schemes for low-income private renters since the late 1950s. Currently over 1 million singles or couples who receive income support payments also receive some level of Commonwealth rent assistance (Australian Institute of Health and Welfare, 2011).

Commonwealth-funded age and invalid pensions were first introduced in Australia in the early 1900s, and indexed to cost of living increases in the 1930s. Means-tested unemployment and sickness benefits were introduced in 1945, and a non-means-tested child endowment payment in 1941. The latter form of support has since shifted to encompass means-tested tax relief and direct support measures for low-income families with dependent children (Australian Bureau of Statistics, 1988). The Australian system differs from those in other OECD countries, where most cash transfers are financed by employer and employee contributions and benefits relate to past earnings—higher income workers receive higher absolute levels of benefits on unemployment or retirement.

In Australia benefits are financed from general revenue and are flat-rate entitlements that are means-tested so that payments reduce as other resources increase. The intention of this approach is to concentrate available resources on those most in need (Whiteford, 2010). Despite some erosion, Australia has a well-developed welfare state that offers support for people in the event of sickness, disability, unemployment, or sole parenthood.

Australian Policy Documents and Statements on Health Inequalities

Australian concern and responses to health inequalities have varied, generally reflecting the trend that Labor governments show more concern than Coalition (Liberal/National) governments in reducing health inequities. These trends are discussed below from the 1970s to the present. We set the initiatives against the background of health sector policies.

The 1970s: Growth of a Community Health Movement

The 1970s were a period of rapid social and political change in Australia. This was very evident in health policy, which saw the growth of a vibrant and progressive community health movement, including Aboriginal and women's health services. The extent of health inequities between Aboriginal and non-Aboriginal people was one of the driving forces behind the establishment of the first Aboriginal-controlled health service in 1971. The progressive Whitlam Labor government introduced the Community Health Program for Australia (CHP) (Hospitals and Health Services Commission, Interim Committee, 1973) in 1973, creating energy and optimism for change in the way health and health services were approached in Australia. The CHP was designed to complement the new universal public health insurance system, to ensure that all Australians had access to basic health services, and to develop new ways of delivering those services. The CHP explicitly sought to address health inequities. The main feature of the program was to be multidisciplinary health centres responsible for the health of a given area (Owen & Lennie, 1992), offering such services as child health, mental health, family planning, dental services, health education, immunization, social work, domiciliary care, and rehabilitation (Sax, 1984, 1067). The program also emphasized prevention of illness. The program review in 1976 (Hospital and Health Services Commission, 1976) showed that it had developed over 700 projects covering a large range of topics.

While the program led to innovation in health service delivery, it was difficult to change the mainstream health system. After the fall of the short-lived Whitlam government, responsibility for community health services devolved back to the states. The Commonwealth initiative had stimulated considerable innovation in Victoria and South Australia, but other states were hostile to the CHP's central ideas. A further review in 1986 found that there was still a reasonably coherent community health program, but the Australian health system was "an illness-focused, residual service providing mainly tertiary and some secondary prevention" (Australian Community Health Association, 1986, 90).

Despite this, Owen and Lennie (1992) point out that the CHP foreshadowed many of the principles of the WHO's 1978 Alma Ata Declaration (World Health Organization, 1981), such as community participation, prevention, and offering locally available services. Raftery (1995), while generally pessimistic about the impact of the CHP, acknowledged that it laid the foundation for reform in the health system in three ways: (1) the development of a cadre of committed community health professionals; (2) some minor inroads into the prevailing biomedical culture; and (3) the provision of a greater range of services.

The 1980s and Early 1990s: Health Inequalities Make It to the Public Policy Agenda

The foundation laid by the CHP meant Australia rapidly incorporated and contributed to the new ideas in public health. By the late 1980s, Australia was regarded as one of the world leaders in public health practice, although behavioural measures in health promotion remained popular. Essentially two approaches developed in parallel: one based on behaviour change and the notion that people would change to healthier habits if they were given information, and the other believing that structural change in the underlying causes of ill health was crucial to improving health and equity.

Initiatives of Federal Labor Governments

The federal minister for health from 1983 to 1990 was Dr. Neal Blewett, a political scientist with a sophisticated understanding of health, who oversaw the introduction of Medicare. Blewett's progressive policy approach was evident when he established the Better Health Commission, whose three-volume report, *Looking Forward to Better Health* (1986), identified cardiovascular disease, nutrition, and injury as three priority areas.

A subsequent report, *Health for All Australians (Health Targets and Implementation Committee, 1988)*, emphasized significant health inequities among different population groups. Unfortunately, the report did not suggest how these should be tackled and fell back on health service responses (McPherson, 1992, 126–127). Its national health goals focused on five key areas: (1) hypertension, (2) nutrition, (3) injury prevention, (4) older people's health, and (5) preventable cancers. So, despite a supportive minister, the final policies still gave most attention to disease. The program established to implement the recommendations, the National Better Health Program (NBHP), did fund a broader range of activities than those linked to lifestyle (see, for example, the evaluation of the South Australian component of the NBHP in Baum, Santich, Craig & Murray, 1996). The Australian Healthy Cities Pilot Program was funded from the NBHP and aimed to develop a variety of health promotion programs that embraced the range of strategies in the Ottawa Charter (Baum & Cooke, 1992).

In the early 1990s the National Health Strategy inquiry reviewed the health system and the need for reform. It did this in a way that considered the importance of primary health care and health promotion, and even produced a specific report on health inequities that was firmly grounded in an appreciation of social, environmental, and economic factors, entitled *Enough to Make You Sick: How Income and Environment Affect Health* (National Health Strategy, 1992).

There was also a series of policies that focused on specific issues or groups, among them the National Women's Health Program (1989), the National Aboriginal Health Strategy (1989), the National Mental Health Policy (1992), the National Rural Health Strategy (1994), the National Campaign against Drug Abuse (started in 1985), the National HIV/AIDS Strategy (started in 1989), and the National Hepatitis C Strategy (started in 1999). These policies all had some focus on equity.

The States and Responses to Health Inequalities

Although federal funds were provided to the states to revive the 1970s' CHP, implementation was patchy (Milio, 1992). Three states—South Australia, Victoria, and New South Wales—continued to develop the community health centres that had been established in the 1970s. These centres were the basis for much advocacy and service development based on addressing inequities. In Victoria the network of community health centres continued to expand (see, for example, Jackson, Mitchell & Wright, 1989). This state also established 43 District Health Councils (DHC) with a mandate to focus on the health of their local communities, giving rise to innovation in community-based health promotion. The Victorian Community Development in Health (CDIH) project also provided leadership in the development of theory and practice on this topic. Both the DHC and the CDIH project had a central focus on health inequities. The Victorian Health Promotion Foundation (now known as VicHealth) was formed in the 1980s and funded from tobacco tax monies. It has consistently drawn attention to health inequities and experimented with ways of reducing them (see Box 3.1).

In South Australia health inequities were central to the state's progressive health developments in the 1980s under a reformist health minister. The state adopted a Primary Health Care Policy (South Australian Health Commission, 1989) and a Social Health Strategy (South Australian Health Commission, 1988), which drew on the WHO Health for All strategy and the Ottawa Charter. These policies created an environment in which experimentation with the concepts of the new public health could flourish (Baum, 2008). Community health centres and women's health centres (Shuttleworth & Auer, 1995) were expanded, the state experimented with community development strategies (Tesoriero, 1995), and a successful Healthy Cities project was launched (Baum & Cooke, 1992). Nutrition (Smith, 1995), drug and alcohol (Cormack, Ali & Pols, 1995), child and adolescent health services (Wigg, 1995), and mental health services (Martin & Davis, 1995) all struggled with making new public health and its focus on health inequities relevant to their particular settings, with some degree of success. The state was one of the first to pass legislation to control tobacco (Reynolds, 1995). More traditional public health activities were maintained and extended, including in local government (Kirke, 1995; Weston & Putland, 1995).

A Retreat from Health Equity, 1996–2007

Policy and actions to address health inequities were subject to further challenges during this period, influenced by the election of a neo-liberal and socially conservative government at the national level.

Health Equity off the Commonwealth Political Agenda

Following election of the Howard Coalition government, policy on health inequities took a backward step with perhaps the exception of rural and Indigenous health. There was little direct policy focus on health inequities, with the exception of a Health Equality Research Collaboration (HERC), which did permit some useful work. The community health movement was not supported, and there were cutbacks in funding to community health centres and services during the 1990s to the detriment of the advocacy and community development (Baum, 1996; Lewis & Walker, 1997). The Howard years saw a retreat from comprehensive models of primary health care and an increased emphasis on chronic disease care and prevention. General practice was supported in preference to the multidisciplinary models of community health. This policy direction saw the development of Australian government-funded Divisions of General Practice, which had no focus on health inequities apart from some limited attention to Indigenous health. Expenditure on rural health was, however, increased. Drought, the downturn in rural industries, recession, depopulation, and the worsening health status of rural people focused attention on their needs. The National Rural Health Strategy (Australian

Box 3.1
VicHealth's Commitment to Action on Health Inequities

The opening statement on "What influences health" in the current VicHealth Business Plan (VicHealth, 2009) says, "How much you earn, your social position, your level of education or your capacity to be involved in activities that help connect you to others in your community are important factors in determining your health and wellbeing" (p. 5).

The business plan also demonstrates VicHealth's explicit commitment to equity: "While working to improve the health of all Victorians, we also focus on the needs of those with the poorest health by targeting many of our activities and supporting research initiatives on health inequalities." Their three core values are to be "brave, just, [and] creative" (p. 7).

In 2005 VicHealth developed a "Position Statement on Health Inequalities." They explicitly link their work to the Commission on the Social Determinants of Health, with its central focus on health inequities and to the *A Fairer Victoria* (2006–2010) document (State Government of Victoria, 2006) that was the policy of the Victorian Labor government, which held power until 2011.

VicHealth's "Key Result Areas" include to:

1.1 Improve the physical and mental health of those experiencing social, economic or geographic disadvantage.
1.2 Contribute to closing the health gap between Indigenous and non-Indigenous Victorians (p. 10)

The Plan also commits to a range of actions including to:

- support research on health inequities, and on the links between poor social and economic environments and a range of unhealthy behaviours
- explore models of good practice in creating environments that benefit the health of priority populations
- inform key stakeholders and the public of existing inequalities in health and the factors underpinning health status disparity
- provide organizational support for housing, education, employment, and peak community organizations to implement and evaluate programs addressing the social and economic determinants of health
- strengthen national and state collaborations across academic, government, and non-government settings to ensure health inequalities are addressed in relevant policy and program reforms
- contribute to state and national policy and programs on health promotion and the prevention of illness focusing on the social and economic determinants of health
- support initiatives on the social, cultural, and economic determinants of Indigenous health

VicHealth's website has a section on health inequalities that describes their current activities, and includes guides for those planning health promotion programs to design interventions that have the greatest potential to reduce health inequalities and investigate the community or neighbourhood level factors that affect child development.

Source: Retrieved from : www.vichealth.vic.gov.au/.

Health Ministers' Conference, 1996) formed the basis of the Howard government's response and has seen improvements in health services provision in rural areas.

Community health in Australia has always been somewhat marginalized and neglected, but has certainly done more than any other part of the health sector to advance action on health inequities. It would have been a sound investment to build on its strengths and provide the sector with sufficient resources to capitalize on the promising work done.

A study of Australian health departments' policies in the period 2000–2006 (Newman, Baum & Harris, 2006) concluded that all jurisdictions had at least some commitment to reducing health inequities and to addressing social determinants. All jurisdictions made a commitment to improving the health of Aboriginal Australians, but beyond this there was significant variation. New South Wales, Tasmania, South Australia, and Victoria were found to have the most commitment to reducing health inequities. The other jurisdictions, including the Australian government, evidenced less concern with inequities.

Under the successive Howard Coalition governments, Aboriginal health did receive some priority. However, in its last year in office, it launched an extremely controversial measure in the Northern Territory. In response to a report on child sexual abuse in that jurisdiction (Wild & Anderson, 2007), it announced a series of policy measures that have become known as "the Northern Territory Intervention." Whilst the intervention aimed to increase investment in housing and health infrastructure, it also included suspension of the Racial Discrimination Act so that welfare conditionality and income management could be introduced for selected Aboriginal communities, compulsory child health checks undertaken, and alcohol and pornographic material restrictions introduced. A health impact assessment conducted on the intervention concluded that while the investment in infrastructure was welcome and likely to be beneficial for health, the psychosocial effects of loss of control and negative effects on spirituality and culture would greatly outweigh the benefits (Australian Indigenous Doctors' Association & Centre for Health Equity Training Research and Evaluation—UNSW, 2010).

State Programs on Health Equity, 1996–2007

Most of the advances in terms of policies on health equity in the decade 1996–2007 happened at a state level (see Newman et al., 2006). Here we discuss some of the policies and initiatives designed to address health inequities from the most active jurisdictions.

New South Wales had the most comprehensive range of structural supports to encourage health equity. A health and equity statement, *In All Fairness* (NSW Department of Health,

2004), provided direction for planning and resource distribution on the basis of population and degree of disadvantage and funding for research. The department encouraged local health services to develop health and equity profiles to identify where action is needed, encourage a review of existing initiatives using an "equity filter," and a review of "best-buy" policies and practices to address health inequities.

The Victorian Labor governments demonstrated a strong philosophical commitment to reducing disadvantage and health inequities. This is reflected in the strategic directions and key objectives of the state strategic plan, *Growing Victoria Together* (Department of Premier and Cabinet, 2005), and those of the Department of Human Services and the Department of Health, which include, for example, reducing "disadvantage in health, education and housing." A plan to reduce disadvantage, called *Fairer Victoria* (State Government of Victoria, 2006), led to a series of neighbourhood renewals in disadvantaged areas. One of the most outstanding examples of a commitment to action on health inequities at a state level is the work of VicHealth in Victoria. It operates as a government-funded body with its own independent board of management (see Box 3.1).

South Australia provides good examples of the use of data, and the state has had a Social Health Atlas available since the late 1980s (Glover, Hetzel, Glover, Tennant & Page, 2006). It also has a South Australian Strategic Plan, which is in many ways a social determinants of health plan and includes health targets, but has only a disaggregated target for Aboriginal Australians compared to non-Aboriginal. Otherwise targets are for the population as a whole.

Labor Governments, 2007–2011

In 2007 a Labor government was elected with health reform as a major plank in its agenda. It established a National Hospital and Health Services Reform Commission, which made "tackling major access and equity issues that affect health outcomes" one of its main priorities (National Health and Hospitals Reform Commission, 2009). The National Preventative Health Taskforce (NPHT) was established in 2008 with terms of reference to "provide a blueprint for tackling the burden of chronic disease currently caused by obesity, tobacco, and excessive consumption of alcohol" (National Preventative Health Taskforce, 2009, 287). Thus, the government immediately limited the scope of their main policy focus on health promotion to chronic disease. Notwithstanding these limited terms, the Taskforce's National Strategy does take account of evidence on inequities in chronic disease and associated risk factors, uses the language of health equity, and argues for actions to address "the unequal distribution of health and risk in Australia" (see also: Baum & Fisher, 2011; National Preventative Health Taskforce, 2009, 32). Two of its seven key strategic directions are to "reduce inequity through targeting disadvantage—especially low SES population groups" and to contribute to "closing the gap" in health outcomes between Indigenous and non-Indigenous Australians (National Preventative Health Taskforce, 2009, 40). It also calls for ongoing measurement of health outcomes and behaviours by "Indigenous status and relative social disadvantage" (2009, 38). However, of the strategy's four key targets, three specify only average gains in health behaviours (2009, 36).

In 2010 the government released *Taking Preventative Action* (TPA), their response to the Taskforce's National Strategy, and in 2011 launched the new Australian National Preventive

Health Agency. TPA's response to Taskforce recommendations frequently appeals to measures already in effect or other policies (e.g., Commonwealth of Australia, 2009; Council of Australian Governments, 2007). Two of these, the Healthy Workers Initiative ($289.4 million) and the Healthy Children Initiative ($325.5 million), promote improved health behaviours in workplaces and among children. In our analysis (Baum & Fisher, 2011), neither of these is specifically intended to target disadvantage. However, elements of the smaller Healthy Communities Initiative ($71.8 million) are targeted (e.g., Commonwealth of Australia, 2010, 51–52). Also, a number of specific measures on tobacco, alcohol, or obesity, and primary health care services are aimed at addressing health behaviours within Indigenous groups, low socio-economic status (SES) communities, and several groups with especially high smoking rates, such as people with mental illness (see analysis in Baum & Fisher, 2011). Otherwise, there is no overt recognition of an association between the overall distribution of socio-economic advantage/disadvantage and chronic disease or health behaviours.

The area in which the current Labor governments have made most commitment to health equity is Aboriginal health. In 2007 the Council of Australian Governments (2007) committed to "Closing the Gap" in life expectancy between Aboriginal and non-Aboriginal Australians in a generation. In February 2008 Prime Minister Rudd delivered a moving apology to the "stolen generation," which refers to successive Australian governments' removal of children from their families for placement in institutions or foster homes. The Labor governments have continued the Northern Territory Intervention, despite protests and evidence that the welfare conditionality is not effective and discriminatory. The "Closing the Gap" commitment has led to a wide range of programs addressing Indigenous health, some of which are addressing the social determinants of health, including education and employment. It includes, among its objectives, increasing access to early childhood education, increasing literacy and numeracy achievements for Indigenous children and improved year 12 completions, and halving the gap in employment outcomes between Indigenous and non-Indigenous Australians within a decade. The 2009–2013 National Health Care Agreement between the states and the Commonwealth is the first to require states and territories to report performance and outcomes by Indigenous status against around 80 percent of the NHCA indicators. The government also has a program to improve Indigenous housing in remote areas, but it has met with only limited success to date.

Advocacy for Health Equity

A number of professional associations have actively advocated for action on health inequities. In the 1980s the Australian Community Health Association was formed and obtained funding from the Australian Labor government. It consistently used the WHO's Health for All strategy to examine Australian health policies and encouraged the development of a community-managed, multidisciplinary community health sector that focused on equity. It organized national and state conferences, and was a strong lobbying voice until its funding was discontinued by the Coalition government in 1997.

The Public Health Association of Australia has been a strong voice for equity since its formation in the 1980s. Its current policy on health inequities says the PHAA will:

Work within the health system, with other health bodies, and organisations in other sectors to build a movement committed to a reduction in health inequities, global trade reform, global economic regulation and health development; and collaborate in advocacy with others to seek commitment from Australian governments to develop a health inequities framework. (Public Health Association of Australia, 2009, 3)

The Royal Australian College of Physicians has also advocated on health inequities, and in 2005 devised a policy statement, *Inequities and Health: A Call to Action: Addressing Health and Social Inequalities in Australia* (Royal Australasian College of Physicians, 2005). The Australian Medical Association has been a strong advocate for the importance of increasing Indigenous life expectancy. Australia also has an active circle of the global People's Health Movement, which is active internationally and in many countries, advocating for health equity and progressive health and social policies.

Research on Health Inequalities in Australia

Australia has well-established and effective institutions to gather data on various aspects of health, health risk, and health inequalities within the population, and systems to fund new health research. See Box 3.2 for organizations' websites.

Institutional and Agency Structures That Support Research into Health Inequalities

Australian government funding of peer-reviewed research occurs through two main agencies, the National Health and Medical Research Council (NHMRC) and the Australian Research Council (ARC). The NHMRC's role is to fund research and provide advice to government in relation to advancement of health objectives. The ARC funds research across science, social science, and the humanities, and aims to encourage partnerships between university-based researchers and industry, government, or non-governmental organizations (NGOs).

A recent NHMRC review of public health research funding in Australia found that public health research is underfunded relative to biomedical research, lacks strategic direction, and is too heavily focused on descriptive rather than implementation-based research. Feedback to the NHMRC review identified health inequalities, Indigenous health, primary health care, and populations with poorer physical or mental health as priorities for additional research effort. The ARC does fund some public health research, although to a lesser extent than the NHMRC (Public Health Research Advisory Committee & Nutbeam, 2008). There has been no formal Australian government response to the findings of the WHO Commission on Social Determinants of Health, including in relation to its health research agenda.

Following an independent review (National Preventative Health Taskforce, 2009), the Australian government has established the Australian National Preventive Health Agency (ANPHA) with a small amount of initial funding for research. The current preventive health policy agenda focuses mainly on interventions to modify individual health behaviour in smoking, diet and exercise, and alcohol use (Baum & Fisher, 2011). Thus, the ANPHA research agenda may also focus on individual health behaviour rather than prioritize research to address social determinants of health inequalities.

Two major federally funded agencies—the Australian Bureau of Statistics (ABS) and the Australian Institute of Health and Welfare (AIHW)—conduct population research in Australia, including in relation to health outcomes. Both generate data and report findings on health inequalities in mental and physical health in various dimensions, including in relation to SES or Indigenous status (e.g., Australian Bureau of Statistics, 2007b, 2010; Australian Institute of Health and Welfare, 2009b, 2010). The Lowitja Institute, Australia's National Institute for Aboriginal and Torres Strait Islander Health Research, facilitates collaborative research involving Aboriginal organizations, academic institutions, and government agencies on Aboriginal and Torres Strait Islanders' health, including a research program on social determinants of health.

Research on health inequalities in Australia is sometimes supported by state governments (e.g., Hetzel, Page, Glover & Tennant, 2004; NSW Department of Health, 2004), and is also a primary focus of work within a number of university-based research groups, including: the Southgate Institute for Health, Society & Equity; the Australian Health Inequities Program (Flinders University, SA); the Public Health Information Development Unit (Adelaide University, SA); the Centre for Primary Health Care & Equity (University of NSW); the QUT School of Public Health (Queensland University of Technology); and the Telethon Institute for Child Health. Australian NGOs have also supported research into health inequalities in Australia (Brown & Nepal, 2010; Vinson, 2007). Important recent research on health inequalities in Australia includes Glover et al. (2006), Turrell et al. (2006), Draper et al. (2004), and Baum et al. (2011).

Findings on Health Inequalities in Australia

The average health and longevity of Australians is high by world standards. Life expectancy at birth is increasing, and in 2011 it was 84 years for women and 79 for men. Mortality rates for cardiovascular disease, cancer, COPD, and asthma are gradually decreasing, as is the propor-

---

Box 3.2

Websites with Information on Research on Health Inequities in Australia

Australian Bureau of Statistics: http://www.abs.gov.au/
Australian Health Inequities Program: http://www.flinders.edu.au/medicine/sites/southgate/
    research/past-projects/ahip/ahip_home.cfm
Australian Institute of Health and Welfare: http://www.aihw.gov.au/
Australian Research Council: http://www.arc.gov.au/
Centre for Primary Health Care & Equity: http://www.cphce.unsw.edu.au/cphceweb.nsf/
    page/home
The Lowitja Institute: http://www.lowitja.org.au/
National Health and Medical Research Council: http://www.nhmrc.gov.au/
Public Health Information Development Unit: http://www.publichealth.gov.au/
QUT School of Public Health: http://www.hlth.qut.edu.au/phsw/
The Southgate Institute for Health, Society & Equity: http://flinders.edu.au/medicine/sites/
    southgate/southgate_home.cfm
Telethon Institute for Child Health: http://www.ichr.uwa.edu.au/

tion of people smoking. In other areas, indicators are less positive. Rates of adult and childhood overweight and obesity are high, and have increased significantly over recent decades (Australian Institute of Health and Welfare, 2010). One in five people experience some form of mental illness within a 12-month period (Australian Bureau of Statistics, 2007b), a far higher rate than in several comparable OECD countries (Wilkinson & Pickett, 2009).

As shown below, health inequalities persist both as social gradients and according to differences of Indigenous status, sex, employment status, and location. Gradients in health are paralleled by steep inequalities in income/wealth across the spectrum of socio-economic status.

Social Gradients in Health: Socio-economic Status
Figures 3.1 to 3.4 describe social gradients in Australia on a range of measures of health, including life expectancy, premature mortality, prevalence of chronic diseases, and risk factors, whether SES is measured by individuals or by a composite index of the socio-economic status of local areas or regions.

Aboriginal and Torres Strait Islanders' Health
Aboriginal Australians are generally subject to significant disadvantage relative to the non-Indigenous population in areas of income, employment, and education (Australian Institute of Health and Welfare, 2010). A greater proportion of Aboriginal peoples live in rural and remote areas, and collectively they have a far younger population profile than the aging non-Indigenous population, with over 50 percent under 20 years of age (Australian Social Inclusion Board, 2010). Aboriginal peoples have significantly worse health outcomes than non-Aboriginals in areas such as psychological distress, injury, diabetes and kidney disease, infant mortality, respiratory disease, and smoking. Aboriginal women are 1.5 times more likely to be obese than non-Aboriginal women (Australian Institute of Health and Welfare, 2009b, 2010). These inequities are reflected in a 10-year gap in overall average life expectancy as shown in Figure 3.1. Figure 3.1 also shows that life expectancy among Aboriginal peoples in the Northern Territory is lower still, which may reflect in part a higher proportion of the Aboriginal population living in remote areas relative to other states.

Gender and Family Composition
In Australia, approximately 6 percent of women are subject to multiple forms of socio-economic and health disadvantage, compared to 4 percent of men. In 2008, 9.7 percent of women were classified as underemployed, compared to 6.4 percent of men. Around 87 percent of single-parent families are headed by women, and these families are one of the most disadvantaged groups in Australia in terms of both household income/wealth and unemployment (Australian Bureau of Statistics, 2007a; Australian Social Inclusion Board, 2010). These differences may be reflected in higher rates of mental illness among women, with the exception of substance abuse disorders (Australian Institute of Health and Welfare, 2010).

Employment/Unemployment
People who are unemployed in Australia display poorer health outcomes in a number of areas, including self-reported health, core activity limitations, and smoking (Australian Institute

Figure 3.1
Australian Life Expectancy at Birth (years) by Quintile of SES & Sex, 2000–2001; by Indigenous Status & Sex, 2005–2007 (inc Northern Territory)

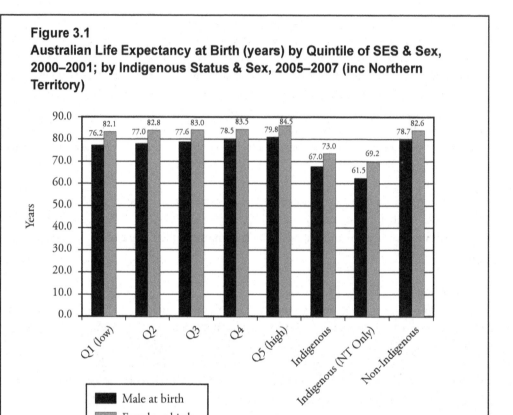

Figure 3.2
Premature Mortality by Quintile of SES and Sex, Ages 16–64 Years, 2003–2007 (per 100,000 pop. (all causes))

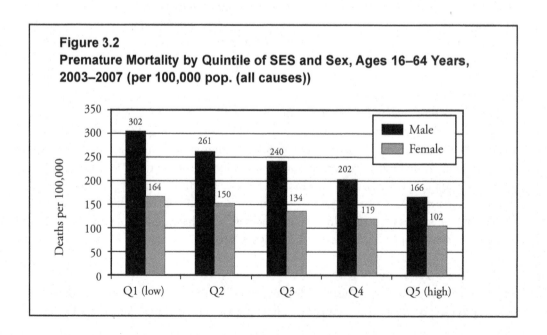

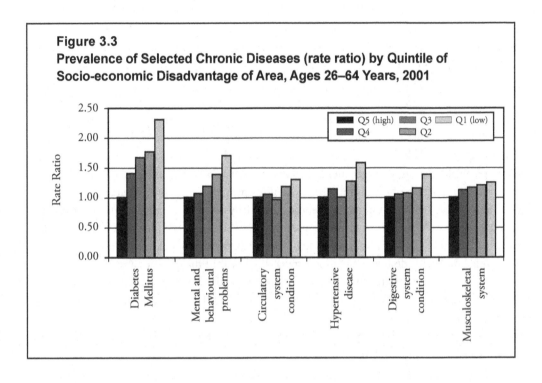

Figure 3.3
Prevalence of Selected Chronic Diseases (rate ratio) by Quintile of Socio-economic Disadvantage of Area, Ages 26–64 Years, 2001

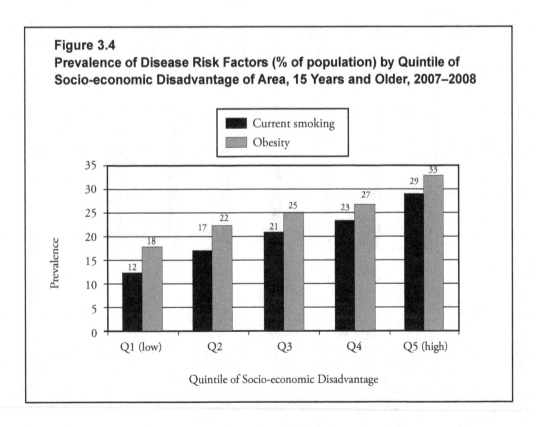

Figure 3.4
Prevalence of Disease Risk Factors (% of population) by Quintile of Socio-economic Disadvantage of Area, 15 Years and Older, 2007–2008

of Health and Welfare, 2010). Unemployment is also associated with higher rates of mental health problems, although a recent study suggests that the unemployed have better mental health than those in jobs of the lowest "psychosocial quality" (Butterworth et al., 2011).

Location

Significant health inequalities in Australia occur according to location. For example, mortality rates follow a gradient of increase according to degree of remoteness. Injury as a cause of death (including self-inflicted) is markedly higher in rural and remote areas compared to major cities, especially among younger men, as shown in Figure 3.5. This is likely to reflect in part the higher proportion of disadvantaged Indigenous peoples living in those areas, higher rates of assault injuries among Indigenous peoples, especially young men, and higher rates of fatal traffic accidents (Australian Institute of Health and Welfare, 2010; Dixon & Welch, 2000). Recent research in Australia has also focused greater attention on areas of concentrated socio-economic and health disadvantage in Australia, both within major cities and in rural/remote areas. Such research indicates that the mix and degree of disadvantage can differ between areas of similar socio-economic status, which may indicate protective effects of factors such as social support and social capital (Vinson, 2007). The number of people living with severe disability is also significantly higher in the most disadvantaged areas of Australian cities (Australian Institute of Health and Welfare, 2009a).

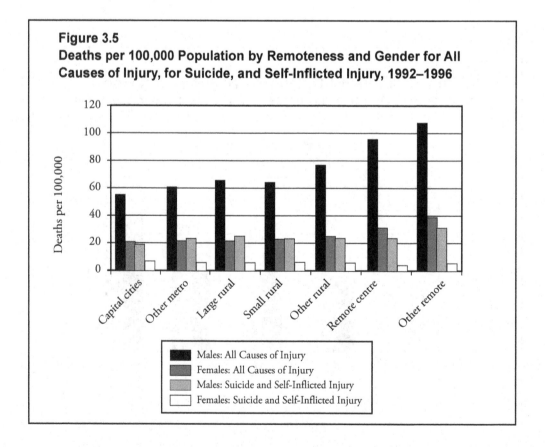

Figure 3.5
Deaths per 100,000 Population by Remoteness and Gender for All Causes of Injury, for Suicide, and Self-Inflicted Injury, 1992–1996

Income Distribution
Australia has relatively high inequality of income distribution among OECD countries (Wilkinson & Pickett, 2009), and the gradient in household wealth inequality is even steeper than that in household disposable income, as shown in Figure 3.6. Fifty percent of single adults with dependent children have both low income and low wealth, a rate far higher than any other household type. The Gini coefficient increased slightly in Australia between 1995 and 2005, from 0.302 to 0.307 (Australian Social Inclusion Board, 2010).

Public Policy and Health Inequalities in Australia

The purpose of this section of the chapter is to provide a brief overview of the main public policy areas in contemporary Australia and to consider the extent to which they make contributions to reducing health inequities. Given the extensive scope of this topic the overview focuses on recent policy directions (within the last decade) and particularly focuses on the past five years.

Taxation
Australia has a system of progressive income taxation, but there are numerous ways in which high-income earners can avoid tax. In the past decade income tax has become less progressive, with taxation rates reduced for high-income earners (Australian Council of Social Services,

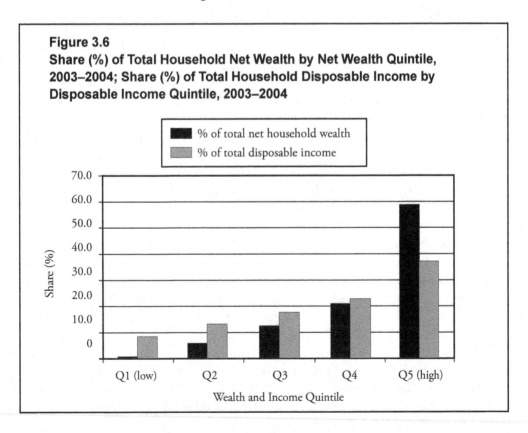

Figure 3.6
Share (%) of Total Household Net Wealth by Net Wealth Quintile, 2003–2004; Share (%) of Total Household Disposable Income by Disposable Income Quintile, 2003–2004

■ % of total net household wealth
▨ % of total disposable income

Share (%)

Wealth and Income Quintile

2009). Prime Minister Rudd proposed a tax on mining profits in 2010 that was defeated following an active campaign by the mining companies. A somewhat watered-down version of this tax has been introduced by the Gillard Labor government at the end of 2011. This government also organized a tax summit in 2011 that saw a wealthy investment banker calling for the wealthiest 15 percent of income earners to pay 15 percent more in income tax (Hartcher, 2011) and at least putting the issue of more progressive taxation on the political agenda. Only the Greens have a policy to raise the top marginal tax rate for high-income earners.

Urban and Housing Policy

Australia has a public housing sector that is funded through an agreement between the Australian government and the states and territories. The trend in the past 20 years has been one of less investment in public housing and as a result, public housing is now welfare housing (Stretton, 2005). All jurisdictions have a community housing sector and a system of women's shelters for women escaping domestic violence. Homelessness has been the focus of a number of policies in recent years that have had mixed success. Homelessness is a particularly significant issue for Aboriginal peoples. Home ownership is the preferred tenure for most Australians— about 70 percent of households own or buy their own home, while 24 percent rent privately and 5 percent rent in social housing. There are generous tax breaks for people who invest in property other than their own home, which is one of the reasons for the high cost of property in Australia. Housing affordability is recognized as a significant and growing problem.

In 2002–2003 over 850,000 low-income households were paying more than 30 percent of income in direct housing costs (housing stress). While 16 percent of all households had high housing cost ratios, 28 percent of low-income households were in housing stress, as were 65 percent of private rental households (Yates & Milligan, 2007).

The Howard Coalition government did not have a concerted policy program on urban areas. The Rudd and Gillard governments have developed such a policy and have established a Major Cities Unit in the Department of Infrastructure and Transport. This unit published an annual *State of Australian Cities* report (Major Cities Unit, 2011), which has a distinct equity focus. It reports on Australia's performance on income inequities against a range of social and health outcomes using Wilkinson and Pickett's (2009) formulation compared with a range of OECD countries. It also reports on low-income households with children and homelessness and on a range of health inequities measures.

Employment Policy

In the past decade Australia has experienced relative low unemployment. This has been a result of a resources boom created by the demand largely from China. During the 1990s changes to industrial relations policy aimed to marginalize the role and power of unions, which had been vested in collective bargaining (Lambert, Gillan & Fitzgerald, 2005). The Howard Coalition government is widely seen to have lost the 2007 election because of the unpopularity of its Work Choices legislation, introduced in 2006. This legislation further reduced union power and swung the balance of industrial relations policy firmly in the direction of employers with measures that made it much easier to dismiss employees. The Australian Council of Trade Unions' campaign against the legislation stressed its impact on health and well-being and won widespread popular support.

The low official unemployment rate also masks significant changes in the patterns of working life. A recent report has identified long-term changes toward more insecure forms of employment, greater demands on flexibility and working hours, and an increasing divide in the workforce between skilled/highly paid and relatively unskilled/insecure/low-paid employment (Rafferty & Yu, 2010). Trade union membership among Australian employees declined from 42 percent in 1988 to 23 percent in 2003 (Australian Bureau of Statistics, 2011b). It would appear that in both housing and employment, there is evidence to suggest that there is a polarizing gap between the haves and have-nots in Australia, with clear implications for health inequities (Rafferty & Yu, 2010; Yates & Milligan, 2007).

Social Protection

The importance of social protection to health and health equity was recognized by the Commission on the Social Determinants of Health (2008). Australia has a system of income support for unemployment, disability, sole parenthood, and old age. In recent years the tests of eligibility for these payments have been tightened and, in some instances, the payments have been made conditional on certain behaviours, such as active job seeking. The decade from 1996 saw successive Howard governments focus on combating welfare dependency through changes to the Social Security Legislation Amendment (Work for the Dole) Act 1997 and reforms adopted under the unambiguously named Work for the Dole program (Stewart & Maley, 2007). This government advanced the notion of "mutual obligation," and Ziguras, Dufty, and Considine (2003) noted that demands for work participation moved from "welfare-to-work" to a "welfare-as-work" policy environment (Marston & McDonald, 2008).

The concept of the "dole bludger"—a welfare claimant who is perceived to be cheating the system—has been used to make welfare policy less generous and had the effect of increasing the social exclusion of welfare recipients. Part of the changes saw the management of welfare payments moved to an agency, Centrelink, and the support for job seekers outsourced to job-search agencies. There is now a significant disparity between unemployment support and other forms of social security such as disability support or old age pensions. Newstart, the current allowance for people who are unemployed, is widely seen by the community sector as insufficient to live on. Newstart is the lowest unemployment payment in the OECD for a single person on an average wage who has just become unemployed (Australian Council of Social Services, 2011).

Social Inclusion

Social inclusion is a direct focus for policy nationally (Australian Social Inclusion Board, 2010; Commonwealth of Australia, 2009) and in three states (South Australia, Queensland, Tasmania) and one territory (Australian Capital Territory). The focus of these initiatives tends to be on excluded groups rather than on the processes of exclusion (see distinction in Popay et al., 2008). Most of the evaluation of these policies is done in-house. One brief appraisal of the South Australian Social Inclusion initiative concluded that overall, the work of the initiative in that state was making some contribution to addressing health inequities through action that addressed the social determinants of health (Baum, Newman, Biedrzycki & Patterson, 2010).

Nationally, the Social Inclusion Initiative (http://www.socialinclusion.gov.au/australian-social-inclusion-board) has a broad remit, which is stated on its website as:

The Australian Government's vision of a socially inclusive society is one in which all Australians feel valued and have the opportunity to participate fully in the life of our society. Achieving this vision means that all Australians will have the resources, opportunities and capability to:
- Learn by participating in education and training;
- Work by participating in employment, in voluntary work and in family and caring;
- Engage by connecting with people and using their local community's resources; and
- Have a voice so that they can influence decisions that affect them.

Much of the work of this initiative has focused on pockets of extreme disadvantage in communities on the fringe of Australia's major cities, which has also been the focus of recent research in the NGO sector (e.g., Vinson, 2007, 2009b). A recent analysis of social exclusion in Australia based on indicators of material resources, employment, education and skills, health and disability, and safety identified "20 to 30 per cent of the Australian population aged 15 years and over as experiencing 'marginal exclusion' at any given point in time. Four to six per cent are 'deeply excluded,' and less than one per cent are 'very deeply excluded'" (Kostenko, Scutella & Wilkins, 2009, 2).

Australia's Refugee Policy: Creating Health Inequities

One of the most sensitive political issues in recent years in Australia has been the treatment of refugee asylum seekers. In the 1970s and 1980s there was bipartisan support for receiving refugees (then mainly coming from Vietnam); they were welcomed and their case for asylum heard while they resided in the community. This policy changed to mandatory detention, first under the Keating Labor government and then under the Howard Coalition government, and refugees were housed in detention centres, first inside Australia and then offshore on the Pacific island of Nauru.

The policy of not processing claims while the refugees live in Australia now has bipartisan support with both major parties seeking deals with other countries to either house detention centres on their land (Nauru in the case of the Coalition) or to return asylum seekers to a third country (Malaysia in the case of the Labor government). Human rights campaigners are very active in campaigning against the policies of both major parties. In August 2011 the High Court of Australia ruled that the planned policy of removing asylum seekers to Malaysia for processing of their claims was illegal. Many refugees are still held in detention centres on the Australian mainland and Christmas Island. Children are no longer held in detention. The considerable health effects, especially on mental health, of life in the detention centres have been documented (Green & Eagar, 2010).

The experience of Australia in the 1970s and 1980s demonstrated that bipartisan political leadership can ensure popular support for a humane approach to refugees and asylum seekers that respects their human rights under international law and provides for their health and well-being.

Health in All Policies

South Australia has implemented an innovative Health in All Policies program through the state Department of Health (Kickbusch & Buckett, 2010). This program of work is led by the Department of Premier and Cabinet and is operationalized through a catalyst unit in the Department of Health. This unit uses "health lens" assessment to consider ways in which particular areas of policy (examples include water security, regional migrant settlement, and transit-oriented development) can be made to enhance rather than detract from health. At this stage, these health lens assessments do not have an explicit equity focus. The Health in All Policies approach does have promise as a means of bringing about action on the social determinants of health.

Conclusion

This chapter has examined the persistent inequities evident in Australian society. We have shown that while Australia does have a well-developed welfare state that offers a publicly funded universal health care scheme, a range of welfare entitlements, and universal free public education, the extent of the welfare provision and the universality of health and education is under constant scrutiny and requires active defence by progressive forces. Since 2007 the federal Labor government's initiatives have seen policy traction on severe social disadvantage and on the most glaring health inequity in the gap between Aboriginal and non-Aboriginal Australians. The Close the Gap strategy has led to an investment of funds in reducing this gap, which does reflect action on a broad number of social determinants of health.

Economic inequities in Australia have increased a little over the past decade. There are worrying signs of a growing divide between haves and have-nots in Australian society. Concerted policy action is required to use progressive taxation and other revenue-raising methods to ensure funding for redistributive policies. Political leadership will be required to create the political will to institute a systematic approach to reducing inequities.

Note

1. There is discussion concerning the preferred term for Australia's Indigenous population. In this chapter we use the terms Aboriginal peoples and Indigenous peoples interchangeably.

Critical Thinking Questions

1. What factors account for the life expectancy gap between Aboriginal and non-Aboriginal Australians?
2. What aspects of political economy in Australia are likely to work for, or against, achieving health equity?
3. Which Australian initiatives to tackle health inequities are likely to succeed?
4. What types of research are now required to inform public policy and action on health inequities in Australia?

Recommended Readings

Baum, F. (2008). *The new public health* (3rd ed.). Melbourne: Oxford University Press.
This is a comprehensive textbook on the new public health. It is relevant to international and Australian audiences. Particular chapters of interest are: Chapter 11: "Changing Health and Illness Profiles in the Twenty-first Century"; Chapter 12: "Patterns of Health Inequities in Australia"; Chapter 13: "The Social Determinants of Health Inequity"; and Chapter 18: "Creating More Equitable Societies."

Carson, B., Dunbar, T., Chenhall, R.D., & Bailie, R. (Eds.). (2007). *Social determinants of Indigenous health.* Crows Nest: Allen & Unwin.
This book provides a comprehensive overview of the social determinants of Indigenous health in Australia.

Keleher, H., & MacDougall, C. (Eds.). (2011). *Understanding health: A determinants approach* (2nd ed.). Melbourne: Oxford University Press.
A useful guide to using a social determinants approach to taking action on health equity.

Stilwell, F., & Jordan, K. (2007). *Who gets what? Analysing economic inequality in Australia.* Port Melbourne, Victoria: Cambridge University Press.
This book provides an analysis of economic inequities in Australia.

Recommended Websites

Australian Indigenous Health InfoNet: www.healthinfonet.ecu.edu.au/
This website contains a comprehensive set of data on many aspects of Aboriginal health status.

People's Health Movement: http://phmovement.org/
The People's Health Movement is a global network of progressive health organizations working for health equity in many countries, including Australia. Its People's Charter for Health argues for economic equity as a prerequisite for health equity.

Public Health Information Development Unit, Adelaide University: www.publichealth.gov.au/
This site contains links to all the Australian Social Health Atlases and a series of interactive mapping tools with databases of health inequities.

Southgate Institute for Health Society & Equity: http://flinders.edu.au/medicine/sites/southgate/southgate_home.cfm
This website provides details of the work of this research institute on health equity.

References

Australian Bureau of Statistics. (1988). *Year book Australia, 1988.* Canberra: Australian Bureau of Statistics.
Australian Bureau of Statistics. (2006a). *Private health insurance: A snapshot, 2004–05.* Canberra: Australian Bureau of Statistics.
Australian Bureau of Statistics. (2006b). *Household wealth and wealth distribution: Australia.* Canberra: Australian Bureau of Statistics.
Australian Bureau of Statistics. (2007a). *Article: One-parent families.* Canberra: Australian Bureau of Statistics.

Australian Bureau of Statistics. (2007b). *National survey of mental health and well being: Summary of results*. Canberra: Australian Bureau of Statistics.

Australian Bureau of Statistics. (2008). *Article: Education across Australia*. Canberra: Australian Bureau of Statistics.

Australian Bureau of Statistics. (2010). *Health and socioeconomic disadvantage*. Canberra: Australian Bureau of Statistics.

Australian Bureau of Statistics. (2011a). 6105.0—Australian labour market statistics, April 2004. Retrieved from: http://www.abs.gov.au/ausstats/abs@.nsf/7d12b0f6763c78caca257061001cc588/592d2f759d9d38a9ca256ec1000766f7!OpenDocument.

Australian Bureau of Statistics. (2011b). 1370.0—Measures of Australia's Progress, 2010. Retrieved from: http://www.abs.gov.au/ausstats/abs@.nsf/Lookup/by%20Subject/1370.0-2010-Chapter-International%20comparisons%20(5.1.6).

Australian Community Health Association. (1986). *Review of the Community Health Program*. Sydney: Australian Community Health Association.

Australian Council of Social Services. (2009). *Progressive tax reform: Reform of the personal income tax system*. Sydney: Australian Council of Social Services.

Australian Council of Social Services. (2011). *Poverty and its causes*. Sydney: Australian Council of Social Services.

Australian Government. (2010). *A stronger, fairer Australia: National statement on social inclusion*. Canberra: Department of Prime Minister and Cabinet, Australian Government.

Australian Health Ministers' Conference. (1996). *National rural health strategy update*. Canberra: AGPS.

Australian Indigenous Doctors' Association & Centre for Health Equity Training Research and Evaluation—UNSW. (2010). *Health impact assessment of the Northern Territory emergency response*. Canberra: Australian Indigenous Doctors' Association.

Australian Institute of Health and Welfare. (2006). *Australia's health 2006*. Canberra: Australian Institute of Health and Welfare.

Australian Institute of Health and Welfare. (2009a). *The geography of disability and economic disadvantage in Australian capital cities*. Canberra: Australian Institute of Health and Welfare, Australian Government.

Australian Institute of Health and Welfare. (2009b). *Measuring the social and emotional wellbeing of Aboriginal and Torres Strait Islander peoples*. Canberra: Australian Institute of Health and Welfare.

Australian Institute of Health and Welfare. (2010). *Australia's health 2010*. Canberra: Australian Institute of Health and Welfare, Australian Government.

Australian Institute of Health and Welfare. (2011). *Housing assistance in Australia 2011*. Canberra: Australian Institute of Health and Welfare.

Australian Social Inclusion Board. (2010). *Social inclusion in Australia: How Australia is faring*. Canberra: Australian Social Inclusion Board, Australian Government.

Baum, F. (1996). Community health services and managerialism. *Australian Journal of Primary Health-Interchange, 2*(4), 31–41.

Baum, F. (2008). *The new public health* (3rd ed.). Melbourne: Oxford University Press.

Baum, F., & Cooke, R. (1992). Healthy Cities Australia: Evaluation of the pilot project in Noarlunga, South Australia. *Health Promotion International, 7*(3), 181–193.

Baum, F., & Fisher, M. (2011). Are the national preventive health initiatives likely to reduce health inequities? *Australian Journal of Primary Health, 17*(4), 320–326.

Baum, F., MacDougall, C., Putland, C., & Ziersch, A. (2011). Differing levels of social capital and mental health in suburban communities in Australia: Did social planning contribute to the difference? *Urban Policy and Research, 29*(1), 35–57.

Baum, F., Newman, L., Biedrzycki, K., & Patterson, J. (2010). Can a regional government's social inclusion initiative contribute to the quest for health equity? *Health Promotion International, 25*(4), 474–482.

Baum, F., Santich, B., Craig, B., & Murray, C. (1996). Evaluation of a national health promotion program in South Australia. *Australian and New Zealand Journal of Public Health, 20*(1), 41–48.

Better Health Commission. (1986). *Looking forward to better health.* Canberra: Better Health Commission, Australian Government.

Brown, L., & Nepal, B. (2010). *Health lies in wealth: Health inequalities in Australians of working age.* Canberra: National Centre for Social and Economic Modelling, Catholic Health Australia.

Butterworth, P., Leach, L.S., Strazdins, L., Olesen, S.C., Rodgers, B., & Broom, D.H. (2011). The psychosocial quality of work determines whether employment has benefits for mental health: Results from a longitudinal national household panel survey. *Occupational and Environmental Medicine, 68,* 806–812.

Commission on the Social Determinants of Health. (2008). *Closing the gap in a generation: Health equity through action on the social determinants of health.* Geneva: World Health Organization.

Commonwealth of Australia. (2009). *A stronger, fairer Australia: National statement on social inclusion.* Canberra: Commonwealth of Australia.

Commonwealth of Australia. (2010). *Taking preventative action—a response to Australia: The healthiest country by 2020—the report of the National Preventative Health Taskforce.* Canberra: Department of Health and Ageing, Commonwealth of Australia.

Cormack, S., Ali, R., & Pols, R.G. (1995). A public health approach to drug issues. In F. Baum (Ed.), *Health for all: The South Australian experience* (pp. 339–361). Adelaide: Wakefield Press.

Council of Australian Governments. (2007). *National Indigenous reform agreement (closing the gap).* Canberra: Council of Australian Governments.

Department of Immigration and Citizenship. (2011a). Fact sheet index. Retrieved from: http://www.immi.gov.au/media/fact-sheets/.

Department of Immigration and Citizenship. (2011b). *The people of Australia: Australia's multicultural policy.* Canberra: Australian Government.

Department of Premier and Cabinet. (2005). *Growing Victoria together: A vision for Victoria to 2010 and beyond.* Melbourne: Victorian State Government.

Dixon, J., & Welch, N. (2000). Researching the rural-metropolitan health differential using the "social determinants of health." *Australian Journal of Rural Health, 8,* 254–260.

Draper, G., Turrell, G., & Oldenburg, B. (2004). *Health inequalities in Australia: Mortality.* Canberra: Queensland University of Technology and Australian Institute of Health and Welfare.

Duckett, S.J. (2007). *The Australian health care system.* Melbourne: Oxford University Press.

Glover, J., Hetzel, D., Glover, L., Tennant, S., & Page, A. (2006). *A social health atlas of South Australia* (3rd ed.). Adelaide: Public Health Information Development Unit, University of Adelaide.

Glover, J.D., Hetzel, D.M., & Tennant, S.K. (2004). The socioeconomic gradient and chronic illness and associated risk factors in Australia. *Australia and New Zealand Health Policy, 1,* 8.

Gray, G. (2010). Health policy. In D. Woodward, A. Parkin & J. Summers (Eds.), *Government, politics, power, and policy in Australia.* Frenchs Forest: Pearson Australia.

Green, J.P., & Eagar, K. (2010). The health of people in Australian immigration detention centres. *Medical Journal of Australia, 192*(2), 65–70.

Hartcher, P. (2011). Left behind: Why the right keeps winning. *The Monthly* (December 2011–January 2012), 20–23.

Health Targets and Implementation Committee. (1988). *Health for all Australians: Report to the Australian health ministers' advisory council and the Australian health ministers' conference.* Canberra: Health Targets and Implementation Committee, Australian Government Publishing Service.

Hetzel, D., Page, A., Glover, J., & Tennant, S. (2004). *Inequality in South Australia: Key determinants of wellbeing. Vol. 1: The evidence.* Adelaide: SA Department of Health.

Hiscock, P. (2008). *Archaeology of ancient Australia.* London: Routledge.

Hospital and Health Services Commission. (1976). *Review of the Community Health Program.* Canberra: AGPS.

Hospitals and Health Services Commission, Interim Committee. (1973). *A Community Health Program for Australia: Report from the National Hospitals and Health Services Commission, Interim Committee.* Canberra: Australian Government.

Hughes, O.E. (1998). *Australian politics* (3rd ed.). South Yarra: Macmillan Australia.

Human Rights and Equal Opportunities Commission. (1997). *Bringing them home: Findings of the national inquiry into the separation of Aboriginal and Torres Strait Islander children from their families.* Sydney: Human Rights and Equal Opportunities Commission.

Jackson, T., Mitchell, S., & Wright, M. (1989). The community development continuum. *Community Health Studies, 13*(1), 66–73.

Jupp, S. (1998). *Immigration* (2nd ed.). Melbourne: Oxford University Press.

Kickbusch, I., & Buckett, K. (Eds.). (2010). *Implementing health in all policies: Adelaide 2010.* Adelaide: Department of Health, Government of South Australia.

Kirke, K. (1995). A state public and environmental health authority. In F. Baum (Ed.), *Health for all: The South Australian experience* (pp. 242–252). Adelaide: Wakefield Press.

Kostenko, W., Scutella, R., & Wilkins, R. (2009). *Estimates of poverty and social exclusion in Australia: A multidimensional approach.* Melbourne: Melbourne Institute of Applied Economic and Social Research, the University of Melbourne, Brotherhood of St. Laurence.

Lambert, R., Gillan, M., & Fitzgerald, S. (2005). Electrolux in Australia: Deregulation, industry restructuring, and the dynamics of bargaining. *Journal of Industrial Relations, 47*(3), 261–275.

Lewis, B., & Walker, R. (1997). *Changing central-local relationships in health service provision: Final report.* Melbourne: School of Health Systems Science, La Trobe University.

Major Cities Unit & Department of Infrastructure and Transport. (2011). *State of Australian cities 2011.* Canberra: Australian Government.

Marginson, S. (1998). Putting the "public" back into public education. In A. Reid (Ed.), *Going public: Education policy and public education in Australia* (pp. 69–76). Adelaide: Australian Curriculum Studies Association.

Marston, G., & McDonald, C. (2008). Feeling motivated yet? Long-term unemployed people's perspectives on the implementation of workfare in Australia. *Australian Journal of Social Issues, 43*(2), 255–269.

Martin, G., & Davis, C. (1995). Mental health promotion: From rhetoric to reality. In F. Baum (Ed.), *Health for all: The South Australian experience* (pp. 406–425). Adelaide: Wakefield Press.

McPherson, P.D. (1992). Health for all Australians. In H. Gardner (Ed.), *Health policy: Development, implementation, and evaluation in Australia* (pp. 119–135). Melbourne: Churchill Livingstone.

Memmott, P., & Moran, M. (2001). *Indigenous settlements of Australia.* Canberra: Department of the Environment and Heritage.

Milio, N. (1992). Keeping the promise of community health policy revival under Hawke 1983–85. In F. Baum, D. Fry & I. Lennie (Eds.), *Community health policy and practice in Australia* (pp. 28–47). Sydney: Pluto Press, Australian Community Health Association.

National Health and Hospitals Reform Commission. (2009). *A healthier future for all Australians: Final report of the National Health and Hospitals Reform Commission.* Canberra: Commonwealth of Australia.

National Health Strategy. (1992). *Enough to make you sick: How income and environment affect health.* Canberra: National Health Strategy.

National Preventative Health Taskforce. (2009). *Australia: The healthiest country by 2020—national preventative health strategy—the roadmap for action.* Canberra: Commonwealth of Australia.

Newman, L., Baum, F., & Harris, E. (2006). Federal, state, and territory government responses to health inequities and the social determinants of health in Australia. *Australian Journal of Health Promotion, 17*(3), 217–225.

Newman, L., Biedrzycki, K., Patterson, J., & Baum, F. (2007). *A rapid appraisal case study of South Australia's social inclusion initiative.* A report prepared for the Social Exclusion Knowledge Network of the World Health Organization's Commission on Social Determinants of Health. Adelaide: Australian Health Inequities Program, Flinders University of South Australia, SA Social Inclusion Unit, Government of South Australia.

NSW Department of Health. (2004). *In all fairness: NSW health and equity statement: Increasing equity in health across NSW*. Sydney: NSW Department of Health.

Owen, A., & Lennie, I. (1992). Health for all and community health. In F. Baum, D. Fry & I. Lennie (Eds.), *Community health: Policy and practice in Australia* (pp. 6–27). Sydney: Pluto Press.

Parkin, A., & Summers, J. (2010). The constitutional framework. In D. Woodward, A. Parkin & J. Summers (Eds.), *Government, politics, power, and policy in Australia* (pp. 51–72). Frenchs Forest: Pearson Australia.

Peterson, N., & Sanders, W. (1998). *Citizenship and Indigenous Australians: Changing conceptions and possibilities* Cambridge: Cambridge University Press.

Popay, J., Escorel, S., Hernández, M., Johnston, H., Mathieson, J., & Rispel, L. (2008). *Understanding and tackling social exclusion: Final report to the WHO Commission on social determinants of health from the Social Exclusion Knowledge Network*. Geneva: WHO Social Exclusion Knowledge Network.

Public Health Association of Australia. (2009). *Policy-at-a-glance: Health inequities policy*. Canberra: PHAA. Retrieved from: http://www.phaa.net.au/documents/policy/20091028HealthInequitiesPolicy.pdf.

Public Health Information Development Unit. (2011). *Monitoring inequality in Australia: Australia, 2010*. Adelaide: PHIDU, Adelaide University. Retrieved from: http://www.publichealth.gov.au/.

Public Health Research Advisory Committee, & Nutbeam, D. (2008). *Report of the review of public health research funding in Australia*. Canberra: National Health and Medical Research Council, Australian Government.

Pusey, M. (1991). *Economic rationalism in Canberra: A nation building state changes its mind*. Cambridge: Cambridge University Press.

Quiggin, J. (2001). Social democracy and market reform in Australia and New Zealand. In A. Glyn (Ed.), *Social democracy in neoliberal times: The left and economic policy since 1980* (pp. 80–109). Oxford: Oxford University Press.

Rafferty, M., & Yu, S. (2010). *Shifting risk: Work and working life in Australia: A report for the Australian Council of Trade Unions*. Sydney: Workplace Research Centre, University of Sydney.

Raftery, J. (1995). The social and historical context. In F. Baum (Ed.), *Health for all: The South Australian experience* (pp. 19–37). Adelaide: Wakefield Press.

Reynolds, C. (1995). Health and public policy: The tobacco laws. In F. Baum (Ed.), *Health for all: The South Australian experience* (pp. 215–229). Adelaide: Wakefield Press.

Robbins, J., & Summers, J. (2010). Indigenous affairs policy. In D. Woodward, A. Parkin & J. Summers (Eds.), *Government, politics, power, and policy in Australia*. Frenchs Forest: Pearson Australia.

Royal Australasian College of Physicians. (2005). *Inequity and health—a call to action: Addressing health and socioeconomic inequality in Australia. Policy Statement 2005*. Sydney: RACP.

Saggers, S., & Gray, D. (1991). *Aboriginal health and society: The traditional and contemporary Aboriginal struggle for better health*. Sydney: Allen & Unwin.

Saint-Arnaud, S., & Bernard, P. (2003). Convergence or resilience? A hierarchical cluster analysis of the welfare regimes in advanced countries. *Current Sociology, 51*, 499–527.

Sax, S. (1984). *A strife of interests: Politics and policies in Australian health services*. Sydney: George Allen & Unwin.

Shuttleworth, C., & Auer, J. (1995). Women's health centres in Adelaide. In F. Baum (Ed.), *Health for all: The South Australian experience* (pp. 253–267). Adelaide: Wakefield.

Smith, B. (1995). Promoting healthy eating. In F. Baum (Ed.), *Health for all: The South Australian experience* (pp. 317–338). Adelaide: Wakefield Press.

South Australian Health Commission. (1988). *A social health strategy for South Australia*. Adelaide: SAHC.

South Australian Health Commission. (1989). *Policy on primary health care*. Adelaide: SAHC.

State Government of Victoria. (2006). *A fairer Victoria: Progress and next steps*. Melbourne: State Government of Victoria.

Stewart, J., & Maley, M. (2007). The Howard government and political management: The challenge of policy activism. *Australian Journal of Political Science, 42*(2), 277–293.

Stilwell, F., & Troy, P. (2000). Multilevel governance and urban development in Australia. *Urban Studies, 37*, 909–929.

Stretton, H. (2005). *Australia fair*. Sydney: University of New South Wales Press.

Tesoriero, F. (1995). Community development and health promotion. In F. Baum (Ed.), *Health for all: The South Australian experience* (pp. 268–280). Adelaide: Wakefield Press.

Trewin, D. (2002). *Year book Australia*. Canberra: Australian Bureau of Statistics.

Turrell, G., Stanley, L., de Looper, M., & Oldenburg, B. (2006). *Health inequalities in Australia: Morbidity, health behaviours, risk factors, and health service use* (vol. 2. AIHW Cat. no. PHE 72). Canberra: Australian Institute of Health and Welfare, Queensland University of Technology.

VicHealth. (2009). *VicHealth strategy and business plan 2009–2013: Promoting health and preventing illness*. Melbourne: Victorian Health Promotion Foundation (VicHealth).

Vinson, T. (2007). *Dropping off the edge: The distribution of disadvantage in Australia*. Melbourne: Jesuit Social Services, Catholic Social Services Australia.

Vinson, T. (2009a). *Social inclusion: Indigenous social exclusion*. Canberra: Department of Education Employment and Workplace Relations, Australian Government.

Vinson, T. (2009b). *Social inclusion: Markedly socially disadvantaged localities in Australia—their nature and possible remediation*. Canberra: Department of Education Employment and Workplace Relations, Australian Government.

Weston, H., & Putland, C. (1995). Public health and local government. In F. Baum (Ed.), *Health for all: The South Australian experience* (pp. 281–306). Adelaide: Wakefield Press.

Whiteford, P. (2010). The Australian tax-transfer system: Architecture and outcomes. *Economic Record, 86*(275), 528–544.

Wigg, N. (1995). Promoting health with children, adolescents, and their families. In F. Baum (Ed.), *Health for all: The South Australian experience* (pp. 393–405). Adelaide: Wakefield Press.

Wild, R., & Anderson, P. (2007). *Ampe Akelyernemane Meke Mekarle "Little Children are Sacred": Report of the Northern Territory Board of Inquiry into the protection of Aboriginal children from sexual abuse*. Darwin: Northern Territory Government Board of Inquiry into the Protection of Aboriginal Children from Sexual Abuse.

Wilkinson, D., Denniss, R., & Macintosh, A. (2004). *The accountability of private schools to public values* Canberra: The Australia Institute.

Wilkinson, R., & Pickett, K. (2009). *The spirit level: Why more equal societies almost always do better*. London: Penguin Books.

Woodward, D., Parkin, A., & Summers, J. (Eds.). (2010). *Government, politics, power, and policy in Australia*. Frenchs Forest: Pearson Australia.

World Health Organization. (1981). *Global strategy for health for all by the year 2000*. Geneva: WHO.

Yates, J., & Milligan, V. (2007). *Housing affordability: A 21st century problem*. Sydney: Australian Housing and Urban Research Institute.

Ziguras, S., Dufty, G. & Considine, M. (2003). *Much obliged: Disadvantaged job seekers' experiences of the mutual obligation regime*. Fitzroy: Brotherhood of St. Laurence, St. Vincent de Paul, University of Melbourne Centre for Public Policy.

Chapter 4

British and Northern Irish Experiences

Katherine E. Smith and Clare Bambra

Introduction

This chapter examines public policy and health inequalities in the UK. It starts by outlining contemporary health inequalities in the UK in their historical context. It then outlines national political organization and structures before providing an overview of key public policy documents on health inequalities in the UK and considers differences between English policies and the approaches of the devolved administrations in Scotland, Wales, and Northern Ireland. The second section is an overview of UK researchers' considerable theoretical and empirical contributions to understanding health inequalities. The final substantive section examines how public policy in the UK has shaped some of the key social determinants of health.

As most overviews of health inequalities research in the UK point out, studies concerned with varying patterns of mortality and life expectancy have a long history, dating back over 300 years to the work of researchers such as William Petty (1623–1687) (Macintyre, 2003). Historically, as now, health-related inequalities have been identifiable between both geographical areas and social groups (Davey Smith, Dorling & Shaw, 2001). For example, in 1838–1841 gentry and professional males residing in rural Bath had a life expectancy of 55, which was more than twice as long as the 25 years predicted for labourers living in the same area (Graham, 2000). A similar gap in the life expectancy rates of contrasting occupational classes was visible in industrial Liverpool during the same period, but with significantly lower life expectancies for both groups than for the equivalent groups living in Bath (Graham, 2000).

Over the past three centuries, despite significant increases in overall life expectancy for all groups, the variations in life expectancy and mortality rates between various regions and social groups appear to have changed remarkably little in Britain. In fact, evidence suggests that the gap between the rich and poor in Britain may be widening, geographically as well as socially (Shaw, Dorling et al., 1998; Shaw, Davey Smith et al., 2005; Marmot, 2010).

National Description and Political Organization and Structure

The UK is made up of the three nations within the island of Britain (England, Scotland, and Wales), plus Northern Ireland. It was one of the richest and most powerful countries in the world during the 19th and early 20th centuries and, although it was overtaken by several other countries in the second half of the 20th century, it remains the world's sixth largest economy, as measured by gross domestic product (World Bank, 2011). By mid-2010, official estimates suggested the resident population of the UK was 62,262,000. In terms of ethnicity, the population is predominantly white British (though some individuals might identify as English, Scottish, Welsh, Northern Irish, or Irish, as opposed to British), but there are significant numbers of South Asian and Afro-Caribbean communities (in part due to the country's colonial past), and a growing number of eastern Europeans (there are few restrictions on the movement of people between the member states of the European Union).

Form of Government

The UK is officially a constitutional monarchy, sharing the same monarch (currently Queen Elizabeth II) as Canada and 14 other Commonwealth countries. However, the monarch's role is largely ceremonial and, in practice, most political power rests with the parliamentary system, which consists of the House of Commons (made up of 650 elected members of Parliament) and the House of Lords (made up of a mixture of hereditary peers, life peers who are chosen by the prime minister and appointed by the monarch, and representatives of the Church of England). The prime minister is accountable to the House of Commons, which is by far the more powerful of the two chambers (the powers of the House of Lords have been significantly reduced over time and are now restricted to suggesting amendments to legislation and/ or delaying its adoption). The prime minister is usually the leader of the political party with the most MPs in the House of Commons. The UK has a first-past-the-post voting system, which has contributed to the long-term dominance of two political parties since the early 20th century: the Conservative (right-leaning) Party and the Labour (left-leaning) Party. As a member of the European Union, an increasing number of policy decisions in the UK are shaped by decisions made at the European level.

Political Organization

Between the immediate postwar period and the 1980s, there was a cross-party consensus supporting many aspects of the UK's welfare state. In particular, there has been long-standing cross-party support for the National Health Service (NHS), which has been free at the point of use for the UK's population since it was established in 1948, funded largely via general taxation. Although the UK's health care service is traditionally associated with social democratic systems (as described in Chapter 1; see also Bambra, 2005), in other regards the UK is a "liberal" political and economic system, in which social support from the state is limited and there is clear support for free-market policies. State support for vulnerable groups is particularly poor in the UK. For example, the benefits system, designed to support those who are either unable to work (due, for example, to ill health or disability) or who are unable to find work, is much less generous in the UK than in comparable countries. As Clegg (2010, 7) reports, "by 2007 the UK benefit system had become the least generous of all the most developed countries, with average replacement rates having fallen below even those of Greece and the US in the period since the late 1990s." (The UK's benefits system is discussed further in later sections.)

So far, this section has focused on the UK as a whole and, indeed, until recently, most legislative decisions were made by the government in London (England) for the UK as a whole, and Northern Ireland, Scotland, and Wales had only limited powers to shape the interpretation and implementation of these policies. However, in the late 1990s, significant political powers were devolved to these three regions and health policy was one of the most significant areas to be devolved (Woods, 2004). However, the scope for genuinely divergent approaches to policies impacting on health has been constrained by the fact that many other policy issues, notably fiscal policy, continue to be largely determined by the UK and, to some extent, the European Union.

Furthermore, in the early years of devolution, the Labour Party dominated all four political contexts, creating a relatively consistent political context. However, following the 2010 UK General Election and the devolved government elections of 2011, different political parties now govern in each of the four regions of the UK for the first time, with a Conservative-Liberal Democrat coalition leading the UK, a minority Labour administration governing in Wales, the Democratic Unionist Party and Sinn Féin sharing power in Northern Ireland, and the left-leaning Scottish National Party governing Scotland. This political divergence means that the policies impacting on health inequalities may now become increasingly different in the constituent parts of the UK. Some key differences are already emerging, which might be expected to impact on health.

For example, in contrast to England, there are currently no prescription charges in Scotland, no university fees, and far greater provision of free personal care for the elderly. There is also some consensus that a "natural experiment" is occurring in UK health care policy (e.g., Greer, 2005, 2009; Bevan, 2010; Connolly, Bevan & Mays, 2010), as England pursues a series of radical, market-oriented reforms to the NHS, while the devolved regions maintain a more social democratic approach to health care (Hunter, 2011). In contrast, there has so far been less obvious divergence in relation to specific public health policies (Smith et al., 2009). However, a recent analysis suggests Scotland may be emerging as a leader of innovative public health policies in the UK (Smith & Hellowell, 2012).

As the following section describes, policy-makers in the UK have often led the way in approaches to tackling health inequalities, from the Labour government's decision to commission an expert-led review of the evidence in the 1970s, to the most recent Labour governments' (in power from 1997 to 2010) strong commitment to reducing health inequalities. Indeed, over the past 15 years, the UK has probably placed more policy emphasis on reducing health inequalities than any other country (as described below). Unfortunately, however, there is little evidence to suggest that the chosen policy responses were effective as health inequalities are continuing to widen by many key measures. One important reason for this may be that policy responsibility for health inequalities was largely placed with the departments of health (in every region of the UK). This is significant both because these departments tend to be preoccupied with the business of the NHS rather than public health (see Hunter et al., 2010), and because many of the policy levers for addressing the social determinants of health inequalities lie outside the realm of these departments.

UK Policy Documents and Statements on Health Inequalities

The need to reduce variations in health across Britain contributed to the decision to establish the National Health Service in 1948. Yet, despite the new service, by the 1970s it was becoming increasingly evident that free access to health care had not been enough to stem the widening inequalities in health and, in 1977, the then Secretary of State for Health and Social Services, David Ennals, faced fresh calls to do something about the issue. Ennals responded by asking the chief scientist, Sir Douglas Black, to appoint a working group of experts to investigate the matter and make policy recommendations (Berridge & Blume, 2003).

The Black Report

In the resulting report (Black, Morris et al., 1980), which is widely referred to as the Black Report, the authors argued that materialist explanations were likely to play the largest role in explaining health inequalities (see below) and, therefore, that policy-makers ought to prioritize the reduction of differences in material and economic circumstances (see Table 4.1). The associated policy recommendations in the report were wholeheartedly rejected by the newly elected Conservative government that had come to power between the commissioning and publication of the report.

Indeed, under the Conservative governments in power from 1979 to 1997, health inequalities were not on the official policy agenda (Berridge & Blume, 2003). Even the term "health inequalities" was discarded and health differences between social groups were instead referred to using the less emotive term "health variations," which implied that health differences could be "natural" and therefore not something for which policy-makers were responsible. Nevertheless, the Black Report had a significant impact on the research community internationally as well as in Britain, and a mass of research on health inequalities was undertaken and published during this period (Berridge & Blume 2003). The Black Report also stimulated some local efforts to address health inequalities in the UK. The northern city of Liverpool was a good example of this; local policy-makers and practitioners worked to produce one of England's first regional reports on public health (Ashton, 1984) and also forged international links with other regional public health efforts, such as those being undertaken in North Karelia in Finland (Hunter et al., 2010).

The Acheson Report

When Labour was elected in 1997, 17 years after the publication of the Black Report, the new government was keen to emphasize the previous Conservative government's failure to implement any of the Black Report's largely structural and socio-economic recommendations. The Labour government initially criticized the Conservatives for placing an "excessive emphasis on lifestyle issues," and casting the responsibility for poor health back onto individuals (Department of Health, 1997). In addition, as promised, the Labour government commissioned a follow-up to the Black Report, announcing an independent inquiry into health inequalities in July 1997 (Department of Health, 1997). The government promised that the *evidence-based* conclusions of the Acheson Inquiry, which became known as the Acheson Report (Acheson, 1998), would inform a new health strategy.

Table 4.1
Overview of the Black, Acheson, and Marmot Reports

	Black Report	Acheson Report	Marmot Report
Background	The Black Report (1980) on health inequalities was commissioned by the outgoing Labour government in 1977, brought health inequalities into the spotlight, and was the first example of a comprehensive strategy to draw attention to health inequalities over the life course. Health inequalities were not recognized as a problem by many at the time.	The Independent Inquiry into Inequalities in Health, chaired by Sir Donald Acheson, was commissioned by the newly elected Labour government in 1997, which committed itself to implementing the evidence-based policy recommendations.	Following publication of the WHO's report on the social determinants of health, Sir Michael Marmot was commissioned to consider the implications for health inequalities in England post-2010. As with the Acheson Inquiry, the Marmot Review was expected to make evidence-based policy recommendations.
Aims	1. To assemble available information about the differences in health status among the social classes and about factors that might contribute to these, including relevant data from other industrial countries 2. To analyze this material in order to identify possible causal relationships, to examine the hypotheses that have been formulated and the testing of them, and to assess the implications for policy 3. To suggest what further research should be initiated	1. To review the latest available information on inequalities of health, to summarize the evidence of inequalities of health and the expectation of life in England, and identify trends 2. In the light of that evidence, to conduct—within the broad framework of the government's overall financial strategy—an independent review to identify priority areas for future policy development, which scientific and expert evidence indicates are likely to offer opportunities for government to develop beneficial, cost effective, and affordable interventions to reduce health inequalities 3. To report to the secretary of state for health; the report will be published and its conclusions, based on evidence, will contribute to the development of a new strategy for health	1. To identify, for the health inequalities challenge facing England, the evidence most relevant to underpinning future policy and action 2. To show how this evidence could be translated into practice 3. To advise on possible objectives and measures, building on the experience of the current Public Service Agreement target on infant mortality and life expectancy 4. To publish a report of the Marmot Review's work that will contribute to the development of a post-2010 health inequalities strategy
Explanatory Theory	Rejected explanations of health inequalities that focused on data artifact or social selection; took a multi-causal approach to explain health inequalities, but suggested that the role of behavioural and cultural determinants in producing inequalities in health were significantly outweighed by the role played by material conditions	Acheson (1998) also supported a multi-causal approach to explaining health inequalities, using a model composed of different layers, including individual lifestyles and the socioeconomic environment; similarly to Black, this approach emphasized the importance of material and structural conditions in shaping other key determinants, such as lifestyle behaviours	The distribution of health and well-being is once again understood to be caused by an interplay of various determinants, with material circumstances playing an important role; however, psychosocial factors, such as social cohesion, and other social stresses are given more prominence in explaining the relationship between material inequalities and health inequalities

(continued)

	Black Report	Acheson Report	Marmot Report
Key Recommendations	Produced 37 recommenda-tions, prioritizing giving children a better start in life within a wider anti-poverty strategy	Produced 39 recommendations; key priorities similar to those of the Black Report, namely: 1. All policies likely to have an impact on health should be evaluated in terms of the impact on health inequalities. 2. High priority should be given to health of families with children. 3. Further steps should be taken to reduce income inequalities and improve living standards of poor households.	Produced six policy objectives: 1. Give every child the best start in life. 2. Enable all children, young people, and adults to maximize their capabilities and have control over their lives. 3. Create fair employment and good work for all. 4. Ensure healthy standard of living for all. 5. Create and develop healthy and sustainable places and communities. 6. Strengthen the role and impact of illhealth prevention.

Sources: C. Bambra, K.E. Smith, K. Garthwaite, K.E. Joyce & D.J. Hunter, A labour of Sisyphus? Public policy and health inequalities research from the Black and Acheson Reports to the Marmot Review, *Journal of Epidemiology and Community Health*, 65(2011), 399–406.

In broad terms, many of the resulting report's (Acheson, 1998) 39 recommendations reflected the conclusions of the earlier Black Report (Birch, 1999): Both highlighted the need to have a multifaceted approach to health inequalities, and both advocated a reduction in income inequalities, with a particular focus on child poverty (see Table 4.1). The key difference was that the Acheson Report was released in a far more favourable political climate than its predecessor and might, therefore, have been expected to have more of a policy impact. However, Labour had also stipulated that the Inquiry's recommendations should recognize the government's fiscal commitments, which, at that time, included a two-year agreement not to increase public spending. This restriction, Davey Smith and colleagues (1998) claim, led to an under-representation of structural and socio-economic determinants in the emerging policy initiatives that were linked to the Acheson Report.

Although the report focused on England, it was acknowledged throughout the UK. A wealth of policy statements referred directly to the report (e.g., Department of Health, 1999; Secretary of State for Scotland, 1999), creating the impression that policy decisions had, as promised, been directly informed by the recommendations in this report. In reality, the relationship between evidence and policy is rarely this direct or linear, and a qualitative study exploring the use of health inequalities evidence in policy over this period found that many official policy responses to health inequalities had already been agreed on before the Acheson Report was published (Smith, 2008). Nevertheless, it is certainly the case that UK policy responses to health inequalities in the period 1997–2003 reflected the ideas set out in the Black and Acheson reports (Smith et al., 2009). For example, as Table 4.2 illustrates, the policies produced in all four regions consistently emphasized the need to tackle the wider social and economic determinants in order to address poor health and health inequalities.

Table 4.2

Illustrative Examples of the Universal Emphasis Placed on Social and Economic Determinants of Health in the Early Post-devolution Years

UK Region	Illustrative Extract
England	From Vision to Reality (Department of Health, 2001, 1): "The worst health problems in the country will not be tackled without dealing with their fundamental causes—poverty, lack of education, poor housing, unemployment, discrimination and social exclusion."
Northern Ireland	Investing for Health (Department of Health, Social Services and Public Safety, 2002, 3): "A large proportion of this unnecessary premature death and disease is determined by social and economic inequalities. The evidence is clear—there is a direct correlation between poverty, social disadvantage and your health."
Scotland	Our National Health (Scottish Executive, 2000, 7): "Poverty, poor housing, homelessness and the lack of educational and economic opportunity are the root causes of major inequalities in health in Scotland. We must fight the causes of illness as well as illness itself."
Wales	Well Being in Wales (Public Health Strategy Division, 2002, 5): "The mix of social, economic, environmental and cultural factors that affect individuals' lives determines their health and well being. We can only improve well being in the long term by addressing these factors."

Source: K.E. Smith & M. Hellowell, Beyond rhetorical differences: A cohesive account of post-devolution developments in UK health policy, *Social Policy and Administration*, 46(2) (2012), 178–198.

Emergent Policies

Although there are some notable differences between the policies that emerged from the four regions in this period, particularly in terms of their different historical legacies and environments, as Table 4.2 illustrates, all four regions initially seemed to be adopting a social and economic model of health, reflecting empirically informed theories about the causes of health inequalities (see later sections). Many other similarities were also evident, including a conceptualization of health inequalities as "health gaps" (rather than as a health gradient) and the articulation of some form of national health inequalities targets, as Table 4.3 summarizes.

The way in which health inequalities are conceptualized is important because it has implications for policy responses (Graham & Kelly, 2004). If policy-makers focus on the health disadvantage facing poorer groups, or on "health gaps" between more and less deprived groups, then policies targeting health improvement measures at deprived groups seems logical (even though it will not reduce health inequalities if the health of advantaged groups continues to improve at a faster rate). Whereas, if health inequalities are framed as a continuous "social

Table 4.3

A Basic Overview of Policy Approaches to Addressing Health Inequalities in the Four UK Constituencies

Aspect of Policy Approach	England	Northern Ireland	Scotland	Wales
Conceptualization of health inequalities	As health gaps resulting from health deprivation	As health gaps resulting from health deprivation	As health gaps resulting from health deprivation	As health gaps resulting from health deprivation
Commitment to a joined-up approach?	Yes	Yes	Yes	Yes
References to evidence base?	Yes	Yes	Yes	Yes
Introduction of targets for reducing health inequalities?	Yes, specific health inequalities targets set in 2001, to be achieved by 2010.	Yes, specific health inequalities targets set in 2002, to be achieved by 2010.	Yes, specific health inequalities targets set in 2004, to be achieved by 2008–2010.	In 2002–2004, "health gain" targets were announced and included "health inequalities targets," but these were non-quantified statements of aspiration.
Articulation of targets?	To reduce health gaps (mainly between areas)	To reduce health gaps (between areas and socio-economic groups)	To improve the health of the most deprived groups at a particular rate	To improve the health of the most deprived groups rapidly
Location of responsibility for meeting health inequalities targets?	Local NHS bodies Primary Care Trusts	Unclear, but "local agencies" are expected to take action to help achieve targets	Local NHS bodies (local health boards)	Local NHS bodies (local health boards)

Source: K.E. Smith & M. Hellowell, Beyond rhetorical differences: A cohesive account of post-devolution developments in UK health policy, *Social Policy & Administration, 46*(2) (2012), 178–198.

gradient" affecting the whole of society (Graham & Kelly, 2004; Marmot, 2010), then targeted interventions alone are likely to appear insufficient. It is therefore notable that all four regions conceptualized health inequalities in terms of health deprivation and health gaps, providing a logical foundation for targeted responses.

Beyond this, all four regions committed to employing cross-cutting policies (Department of Health, 1999; Department of Health, Social Services, and Public Safety, 2002; Public Health Strategy Division, 2002; Scottish Executive, 2000), and all four drew on empirical data in refining their implementation strategies (Acheson, 1998; McWhirter, 2004; Scottish Executive, 2003; Townsend, 2001), although only England and Wales initially commissioned reviews of the available evidence to inform their strategies (Acheson, 1998; Townsend, 2001). By 2004, all four regions had also articulated targets to reduce health inequalities of some kind (see Bauld et al., 2008; Smith et al., 2009), although the targets in Wales remained unquantified.

The way in which the targets were framed in all four regions reinforced the idea that policy-makers could tackle health inequalities through targeted health improvement measures (Bauld et al., 2008; Smith et al., 2009). This is perhaps one reason why, in the period 2004–2007, the public health strategies of England, Scotland, and Wales all moved away from the initial concern with social and economic determinants (Table 4.2) and instead focused increasingly on health services and lifestyle behaviours (Smith et al., 2009). This shift was associated with a reduction in the level of responsibility that central government appeared to be taking for health inequalities, as policy documents increasingly emphasized the importance of individual responsibility for health outcomes (see Table 4.4).

The way in which health inequalities were conceptualized is likely to have aided this shift. However, there were also some distinct contextual reasons underlying the shift in each region. In England, where a performance assessment regime was most deeply embedded, the time-limited, specific targets contributed to policy-makers seeking "quick wins" via the increased prescription of drugs to reduce strokes and heart attacks and greater investment in smoking cessation aids (Bauld et al., 2007; Blackman, 2007). In Wales, increasing media interest in the relatively worse NHS waiting times (as compared to England) appears to have caused health policy-makers to sideline public health policies in their efforts to ensure that Welsh waiting times became more consistent with English ones (Smith et al., 2009; BMA, 2010). The inability of Welsh policy-makers to pursue what had initially been the most radical public health policy of the four regions also relates to the limited powers of the Welsh Assembly (Greer, 2004).

It is less clear why policies in Scotland (where policy-makers had greater powers) also shifted toward a focus on lifestyle behaviours and health services in this period (albeit in a somewhat less pronounced manner). However, the specific and time-limited nature of the targets may have played a role here too, as may have the fact that the same political party dominated both contexts (Smith et al., 2009). In Northern Ireland, the situation is somewhat different as there is less evidence of a policy shift away from socio-economic concerns (e.g., Department of Health, Social Services, and Public Safety, 2005, 2006). However, the suspension of the Northern Irish Assembly between 2002 and 2007 (due to the long-term conflict about the position of Northern Ireland in relation to the UK and the Republic of Ireland) resulted in a reduced focus on non-essential matters, leaving much public health decision-making to the local level (Greer, 2004).

The fact that different reasons appeared to underpin a similar shift in policy focus is important because it suggests that subsequent policies may diverge more in the future. Indeed, in the period between 2008 and now, it appears that approaches to health inequalities *are* becoming increasingly distinct (Smith & Hellowell, 2012). There has been little change in Wales, with the focus on health promotion (as opposed to tackling health inequalities) outlined in *Health Challenge Wales* continuing, although a 2011 *Lancet* editorial (*The Lancet*, 2011) argues that Welsh policy-makers are still committed to a more radical public health agenda. Meanwhile,

Table 4.4
The Shift away from Central Government Responsibility and toward Individuals

Context	Illustrative Extracts—England	Illustrative Extracts—Scotland
Pre-2003 Policies	*Saving Lives* (Secretary of State for Health 1999, pt4.9): "While the roots of health inequality run deep, we refuse to accept such inequality as inevitable. Moreover, we fully accept the responsibility of Government to address such deep-seated problems. That is why we are committed to a wide-ranging programme of action, right across Government, to tackle them."	*Towards a Healthier Scotland* (Secretary of State for Scotland, 1999, chp6): "A Public Health Strategy Group, led by the Minister for Health and drawn from all Scottish Office Departments, will ensure the integration of policies and initiatives with health implications within The Scottish Office, and encourage the use of Health Impact Assessment."
2003+ Policies	*Choosing Health* (Secretary of State for Health, 2004, 6): "People cannot be instructed to follow a healthy lifestyle in a democratic society. Health improvement depends upon people's motivation and their willingness to act on it. The Government will provide information and practical support to get people motivated and improve emotional wellbeing and access to services so that healthy choices are easier to make." And: "In our survey, 88% of respondents agreed that individuals are responsible for their own health. Health is a very personal issue."	*Fair to All, Personal to Each* (Scottish Executive, 2004, 1): "[K]ey decisions affecting our health lie in our own hands. The Government can't make us eat more healthily or give up smoking. Each of us needs to take responsibility for our own health by choosing a healthier lifestyle and the Government can help by providing appropriate opportunities and ensuring services are accessible and available." *Delivering for Health* (Scottish Executive, 2005, vi): "We are working to encourage people to take greater control over their own health."

Source: K.E. Smith (2008), *Health inequalities in Scotland and England: The translation of ideas between research and policy,* Ph.D. thesis, University of Edinburgh.

the restoration of powers to the Northern Ireland Assembly appears to have facilitated a fresh concern with public health, with a new Public Health Agency established in 2009, although there is still little to indicate the extent of the focus that will be placed on health inequalities or social and economic determinants.

The most significant developments have occurred in Scotland and England, where policies appear to be moving in opposite directions. In Scotland, *Equally Well* (Scottish Government, 2008) and the follow-up review (Scottish Government, 2010) both articulate an evidence-informed approach to tackling health inequalities, which takes social and economic determinants seriously and which accepts the need for central government action. In contrast, the UK Coalition government's Public Health White Paper (Secretary of State for Health, 2010) pays little more than lip service to wider social and economic determinants of health, choosing instead to stress that the causes of premature death are dominated by "diseases of lifestyle" for which the government accepts only limited responsibility.

One area in which there does appear to have been some convergence is the approach to targets; by 2011 the deadline had passed for all of the quantified national health inequalities targets and none have yet been replaced. The recent policy documents emerging from England and Scotland (Scottish Government, 2008, 2010; Secretary of State for Health, 2010) suggest there is an increasing preference for monitoring health inequalities via a series of lower-level indicators, rather than focusing on tightly defined, high-level targets. This may be a result both of the failure to achieve the national targets and of criticisms relating to the targets that were set (e.g., Bauld et al., 2008).

The Marmot Review

Perhaps the most significant recent development in relation to health inequalities policy development in the UK was the outgoing Labour government's decision to commission a post-2010 strategic review of the evidence on health inequalities. The report, published in February 2010 (shortly before the General Election, which led to a new Coalition government), was led by Michael Marmot and quickly became known as the Marmot Review (Marmot, 2010). It built on the earlier Black and Acheson reports, although following 13 years of policy efforts to reduce health inequalities, it had far more evidence upon which to draw. Nevertheless, as Table 4.1 outlines, the Marmot Review's policy recommendations mirror those of the earlier Black and Acheson reports. As Bambra and colleagues (2011) note, this raises questions about both the adequacy of policy responses to these earlier reports and the purpose of all the subsequent research into health inequalities. For, despite the vast quantities of research that has been undertaken on health inequalities, it is unclear how much of this evidence has had a direct impact on policy, and there appears to have been only limited progress in moving our understanding of health inequalities beyond what was known by the authors of the Black Report more than three decades ago. It is possible that all of this research will contribute to substantial shifts in policy and public perceptions in the long term, which is how Weiss (1977, 1979) suggests research most commonly influences policy. Yet, it is also possible that the research community should do more to ensure that health inequalities research influences policy (a point returned to in later sections).

Institutions Responsible for Researching and Tackling Health Inequalities

Most health inequalities research in the UK is undertaken within universities, and the most prominent here are Bristol, Durham, Edinburgh, Glasgow, Liverpool, University College London, and York. There are also some important research units outside of universities, as well as some government-funded health agencies and some internal government research. The three main funders of health inequalities research within universities in the UK are the Economic and Social Research Council (ESRC), the National Institute for Health Research (NIHR), and the Medical Research Council (MRC). However, some other funders, including charities and government funding organizations, have also played an important role.

In 1986, the Health Education Council (HEC), a government-funded agency, commissioned Margaret Whitehead to update the Black Report's analysis. Whitehead's report, called *The Health Divide*, was published in 1987. It played a significant role in further promoting the need for policy-makers to take action to reduce health inequalities (Berridge, 2003). In the same year that *The Health Divide* was released, HEC was replaced by the less independent Health Education Authority (HEA). HEC's director, David Player, was not offered the directorship of the new HEA and he attributed this to growing government frustration at HEC's efforts to draw attention to problematic public health policies (Berridge, 2003).

By 2000, this agency's activities had been significantly reduced; those that remained were incorporated into the newly created Health Development Agency (HDA) (Hunter et al., 2010). In 2005, the functions of the HDA were transferred to the National Institute for Clinical Excellence (NICE) (Hunter et al., 2010). This agency, which still existed when this book was sent to print, was renamed the National Institute for Health and Clinical Excellence, but it continued to use the acronym NICE (Hunter et al., 2010). All of these agencies have produced work on health inequalities.

During the 1980s, the MRC Medical Sociology Unit in Aberdeen (which moved to Glasgow in 1984) also produced some important work on health inequalities. In 1998, this unit, which was directed by Sally Macintyre, merged with the Public Health Research Unit, becoming the MRC Social and Public Health Sciences Unit. This unit, which is still directed by Sally Macintyre, is funded jointly by the MRC and the Chief Scientist Office of the Scottish government.

The Office of Population Censuses and Surveys, which became part of the Office of National Statistics (ONS) in 1996, was another government agency that undertook significant work on health inequalities during the 1980s. Much of the OPCS's work drew on longitudinal data (e.g., Fox, Goldblatt et al., 1985; Goldblatt, 1990). Other significant funders of health inequalities research during the 1980s and early 1990s included the ESRC and the MRC, the British Medical Association (a professional group representing medics), and the charity (sometimes referred to as a think tank) called The King's Fund (see Macintyre, 2003).

Perhaps the most significant program of research focusing on health inequalities to commence prior to 1997 was the ESRC's Health Variations Programme, which ran from 1996 to 2001 and involved 26 projects undertaken by academics across a range of UK universities (http://www.lancs.ac.uk/fass/apsocsci/hvp/intro.htm). The program was headed by Hilary Graham, who was at that time based at the University of Lancaster. Between them, the 26 projects aimed to develop multidisciplinary research that would advance the understanding of the processes and factors underlying socio-economic inequalities in health. The program was called Health Variations rather than Health Inequalities because the very term "health inequalities" was deemed politically sensitive at the time (Smith, 2008). Many of the academics involved in this program had been undertaking research into health inequalities without substantial funding while the issue was off the policy agenda, including Mel Bartley, George Davey Smith, Danny Dorling, Sally Macintyre, and Margaret Whitehead.

Once health inequalities moved onto the official policy agenda with the election of New Labour in 1997, the opportunities for health inequalities research funding grew (Smith, 2008). Work continued to be funded by the ESRC and the MRC, to be undertaken in universities and in the new agencies, the HDA and ONS, but significantly more research funding also became available through other routes, notably via direct government and NHS funding. A new National Institute for Health Research Service Delivery and Organisation (NIHRSDO) was established in 1999 as part of the NHS, and this represented a new major funding stream for public health (including health inequalities) research. In January 2012, the Service Delivery and Organisation (SDO) program was merged with the Health Services Research (HSR) program to form a new NIHR Health Services and Delivery Research (HS&DR) program.

Significant funding for health inequalities has also been made available over the past 15 years by some major charities, including the Joseph Rowntree Foundation (e.g., Exworthy et al., 2003 and Mitchell et al., 2000) and The King's Fund, which has tended to focus on research exploring the impact of policy reforms (particularly NHS reforms) on health inequalities in the UK (e.g., Hutt & Gilmour, 2010).

In 2006, many of the major funders of health inequalities research in the UK (including the ESRC, the MRC, various charities, and government agencies in England, Wales, and Northern Ireland) collaborated to fund five major public health "centres of excellence" via the UK Clinical Research Collaboration (UKCRC): the UKCRC Centre for Tobacco Control Studies, the UKCRC Centre for Public Health Translational Research, the UKCRC Centre for the Development and Evaluation of Complex Interventions for Public Health Improvement, the UKCRC Northern Ireland Centre of Excellence for Public Health Research, and the UKCRC Diet and Physical Activity Public Health Research Centre. None of these centres focuses exclusively on health inequalities, but they all incorporate aspects of health inequalities research.

Research on Health Inequalities in the UK

As noted earlier, there is a long history of research into health inequalities in the UK. Indeed, UK research has been at the forefront of the study of health inequalities (theoretically and empirically) for many decades, internationally leading the way in examining and explaining the etiological pathways underpinning health inequalities in advanced Western democracies. Much of this work dates back to the 1980 Black Report, which outlined four distinctive explanations of health inequalities: artifact, selection, cultural-behavioural, and materialist. More recently, additional theories of health inequalities that have been led by UK research include the psychosocial model, the life course approach, and the political economy approach.

Artifact

The first explanation the Black Report considered was that the relationship between health and "social class" could potentially be an artifact of the measurement process. In particular, the report considered whether the apparent class-health relationship could be a result of upward social mobility, with healthier and younger members of the lower classes moving up the social class scale, leaving a residual older and/or less healthy population at the bottom of the social class scale. After examining the empirical data, the authors rejected this explanation and, since then, a variety of studies have confirmed that the inverse social class-health relationship is not due to any kind of statistical bias and cannot be wholly (or even largely) explained in terms of upward social mobility (e.g., Fox, Goldblatt et al., 1985; Power, Matthews et al., 1997). A consensus, therefore, now exists that there is an inverse gradient linking health and "social class" or wealth, which artifact cannot explain (Graham, 2000).

Natural/Social Selection

The Black Report also considered whether natural or social selection might play a significant role in explaining the gradient separately. This idea suggests that the social gradient in health results from poor health limiting people's access to financial and other resources, which, as a result, determines their "social class." This rather Social Darwinian notion of "natural selection," which assumes that physically fitter people are more successful in life, was also rejected by the authors of the Black Report. However, some evidence has subsequently emerged to suggest that social mobility is likely to play a role in health inequalities, albeit a small one (Blane, Davey Smith et al., 1993). Furthermore, recent developments in genetic research, particularly the human genome project, suggest the health inequalities researchers will soon need to consider the implications of new types of genetic explanations for health inequalities (Davey Smith, Ebrahim et al., 2005).

Cultural-Behavioural

The cultural-behavioural approach asserts that the link between social class and health is a result of differences between socio-economic class in terms of their health-related behaviour (smoking rates, alcohol and drug consumption, dietary intake, physical activity levels, sexual behaviour, and health service usage). The "hard" version of the cultural-behavioural approach asserts that the differences in health between socio-economic classes are wholly accounted for by differences in these unhealthy behaviours. The "softer" version posits that behaviour is a contributory factor to the social gradient, but not the entire explanation (Macintyre, 1997).

Although the Black Report (Black, Morris et al., 1980) acknowledges that lifestyle behaviours contribute to health inequality patterns in the UK, it quickly rejects this as a sufficient explanation for health inequalities on the basis that lifestyle behaviours are significantly affected by the socio-economic contexts within which people live. More recent versions of the behavioural model take cultural norms into account. Unhealthy behaviours are more common in lower social classes where these behaviours represent the cultural norm and are more acceptable, possibly as a result of long-standing industrial work cultures.

Materialist

The materialist explanation focuses on income, and on what income enables, in the relationship between social class and health. Important dimensions of what income enables include access to goods and services and the limitation of exposures to physical and psychosocial risk factors. By way of illustration, a decent income can enable greater access to health care, transport, an adequate diet, good-quality education and housing, and opportunities for social participation, all of which are recognized as health promoting. Material wealth also enables people to limit their exposures to known risk factors for disease, such as physical hazards at work or adverse environmental exposures. The role of public policy and public services, such as schools, transport, and welfare, are thus highlighted in the social patterning of inequality (Bartley, 2004).

The materialist perspective was the one most supported by the authors of the Black Report and it is evident in a great deal of the research on health inequalities that has been undertaken in the UK since (e.g., Graham, 2004; Davey Smith, Dorling & Shaw, 2001; Whitehead, 1987), and there is now a significant consensus that material determinants of health do affect health (Graham, 2004). In this sense, the materialist explanation remains a favoured explanation for health inequalities in the UK (Graham, 2002). However, there have also been some important critiques of this explanation, one of the most common of which is that material approaches fail to fully account for why inequalities in health persist within countries where the material standard of living has significantly increased, such as the UK.

Psychosocial

The income inequalities hypothesis—which suggests that beyond a certain basic level of wealth, health is more closely linked to how egalitarian a society is than to national economic performance or specific levels of poverty—has contributed to an increasing interest in "psychosocial" explanations of health inequalities (Wilkinson, 2005; Wilkinson & Pickett, 2009). Psychosocial explanations focus on how social inequality makes people feel and the effects of the biological consequences of these feelings on health. Bartley (2004) describes how feelings of subordination or inferiority stimulate stress responses that can have long-term consequences for physical and mental health, especially when they are prolonged (chronic). For example, it may not simply be income level or an adequate working environment alone that leads to good health, but rather how good income and good-quality work can make people feel, especially in relation to others (Bartley, 2004). Here perceptions of social status and in particular perceptions of status in comparison to other people in society are significant constructs—what matters is how individuals value themselves. If these value judgments are negative, feelings of inferiority or subordination can invoke harmful stress responses.

Much of the UK research on psychosocial pathways focuses on the workplace and how a sense of control, security, and esteem influences health outcomes (e.g., Marmot, Bosma et al., 1997; De Vogli, Ferrie et al., 2008). This is largely as a result of the findings of the highly influential Whitehall civil service cohort study, which found that occupational grade is inversely associated with incidence of coronary heart disease and related conditions (Marmot et al., 1991, 1997), all-cause mortality, and non-coronary heart disease mortality (Marmot & Brunner, 2005).

Life Course

One approach to understanding health inequalities that has held particular sway since the 1990s is the life course perspective. This is not, in itself, an etiological explanation for health inequalities; rather, it is a perspective that suggests it is essential for theories about the causes of health inequalities to consider the importance of timing and to think about the whole life course rather than just particular points within it. Taking a life course perspective, therefore, involves considering the various risks that individuals are exposed to across their life courses, from fetal development through to old age (Barker, 1992; Bartley, 2004). This is particularly important for chronic diseases, many of which are known to have long latency periods (Lynch & Davey Smith, 2005). Health inequality between socio-economic classes, therefore, results from inequalities in the accumulation of social, psychological, and biological advantages and disadvantages over time.

The notion of critical social transitions is also used to explain how certain important changes in social status (e.g., entry into the labour market or movement between jobs) can have long-term consequences for health and future life chances (Blane, 2006). Longitudinal cohort studies have shown that disadvantage tends to cluster in the present and accumulate over time (Blane, 2006). In this way, individuals who are exposed to adverse conditions in one respect—for example, work—are also more likely to encounter disadvantage in others, such as poor and damp housing, exposure to environmental pollution, inadequate nutrition, limited social participation, and lack of access to green spaces. Moreover, any disadvantage encountered in the past, such as unemployment, is likely to increase the chances of accumulating further disadvantage in the future.

Political Economy

The political economy approach draws on the materialist and psychosocial explanations, but argues that the social determinants of health are themselves shaped by macro-level structural determinants: politics, the economy, the state, the organization of work, and the labour market (Doyal & Pennell, 1979; Bambra, 2011). Politics and the balance of power between key political groups determine whether there are collective interventions and a strong welfare state to reduce inequality, and whether policy interventions are individually, environmentally, or socially focused. So in this explanation, health and health inequalities are politically and economically determined (Bambra et al., 2007a). This explanation is supported by comparative research, which demonstrates that not all advanced economies have the same levels of population health or health inequalities. For example, Coburn's (2004) research concluded those countries that were the least neo-liberal in their economic and social policy orientation (i.e., the Scandinavian welfare states) had significantly lower infant mortality rates, lower overall mortality rates, and less mortality at younger ages. Similarly, studies by Navarro and colleagues indicate that long-term rule by social democratic parties results in better health outcomes than those with more neo-liberal governments (Navarro et al., 2003, 2006).

Public Policy and Health Inequalities in the UK

There are various influences on health, from individual characteristics, which cannot be easily altered, through a range of factors over which individuals have some control, such as lifestyle, education, and employment, but which all exist within, and are influenced by, the macro social, economic, cultural, and environmental context. The main social determinants of health are widely considered to be: access to essential goods and services (specifically, water, sanitation, and food), housing and the living environment, "lifestyle" factors, access to health care, education, unemployment and social security, working conditions, and transport (Dahlgren & Whitehead, 1991).

Access to clean water and hygienic sanitation systems are the most basic prerequisites for good public health, as is the quality, quantity, price, and availability of food (Dahlgren, Nordgren & Whitehead, 1996). Housing is also an important determinant; poor-quality housing results in higher prevalence of respiratory disease, while housing costs can also indirectly have a negative effect on health by limiting expenditure in other areas, such as diet (Stafford & McCarthy, 2006). In terms of lifestyle factors, smoking remains the most important preventable cause of mortality in the advanced capitalist world (Jarvis & Wardle, 2006). Access to health care is a fundamental determinant of health, particularly in terms of the treatment of pre-existing conditions (Tudor Hart, 1971). Unemployment is associated with an increased likelihood of morbidity and mortality (Bartley, Ferrie et al., 2006), and the physical work environment can impact negatively on health via exposure to dangerous substances (e.g., lead, asbestos, etc.), or via ergonomic problems (Bambra, 2011). Epidemiological research has also found a relationship between the psychosocial work environment and inequalities in health status (as outlined earlier).

Transport works as a social determinant of health in three ways: as a source of pollution, as a cause of accidents, and as a form of exercise. Public policy clearly has a major role in shaping all these social determinants. In this section we examine the impact of UK public policy since the 1980s on four of these key social determinants of health: access to health care services, lifestyle behaviours, the work environment, and unemployment.

Access to, Use of, and Quality of Health Services

As outlined above, all four UK jurisdictions have a health care system, known as the National Health Service, which is funded from general taxation and largely delivered by public service providers. This means that in the UK (as in Canada), there is rather less concern about the role that access to health care services plays in health inequalities than there is in countries in which health care services are dependent upon individual contributions (either through direct, out-of-pocket payments or via payments to health care insurers). However, in 1971 Julian Tudor Hart (a general practitioner working in Wales) put forward the notion that an "inverse care law" was operating in the UK despite the NHS (Tudor Hart, 1971), which meant that the availability of medical care was varying inversely with the need of the population (Black, Morris et al., 1980, 113).

It has been posited that this is partly because health care professionals choose to live and work in more advantaged areas, and partly because poorer communities have higher rates of morbidity, which means the demand for health services is greater in poorer areas. Recent research that lends support to this thesis includes Powell and Exworthy's (2003) analysis of NHS policies, which indicates that equal access to health care is still far from a reality in Britain, and Benzeval and Judge's (1996) study, which suggests that considerable inequalities remain in access to GP services in England. Other studies suggest that once people enter the health care system, patients from more privileged backgrounds may be offered better (or more intensive) treatment options than patients from lower socio-economic groups (e.g., Pell, Pell et al., 2000).

This evidence suggests that the NHS has a potentially important role to play in helping to reduce health inequalities in the UK. Reflecting this, ever since health inequalities moved onto the policy agenda in 1997, policy-makers have made it clear that they expected the NHS to take a leading role in reducing health inequalities. Indeed, in 2000, the principle that the NHS should "work to reduce health inequalities" was included in one of 10 "core principles" that the government established for the NHS (Department of Health, 2000). Furthermore, as Table 4.3 summarizes, the responsibility for achieving national health inequalities targets in the UK has generally been passed from central government to the NHS. Yet, given the consensus that social and material factors are important determinants of health inequalities, it is far from clear how significantly the NHS could be expected to reduce health inequalities.

In the UK, the formula used to distribute NHS funds does try to take the higher health needs of poorer socio-economic groups into consideration (Patterson & Judge, 2002). Furthermore, while Labour was in power (1997–2010), efforts were made to ensure that NHS services were more easily accessible to people whose hours of work clashed with traditional NHS opening hours and to those who were not registered with general practitioners, which was the case for many homeless people. For example, a series of NHS walk-in centres was introduced (see Salisbury et al., 2002) to make services more accessible to non-registered patients and an NHS telephone service (NHS Direct) was established. However, it remains unclear how successful these efforts to improve access to health care were. Goddard (2009) argues that their success is likely to be limited because they largely failed to recognize the source of barriers to access.

In addition, recent NHS policies that have explicitly aimed to reduce health inequalities include the provision (and targeting) of smoking cessation services and the increased prescription of statins (as a means of helping to prevent heart attacks) and other pharmaceuticals, such as antidepressants (Blackman, 2007). Although these kinds of measures, which are based on a medical (rather than a social) model of health, may have had a small impact on reducing aspects of health inequalities (e.g., Bauld et al., 2007), they are short-term measures that do little to address the determinants underlying health inequalities and that, therefore, cannot be expected to significantly reduce health inequalities. Furthermore, the NHS has also been subject to incessant organizational reforms and political pressure to address media scandals concerning health care. All of this has diverted attention away from long-term public health issues (such as tackling health inequalities) and toward short-term clinical issues such as reducing waiting times and improving survival rates (Hunter et al., 2010).

Lifestyle Behaviours

As outlined above, while health inequalities are closely linked to unhealthy lifestyle behaviours, such as smoking, alcohol consumption, and obesity, the unequal distribution of the lifestyle behaviours is widely understood to be symptomatic of more "upstream" determinants, such as social and economic circumstances. Despite the explicit recognition of this within most of the UK public health policy documents produced in the post-1997 era, it is also evident that what has been termed "lifestyle drift" occurred (Whitehead & Popay, 2010), in which the emphasis placed on lifestyle behavioural interventions (as mechanisms for reducing health inequalities) increased the longer that Labour remained in power (see sections above). The growing pressure on targeted smoking cessation services to help achieve national health inequalities targets was an obvious example of this (Smith et al., 2009).

More broadly, UK governments have introduced a raft of policies that focus on trying to improve lifestyle behaviours, and many of these policies do not explicitly consider health inequalities. They may, nevertheless, impact on health inequalities and could even unintentionally increase health inequalities if, for example, they have a greater impact on wealthier groups than more deprived groups (Macintyre et al., 2001). A key factor that shapes the likelihood of this is the extent to which policies designed to improve lifestyle behaviours rely on individuals' ability to change their behaviours in spite of their circumstances. For example, health education campaigns that encourage people to adopt healthier livestyles may have most impact on individuals living in comfortable circumstances who are already focused on trying to improve (or maintain) their health (a group sometimes referred to as the "worried well"). In contrast, policies that focus on increasing the cost of engaging in health-damaging activities, such as smoking and drinking alcohol, by raising prices tend to have a bigger impact on poorer communities and are therefore more likely to help reduce health inequalities (e.g., IARC, 2011).

In this respect, there are important differences in the policy approaches that have been taken to address different "lifestyle behavioural" problems in the UK. As Table 4.5 demonstrates, there is a lack of policy coherence between policies designed to reduce smoking (which have, in recent years, focused on significant state interventions, such as high taxes and legislative restrictions on smoking in public places) and policies intended to reduce alcohol misuse and obesity (which have tended to focus on voluntary, non-legislative measures that rely on individual and corporate action). The implications of this increasingly obvious policy divergence for health inequalities have not yet been adequately assessed. However, based on what is known about both the determinants of health inequalities (as discussed in earlier sections) and corporate non-compliance with voluntary agreements (Gilmore et al., 2011), it might be expected that the policy approaches taken to reduce smoking will help reduce health inequalities, while the policy approaches to tackling alcohol misuse and obesity might (unintentionally) exacerbate health inequalities.

Work Environment

The work environment has long been acknowledged as an important determinant of health and health inequalities in the UK. Physical working conditions and stressful psychosocial work environments are prominent determinants of health, and exposure to them exhibits a strong social gradient that influences inequalities in health among employees (Bambra, 2011). Historically and comparatively, the UK has had a strong health and safety at work legislative framework that was underpinned by trade union and social democratic party action (e.g., the introduction of the Health and Safety at Work Act by the UK Labour government in 1975). However, since the 1980s, Conservative governments, motivated by neo-liberal ideology, have sought to dismantle this framework. For example, in 2011 it was announced that health and safety legislation would be streamlined in the UK, and that the enforcement agency, the Health and Safety Executive, would be downsized.

Furthermore, the actual enforcement of health and safety legislation has been limited (Bambra, 2011) with low employer fines common for breaches. For example, the 1,245 prosecutions by the UK Health and Safety Executive in 2008–2009 resulted in an average company fine of just £20,000 (20 percent below the median UK wage of £25,000). Actions to reduce health and safety legislation went alongside restrictions on trade union activities in the 1980s, which further decreased employees' rights. In addition, despite a strong evidence base to sug-

Table 4.5
A Brief Summary of Recent UK Regional Approaches to Alcohol, Food, and Tobacco

Region	Policy Approach to Alcohol	Policy Approach to Food and Obesity	Policy Approach to Tobacco
England	• In 2009, the chief medical officer recommended that the government introduce a minimum price per unit of alcohol at a rate of 50p per unit. In January 2011, the Coalition government announced it was working on the less radical plan of introducing a ban on the sale of below-cost alcohol. • In 2010, a UK-wide consultation on alcohol labelling was undertaken. Subsequent proposals remain unclear.	• Focus is on health promotion and education, with efforts to encourage people to take more exercise and improve their diets. There is some attention to tackling "obesogenic environments." • Voluntary approaches are explicitly preferred to government intervention (e.g., voluntary rather than compulsory "traffic light" food labelling system).	• Smoking in public places was banned in July 2007. • Legislation was passed in 2009 to ban cigarette sales from vending machines and point-of-sale displays. Implementation of the vending machine ban is planned for October 2011. Implementation for the display ban is planned for April 2012–2015, depending on the size of the retailer. • Commitment to undertake consultation on plain packs.
Northern Ireland	• In March 2011, Northern Ireland's power-sharing executive indicated that it intended to become the first UK government to introduce minimum pricing for alcohol, and launched a consultation process calling for a minimum price of between 40p and 70p per unit of alcohol. • On labelling, see England.	• Approach was similar to England's.	• Smoking in public places was banned in April 2007. • It is covered by the UK legislation relating to ban in vending machines and point-of-sale displays, although it is unclear when the legislation will be implemented. • It is covered by the UK's commitment to consultation on plain packs.

Scotland	• There is a clear commitment to (re) introduce a Minimum Pricing Bill, following a previous failed attempt, which will set rates for alcohol at 45p per unit. • On labelling, see England.	• The approach is similar to England's, although in August 2010, the Scottish government extended the free school lunch entitlement to all P1–P3 pupils, with the aim of improving diets in early years.	• Smoking in public places was banned in March 2006. • Legislation was passed in 2010 banning cigarette sales from vending machines and point-of-sale displays. Implementation of the vending machine ban was planned for October 2011. Following a legal challenge, implementation for the display ban is anticipated for April 2012–2015.
Wales	• The English approach to minimum pricing will apply to Wales. It is unclear, despite expressed support for minimum pricing among some Welsh Assembly ministers, whether additional legislation will be introduced. • On labelling, see England.	• The approach is similar to England's.	• Smoking in public places was banned in April 2007. • It is covered by the UK legislation relating to ban in vending machines and point-of-sale displays, although it is unclear when the legislation will be implemented. • It is covered by the UK's commitment to consultation on plain packs.

Source: K.E. Smith & M. Hellowell, Beyond rhetorical differences: A cohesive account of post-devolution developments in UK health policy, *Social Policy & Administration, 46*(2) (2012), 178–198.

gest that interventions that increase employee control can be beneficial for health and productivity (Egan et al., 2007; Bambra et al., 2007b), the UK lacks any legislative requirement for employees to be consulted by their employers, except where trade unions are recognized.

Under the 1997–2010 Labour administration, some more progressive work environment legislation was enacted, such as the right to request flexible working arrangements (e.g., teleworking or reduced hours) for all UK employees with children up to the age of 16 or caregiving responsibilities. Flexible working has been shown to have positive health effects for employees (Joyce et al., 2010). The European Union, of which the UK is a member, has also continued to advance health and safety legislation, although this has usually focused on educating workers about dangerous work environments and requiring them to wear protective clothing rather than requiring company action (Bambra, 2011). It should be noted that comparative studies have shown that countries with stronger work environment legislation, such as Sweden, have lower levels of stress and ill health among all employees, and smaller inequalities in health between employees (Dragano et al., 2011).

Unemployment

Unemployment is associated with an increased likelihood of morbidity and mortality (Bambra, 2010). At the individual level, studies have particularly shown that unemployment is associated with worse mental health, including suicide and attempted suicide. It has also been linked to higher rates of all-cause mortality as well as limiting long-term illness and, in some studies, a higher prevalence of risky health behaviours (among young men), including problematic alcohol use and smoking (Bambra, 2011). At the area level, rates of unemployment, especially when used as indicators of deprivation, correlate with poorer neighbourhood health, and at the national level increases in the unemployment rate have been associated with increased mortality (Bambra, 2011).

The negative health experiences of unemployment are not limited only to the unemployed, but also extend to their families and the wider community. Links between unemployment and poorer health have conventionally been explained through two interrelated concepts: the material consequences of unemployment (e.g., wage loss and resulting changes in access to essential goods and services), and the psychosocial effects of unemployment (e.g., stigma, isolation, and loss of self-worth). Research has also drawn attention to the contributory role of ill health itself as a factor behind unemployment (direct health selection) (Popham & Bambra, 2010). Studies from various countries have identified poverty as an important intermediary factor in the relationship between unemployment and health (Bambra, 2011).

Unemployment benefits are, therefore, an important mediator of this negative relationship (Bartley & Blane, 1997) with those countries that provide higher levels of benefits exhibiting a weaker relationship between unemployment and poor health (Bambra & Eikemo, 2008). In the UK welfare system, unemployment benefits have generally been very low in comparison to average wages and well below the poverty line. In the early 1980s, the value of UK unemployment benefit as a percentage of average wages (excluding housing costs) was 45 percent, but by 1999 this had decreased to 16 percent (Bambra & Eikemo, 2008). In 2011, the benefit was worth £65 per week, compared to an estimated poverty line of £115 per week (excluding housing costs) (Bambra, 2011). This decrease was largely as a result of reforms to the welfare state during the Thatcher-led governments of the 1980s. In addition to reductions in the value of unemployment benefit, these reforms (and later ones) saw an increase in means-testing so that only the very poor are now entitled to any support from the welfare state after six months of unemployment. This entitlement restriction, alongside increases in the work history required prior to unemployment (qualifying conditions), has resulted in a decrease in those covered by unemployment benefit in the UK from 90 percent in 1980 to 77 percent in 1999 (Bambra & Eikemo, 2008). Studies have shown that those on means-tested benefits have worse health than those on entitlement benefits (Rodriguez, 2001). The unemployed are also subject to compulsory participation in return-to-work programs such as Pathways to Work and, since 2011, the Work Programme. Some have suggested that there are negative effects on mental health as a result of participation in these programs, particularly for the young (Dorling, 2009).

Conclusion

The UK has a long history of health inequalities research and, following the election of a Labour government on a mandate that included a commitment to reducing health inequalities and implementing evidence-based policy in 1997, the UK became the first European country in which policy-makers systematically and explicitly attempted to reduce inequalities in health (Mackenbach, 2011). A raft of policy measures designed to reduce health inequalities have been announced since 1997 and, although the UK's political system has become increasingly fragmented as a result of political devolution in Northern Ireland, Scotland, and Wales, health inequalities have remained consistently high on policy agendas throughout the UK.

Despite all this, by the time Labour left office in 2010, mounting evidence indicated that health inequalities in the UK had continued to widen (Marmot, 2010; National Audit Office, 2010). This failure has triggered some despair within the health inequalities community (Mackenbach, 2010). A variety of accounts of why UK health inequalities policies in this period were not successful exist, including claims that: (1) cultural and institutional gaps between researchers and policy-makers prevented the effective use of evidence (e.g., Mackenbach, 2011); (2) a policy orientation toward a medical, individualized model of health diminished the influence of research concerning wider, social determinants of health (Hunter, 2003); (3) dominant social, political, and economic ideologies prevented much of the existing evidence from influencing policy (Carlisle, 2001); and (4) policy-makers did not feel they had a democratic mandate to implement many of the policies that the evidence suggested would be necessary to reduce health inequalities (Mackenbach, 2011).

In response to these problems, health inequalities scholars in the UK have begun to call for stronger links between academics and policy-makers, in which the two groups work collaboratively to co-produce research (Hunter, 2009); greater efforts to engage in public health advocacy and work with communities (Whitehead & Popay, 2010; Mackenbach, 2011); and more awareness of the actors and forces influencing policies in ways that are likely to be counterproductive for health inequalities (Navarro, 2009).

Critical Thinking Questions

1. To what extent were policies to tackle health inequalities in the UK (in the 1997–2010 period) informed by the available research evidence?
2. What might explain some of the differences between the available evidence on health inequalities and the policy approaches taken in the UK?
3. How might the failure of the UK to measurably reduce health inequalities in the 1997–2010 period be explained?
4. What can other countries learn from the UK's approach to reducing health inequalities?

Recommended Readings

Bambra, C., Smith, K.E., Garthwaite, K., Joyce, K., & Hunter, D. (2011). A labour of Sisyphus? Public policy and health inequalities research from the Black and Acheson Reports to the Marmot Review. *Journal of Epidemiology and Community Health, 65,* 399–406.
> This article provides a more detailed overview of the three UK government-commissioned reviews of health inequalities evidence that are mentioned in this chapter. It comparatively assesses the recommendations emerging from each of the three reviews and reflects on their impact on policy and research.

Hunter, D.J., Marks, L., & Smith, K.E. (2010). *The public health system in England.* Bristol: Policy Press.
> This short book provides a detailed overview of the public health system in England from the mid-1970s until 2010, and sets this against broader UK, European, and international developments. It draws out the recurrent tensions and themes that have dominated public health policy in England over this period.

Mackenbach, J.P. (2010). Can we reduce health inequalities? An analysis of the English strategy (1997–2010). *Journal of Epidemiology and Community Health.* doi: 10.1136.
> This article reflects on the Labour government's efforts to reduce health inequalities during the 1997–2010 period. It tries to assess whether these policy efforts were successful and draws out potential lessons. The article argues that public health advocacy is needed to ensure that governments have a democratic mandate to make the necessary policy changes to address health inequalities.

Wilkinson, R., & Pickett, K. (2010). *The spirit level: Why more equal societies almost always do better.* London: Penguin.
> This book uses a variety of empirical sources to argue in favour of efforts to achieve more equal societies. The authors claim that societies in which resources are more equally distributed tend to have a variety of much better social outcomes, including in relation to health. This book has generated a great deal of political, public, and media interest and debate in the UK.

Recommended Websites

Equality Trust: www.equalitytrust.org.uk
> This is the official website for the Equality Trust, which was founded by Richard Wilkinson and Kate Pickett, the authors of *The Spirit Level,* which is one of the most popular books setting out the links between health inequalities and other forms of inequality and making the case for psychosocial explanations. The website provides links to summaries of the books as well as a host of other related resources.

Health Inequalities Blog: http://inequalitiesblog.wordpress.com
> A blog concerned with health inequalities research that has a particular focus on the UK and the US, providing an up-to-date summary of recent contributions to the health inequalities field.

Marmot Review: www.marmotreview.org
> Website for the 2010 Marmot Review. In addition to listing the full report and associated documents (including an executive summary of the report), this site provides lots of further resources, such as video and audio clips about the report and its impact.

Social and Spatial Inequalities Research Group at the University of Sheffield: http://sasi.group.shef.ac.uk/presentations
> This website provides access to a selection of material from lectures, presentations, and talks by Danny Dorling, one of the leading health inequalities scholars in the UK, and some of his colleagues.

References

Acheson, D.C. (1998). *Independent inquiry into inequalities in health.* London: The Stationery Office.

Ashton, J. (1984). *Health in Mersey: A review.* Liverpool: Department of Community Health, Liverpool University Medical School.

Bambra, C. (2005). Worlds of welfare and the health care discrepancy. *Social Policy and Society, 4,* 31–41.

Bambra, C. (2010). Yesterday once more? An analysis of unemployment and health in the 21st century. *Journal of Epidemiology and Community Health, 64,* 213–215.

Bambra, C. (2011). *Work, worklessness, and the political economy of health.* Oxford: Oxford University Press.

Bambra, C., Egan, M., Thomas, S., Petticrew, M., & Whitehead, M. (2007a). The psychosocial and health effects of workplace reorganisation 2: A systematic review of task restructuring interventions. *Journal of Epidemiology and Community Health, 61,* 1028–1037.

Bambra, C., & Eikemo, T. (2008). The welfare state: A glossary for public health. *Journal of Epidemiology and Community Health, 62,* 3–6.

Bambra, C., Fox, D., & Scott-Samuel, A. (2007b). A politics of health glossary. *Journal of Epidemiology and Community Health, 61,* 571–574.

Bambra, C., Smith, K.E., Garthwaite, K., Joyce, K., & Hunter, D. (2011). A labour of Sisyphus? Public policy and health inequalities research from the Black and Acheson Reports to the Marmot Review. *Journal of Epidemiology and Community Health, 65,* 399–406.

Barker, D.J.P. (1992). Foetal and infant origins of adult disease, *BMJ* (301), 1111.

Barker, D.J.P., Eriksson, J.G., et al. (2002). Fetal origins of adult disease: Strength of effects and biological basis. *International Journal of Epidemiology, 31,* 1235–1239.

Bartley, M. (2004). *Health inequality: An introduction to theories, concepts, and methods.* Cambridge: Polity Press in association with Blackwell Publishing Ltd.

Bartley, M., & Blane, D. (1997). Health and the lifecourse: Why safety nets matter. *BMJ, 314,* 1194–1196.

Bartley, M., Ferrie, J., & Montgomery, S. (2006). Health and labour market disadvantage: Unemployment, non-employment, and job insecurity. In M. Marmot & R.G. Wilkinson (Eds.), *Social determinants of health* (pp. 78–96). Oxford: Oxford University Press.

Bauld, L., Day, P., & Judge, K. (2008). Off target: A critical review of setting goals for reducing health inequalities in the United Kingdom. *International Journal of Health Services: Planning, Administration, Evaluation, 38*(3), 439–454.

Bauld, L., Judge, K., & Platt, S. (2007). Assessing the impact of smoking cessation services on reducing health inequalities in England: Observational study. *Tobacco Control, 16*(6), 400–404.

Benzeval, M., & Judge, K. (1996). Access to health care in England: Continuing inequalities in the distribution of GPs. *Journal of Public Health, 18*(1), 33–40.

Berridge, V. (Ed.). (2003). Witness seminar: The Black Report and the health divide. In V. Berridge & S. Blume (Eds.), *Poor health: Social inequalities before and after the Black Report* (pp. 131–171). London: Frank Cass.

Berridge, V., & Blume, S. (Eds.). (2003). *Poor health: Social inequality before and after the Black Report.* London: Frank Cass.

Bevan, G. (2010). Impact of devolution of healthcare in the UK: Provider challenge in England and provider capture in Wales, Scotland, and Northern Ireland? *Journal of Health Services Research and Policy, 15*(2), 67–68.

Birch, S. (1999). The 39 steps: The mystery of health inequalities in the UK. *Health Economics, 8,* 301–308.

Black, D., Morris, J.N., et al. (1980). *Inequalities in health: Report of a research working group.* London: Department of Health and Social Services.

Blackman, T. (2007). Statins, saving lives, and shibboleths. *BMJ, 334*(7599), 902.

Blane, D. (2006). The life course, the social gradient, and health. In M. Marmot & R.G. Wilkinson (Eds.), *Social determinants of health* (pp. 54–77). Oxford: Oxford University Press.

Blane, D., Davey Smith, G., et al. (1993). Social selection: What does it contribute to social class differences in health? *Sociology of Health & Illness, 15*(1), 1–15.

BMA. (2010). *Devolution—a map of divergence.* London: BMA.

Carlisle, S. (2001). Inequalities in health: Contested explanations, shifting discourses, and ambiguous policies. *Critical Public Health, 11*(3), 267–281.

Clegg, D. (2010). Labour market policy in the crisis: The UK in comparative perspective. *Journal of Poverty and Social Justice, 18*(1), 5–17.

Coburn, D. (2004). Beyond the income inequality hypothesis: Class, neo-liberalism, and health inequalities. *Social Science & Medicine, 58*, 41–56.

Connolly, S., Bevan, G., & Mays, N. (2010). *Funding and performance of healthcare systems in the four countries of the UK before and after devolution.* London: The Nuffield Trust.

Dahlgren, G., Nordgren, P., & Whitehead, M. (1996). *Health impact assessment of the EU Common Agricultural Policy.* London: Swedish National Institute of Public Health & The King's Fund.

Dahlgren, G., & Whitehead, M. (1991). *Policies and strategies to promote social equity in health.* Stockholm: Institute for Futures Studies.

Davey Smith, G., Dorling, D., & Shaw, M. (Eds). (2001). *Poverty, inequality, and health in Britain: 1800–2000—a reader.* Studies in Poverty, Inequality, and Social Exclusion: A Series by the Policy Press. Bristol: The Policy Press.

Davey Smith, G., Ebrahim, S., et al. (2005). Genetic epidemiology and public health: Hope, hype, and future prospects. *The Lancet, 366*, 1484–1498.

Davey Smith, G., Morris, J.N., & Shaw, M. (1998). The independent inquiry into inequalities in health is welcome, but its recommendations are too cautious and vague. *BMJ, 317*, 1465–1466.

Department of Health. (1997). *Press release: Public health strategy launched to tackle the root causes of ill-health.* London: Department of Health.

Department of Health. (1999). *Reducing health inequalities: An action report.* London: The Stationery Office.

Department of Health. (2000). *The NHS plan: A plan for investment, a plan for reform.* London: The Stationery Office.

Department of Health. (2001). *From vision to reality.* London: Department of Health.

Department of Health, Social Services, and Public Safety. (2002). *Investing for health.* Belfast: Northern Ireland Executive.

Department of Health, Social Services, and Public Safety. (2005). *Investing for health update 2005.* Belfast: Health Promotion Agency for Northern Ireland on behalf of the DHSSPS.

Department of Health, Social Services, and Public Safety. (2006). *Investing for health update report 2006.* Belfast: Health Promotion Agency for Northern Ireland on behalf of the DHSSPS.

De Vogli, R., Ferrie, J.E., et al. (2008). Unfairness and health: Evidence from the Whitehall II study. *Journal of Epidemiology and Community Health, 61*, 513–518.

Dorling, D. (2009). Unemployment and health: Health benefits vary according to the method of reducing unemployment. *BMJ, 338*, 1091–1092.

Doyal, L., & Pennell, I. (1979). *The political economy of health.* London: Pluto Press.

Dragano, N., Siegrist, J., & Wahrendorf, M. (2011). Welfare regimes, labour policies, and psychosocial working conditions: A comparative study with 9,917 older employees from 12 European countries. *Journal of Epidemiology and Community Health, 65*(9), 793–799.

Egan, M., Bambra, C., Thomas, S., Petticrew, M., Whitehead, M., & Thomson, H. (2007). The psychosocial and health effects of workplace reorganisation 1: A systematic review of organisational-level interventions that aim to increase employee control. *Journal of Epidemiology and Community Health, 61*, 945–954.

Exworthy, M., Stuart, M., Blane, D., & Marmot, M. (2003). *Tackling health inequalities since the Acheson Inquiry.* Bristol: The Policy Press for the Joseph Rowntree Foundation.

Fox, A.J., Goldblatt, P.O., et al. (1985). Social class mortality differentials: Artefact, selection, or life circumstances? *Journal of Epidemiology and Community Health, 39*(1), 1–8.

Gilmore, A.B., Savell, E., & Collin, J. (2011). Public health, corporations, and the New Responsibility Deal: Promoting partnerships with vectors of disease? *Journal of Public Health, 33*(1), 2–4.

Goddard, M. (2009). Access to health care services—an English policy perspective. *Health Economics, Policy, and Law, 4*, 195–208.

Goldblatt, P.O. (1990). *Longitudinal study: Mortality and social organisation.* London: HMSO.

Graham, H. (2000). *Understanding inequalities in health.* Buckingham: Open University Press.

Graham, H. (2002). Building an inter-disciplinary science of health inequalities: The example of life-course research. *Social Science & Medicine, 55*(11), 2005–2016.

Graham, H. (2004). Social determinants and their unequal distribution: Clarifying policy understandings. *The Milbank Quarterly, 82*(1), 101–124.

Graham, H., & Kelly, M.P. (2004). *Health inequalities: Concepts, frameworks, and policy.* London: HDA.

Greer, S. (2004). *Territorial politics and health policy: UK health policy in comparative perspective.* Manchester: Manchester University Press.

Greer, S. (2005). The territorial bases of health policymaking in the UK after devolution. *Regional and Federal Studies, 15*, 501–518.

Greer, S. (2009). Devolution and divergence in UK health policies. *BMJ, 338*, 78–80.

Hunter, D.J. (2003). *Public health policy.* Oxford: Polity Press.

Hunter, D.J. (2009). Relationship between evidence and policy: A case of evidence-based policy or policy-based evidence? *Public Health, 123*(9), 583–586.

Hunter, D.J. (2011). Change of government: One more big bang health care reform in England's National Health Service. *International Journal of Health Services, 41*(1), 159–174.

Hunter, D.J., Marks, L., & Smith, K.E. (2010). *The public health system in England.* Bristol: Policy Press.

Hutt, P., & Gilmour, S. (2010). *Tackling inequalities in general practice.* Research paper. London: The King's Fund.

IARC (International Agency for Research on Cancer, World Health Organization). (2011). Handbook Vol. 14: *Effectiveness of tax and price policies for tobacco control.* IARC: Lyon.

Jarvis, M., & Wardle, J. (2006). Social patterning of individual health behaviours: The case of cigarette smoking. In M. Marmot & R. Wilkinson (Eds.), *The social determinants of health* (pp. 224–237). Oxford: Oxford University Press.

Joyce, K., Pabayo, R., Critchley, J.A., & Bambra, C. (2010). *Flexible working conditions and their effects on employee health and wellbeing.* Cochrane Database of Systematic Reviews 2010, Issue 2.

The Lancet. (2011). Editorial: Public health in Wales: A nation comes of age. *The Lancet, 378*, 374.

Lynch, J.W., & Davey Smith, G. (2005). A life course approach to chronic disease epidemiology. *Annual Review of Public Health, 26*, 1–35.

Macintyre, S. (1997). The Black Report and beyond: What are the issues? *Social Science & Medicine, 44*(6), 723–745.

Macintyre, S. (2003). Before and after the Black Report: Four fallacies. In V. Berridge & S. Blume (Eds.), *Poor health: Social inequalities before and after the Black Report* (pp. 198–219). London: Frank Cass.

Macintyre, S., Chalmers, I., Horton, R., & Smith, R. (2001). Using evidence to inform health policy: Case study. *BMJ, 322*(7280), 222–225.

Mackenbach, J.P. (2010). Has the English strategy to reduce health inequalities failed? *Social Science & Medicine, 71*, 1249–1253.

Mackenbach, J.P. (2011). Can we reduce health inequalities? An analysis of the English strategy (1997–2010). *Journal of Epidemiology and Community Health, 65*, 568–575.

Marmot, M. (2004). *The status syndrome: How social standing affects our health and longevity.* New York: Times Books.

Marmot, M. (Chair). (2010). *Fair society, healthy lives: The Marmot review.* London: University College.

Marmot, M., Bosma, H., Hemingway, H., Brunner, E., & Stansfeld, S. (1997). Contribution of job control and other risk factors to social variations in coronary heart disease. *The Lancet, 350*, 235–240.

Marmot, M., & Brunner, E. (2005). Cohort profile: The Whitehall II study. *International Journal of Epidemiology, 34*, 251–256.

Marmot, M., Stansfeld, S., Patel, C., North, F., Head, J., White, I., et al. (1991). Health inequalities among British civil servants—the Whitehall II study. *The Lancet, 337*, 1387–1393.

McWhirter, L. (2004). *Equality and inequalities in health and social care in Northern Ireland: A statistical overview.* Belfast: DHSSPS.

Mitchell, R., Shaw, M., & Dorling, D. (2000). *Inequalities in life and death—what if Britain were more equal?* Bristol: Joseph Rowntree Foundation and The Policy Press.

National Audit Office. (2010). Department of Health: *Tackling health inequalities in life expectancy in areas with the worst health deprivation.* London: The Stationery Office.

Navarro, V. (2009), What we mean by social determinants of health. *Global Health Promotion, 16*, 5–16.

Navarro, V., Borrell, C., Benach, J., & Muntaner, C. (2003). The importance of the political and the social in explaining mortality differentials among the countries of the OECD, 1950–1998. *International Journal of Health Services Research, 33*, 419–494.

Navarro, V., Muntaner, C., Borrell, C., & Benach, J. (2006). Politics and health outcomes. *The Lancet, 368*, 1033–1037.

Patterson, I., & Judge, K. (2002). Equality of access to healthcare. In J. Mackenbach & M. Bakker (Eds.), *Reducing inequalities in health: A European perspective* (pp. 169–186). London: Routledge.

Pell, J.P., Pell, A.C.H., et al. (2000). Effect of socio-economic deprivation on waiting time for cardiac surgery: Retrospective cohort study. *BMJ, 320*(7226), 15–18.

Popham, F., & Bambra, C. (2010). Evidence from the 2001 English Census on the contribution of employment status to the social gradient in self-rated health. *Journal of Epidemiology and Community Health, 64*, 277–280.

Powell, M., & Exworthy, M. (2003). Equal access to health care and the British National Health Service. *Policy Studies, 24*(1), 51–64.

Power, C., Matthews, S., et al. (1997). Inequalities in self-rated health in the 1958 birth cohort: Lifetime social circumstances or social mobility? *BMJ, 313*, 449–453.

Public Health Strategy Division. (2002). *Well being in Wales.* Cardiff: Office of the Chief Medical Officer.

Rodriguez, E. (2001). Keeping the unemployed healthy: The effect of means-tested and entitlement benefits in Britain, Germany, and the United States. *American Journal of Public Health, 91*, 1403–1411.

Salisbury, C., Chalder, M., Scott, T.M., Pope, C., & Moore, L. (2002). What is the role of walk-in centres in the NHS? *BMJ, 324*, 399–402.

Scottish Executive. (2000). *Our National Health: A plan for action, a plan for change.* Edinburgh: The Stationery Office.

Scottish Executive. (2003). *Inequalities in health: Report of the Measuring Inequalities in Health Working Group.* Retrieved from: www.scotland.gov.uk/library2/doc07/sjmd.pdf.

Scottish Executive. (2004). *Fair to all, personal to each.* Edinburgh: Department of Health.

Scottish Executive. (2005). *Delivering for health.* Edinburgh: Department of Health.

Scottish Government. (2008). *Equally well: Report of the Ministerial Task Force on Health Inequalities.* Edinburgh: Scottish Government.

Scottish Government. (2010). *Equally well review.* Edinburgh: Scottish Government.

Secretary of State for Health. (1999). *Saving lives: Our healthier nation.* London UK: Department of Health.

Secretary of State for Health. (2004). *Choosing health: Making healthy choices easier.* London UK: Department of Health.

Secretary of State for Health. (2010). *Healthy lives, healthy people: Our strategy for public health in England.* White Paper. Norwich: The Stationery Office.

Secretary of State for Scotland. (1999). *Towards a healthier Scotland: A White Paper on Health.* London: The Stationery Office.

Shaw, M., Davey Smith, G., et al. (2005). Health inequalities and New Labour: How the promises compare with real progress. *BMJ, 330*(7498), 1016–1021.

Shaw, M., Dorling, D., et al. (1998). Changing the map: Health in Britain 1951–1991. In M. Bartley, D. Blane & G. Davey Smith (Eds.), *The sociology of health inequalities*. Oxford: Blackwell.

Smith, K.E. (2008). *Health inequalities in Scotland and England: The translation of ideas between research and policy*. PhD thesis, University of Edinburgh.

Smith, K.E., & Hellowell, M. (2012). Beyond rhetorical differences: A cohesive account of post-devolution developments in UK health policy. *Social Policy & Administration, 46*(2), 178–198.

Smith, K.E., Hunter, D.J., Blackman, T., Williams, G., McKee, L., Harrington, B., Elliott, E., Marks, L., & Greene, A. (2009). Divergence or convergence? Health inequalities & policy in a devolved Britain. *Critical Social Policy, 29*(2), 216–242.

Stafford, M., & McCarthy, M. (2006). Neighbourhoods, housing, and health. In M. Marmot & R. Wilkinson (Eds.), *The social determinants of health* (pp. 297–317). Oxford: Oxford University Press.

Townsend, P. (2001). *Targeting poor health: Professor Townsend's report of the Welsh Assembly's National Steering Group on the Allocation of NHS Resources* (Vol. 1). Cardiff: National Assembly for Wales.

Tudor Hart, J. (1971). The inverse care law. *The Lancet, 1*(7696), 405–412.

Weiss, C. (1977). Research for policy's sake: The enlightenment function of social research. *Policy Analysis, 3*, 531–547.

Weiss, C. (1979). The many meanings of research utilization. *Public Administration Review, 39*(5), 426–431.

Whitehead, M. (1987). *The health divide: Inequalities in health in the1980's*. London: Health Education Authority.

Whitehead, M., & Popay, J. (2010). Swimming upstream? Taking action on the social determinants of health inequalities. *Social Science & Medicine, 71*, 1234–1236.

Wilkinson, R. (2005). *The impact of inequality: How to make sick societies healthier*. New York: The New Press.

Wilkinson, R., & Pickett, K. (2009). *The spirit level: Why more equal societies almost always do better*. London: Penguin.

Woods, K.J. (2004). Political devolution and the health services in Great Britain. *International Journal of Health Services, 34*(2), 323–339.

World Bank. (2011). World Development Indicators database: Gross domestic product 2010. Retrieved from: http://siteresources.worldbank.org/DATASTATISTICS/Resources/GDP.pdf.

Chapter 5

Canadian Experiences

Dennis Raphael

Introduction

Canada is a wealthy developed nation that has been seen as a leader in developing health promotion and population health concepts that emphasize the importance of identifying and tackling health inequalities (Hancock, 2011). Yet, Canadian governmental authorities have repeatedly been identified as laggards in implementing these concepts through public policy activity (Bryant, Raphael, Schrecker & Labonte, 2011). In fact, international authorities chide Canada on an ongoing basis for failing to provide many of its citizens with the basic requirements necessary for health (Raphael, 2011f). Unlike many other member nations of the Organisation for Economic Co-operation and Development (OECD), Canada has not endorsed the reduction of health inequalities as a major policy objective.

Much of this has to do with Canada being a liberal welfare state where governmental concern with providing citizens with economic and social security has always been rather limited (Raphael & Bryant, 2006). Comparative analyses of Canada's approaches toward social provision find it to be more similar to the US than to the European member nations of the OECD (Bernard & Saint-Arnaud, 2004).

Evidence indicates that the extent of income-related health inequalities in Canada is greater than in many other wealthy developed nations (Humphries & van Doorslaer, 2000). More specifically, the extent of inequality in self-assessed health is higher than that found in Sweden, Finland, Germany, Netherlands, Switzerland, and Spain, but not different from the UK and the US. "It also appears as if Canada's health inequality is higher than what would be expected on the basis of its income inequality" (p. 663).

This public policy situation has worsened over the past three decades as Canada underwent significant welfare state retrenchment that resulted in growing inequality in the distribution of the social determinants of health (Bryant et al., 2011). There is also evidence of growing health inequalities in key areas such as infant mortality, mortality from diabetes, and life expectancy, among others (Manitoba Centre for Health Policy, 2010; Wilkins, 2007).

While there is much evidence concerning the extent of health inequalities in Canada, tackling these is not on the public policy agenda of the federal or any provincial or territorial government such that the issue plays a negligible, if any, role in shaping public policy (Hancock, 2011; Raphael, 2007). In fact, Canada has been described as being "A land of lost opportunities for addressing the social determinants of health" (Bryant et al., 2011, abstract), with federal and provincial governments failing in their "duty to the public to improve health and reduce inequalities in health" (Hancock, 2011, 264).

This chapter describes Canada's contributions to understanding and tackling health inequalities. It then details the extent of health inequalities in Canada. The gap between Canada's conceptual contributions and its action in tackling health inequalities is explained in terms of Canada's approach to public policy-making, which shapes the distribution of the social determinants of health. The chapter concludes by suggesting areas of research and citizen activity that can heighten awareness among the public and promote action on tackling health inequalities by governmental authorities.

National Description and Political Organization and Structure

Canada is a North American nation recently ranked as eighth in household wealth among the industrialized nations of the OECD (Conference Board of Canada, 2011a). A natural resource-rich nation, it is the second largest in geographic area with much of its relatively small population of 34.6 million living in cities close to its long border with the US. Canada's status as a nation dates from the British North America Act of 1867, which amalgamated several former British colonies. The 1982 Canada Constitution Act amended this Act and also added a Charter of Rights and Freedoms (Forsey, 2007).

Canada operates under a federal system by which its 10 provinces and three territories are responsible for significant governmental sectors that include health care and public health and other policy areas such as housing and social assistance that impact the extent of, and response to, health inequalities. Historically, the central government in Ottawa influenced many of these public policy areas through its tax collection and cost-sharing powers (Bryant, 2009). The past three decades has seen federal withdrawal from many of these policy-influencing activities.

Population Demographics

Canada's cultural history is one of appropriation of lands and domination of its Native populations, which consist of First Nations, Inuit, and Métis (Smylie, 2009). Approximately 1.2 million or 3.8 percent of the Canadian population is of Native descent. Of these, about 60 percent identify as North American "Indian," 33 percent as Métis, 4 percent as Inuit, and 3 percent as more than one Aboriginal group or as members of First Nations bands who do not identify as Aboriginal. As a group, Native peoples experience a range of unfavourable living and working conditions and, as a result, show a wide range of adverse health outcomes (Smylie, 2009).

Since its founding, Canada has been an overwhelmingly white nation with the great proportion of its population of European descent. Shifts in immigration practices dating from the 1960s saw an increase in non-European immigration such that by the 1980s and 1990s, 75 percent of immigrants came from the Third World or global South (Galabuzi, 2009). Most of these were people of colour or racialized immigrants. In 2006, people of colour numbered 5.1 million and constituted 16.2 percent of Canada's total population (National Resources Canada, 2009). Evidence indicates that these new non-European immigrants are more likely to be unemployed, underemployed, and living in poverty (Galabuzi, 2009). They are also the Canadians most likely to show declines in health status over time (Ng, Wilkins, Gendron & Berthelot, 2005).

Form of Government and Political Parties

Canada is a constitutional monarchy—Queen Elizabeth II is its current sovereign—within a parliamentary system modelled after that of the United Kingdom. It consists of a House of Commons with elected members from 308 ridings and an appointed Senate of 105 members, which has the power to review legislation passed by the House of Commons. Unlike most other wealthy developed nations that apply proportional representation to the election process, Canada's selection of members of the House of Commons operates through a first-past-the-post electoral system. The provinces and territories have similar structures, but without corresponding Senate-like houses (Forsey, 2007).

Though provinces and territories have primary responsibilities for a variety of public sectors, historically, the federal government significantly influenced pan-Canadian developments through its control of taxation and spending. As one example, state-insured universal health care was incrementally introduced in the Province of Saskatchewan over the period 1947–1962 (Bryant, 2009), but was applied across the nation in 1966 by the federal government's offer to share costs 50/50 with the provinces. In return for its funding, the federal government imposed numerous requirements for health care access and delivery, which are enshrined in the Canadian Health Act of 1985.

Similarly, in 1966, the federal government introduced legislation to help finance social assistance costs of the provinces and territories. In order to receive these funds, the provinces were required to provide assistance to those in need under a framework that forbade forced activity or workfare to receive such benefits (Raphael, 2011f). However, the current share of federal support of medicare is now at only 20 percent (Canadian Institute for Health Information, 2011) and changes in federal legislation now allow the provinces and territories to impose workfare as a condition for receipt of social assistance (Raphael, 2011f).

The federal government is responsible for organization and delivery of Canada's unemployment benefit system and, with the exception of Quebec, old age pensions (Forsey, 2007). Social assistance, labour legislation, housing, and numerous other health inequality-related public policies are managed by the provinces and territories. Municipal governments operate within the shadow of provincial and territorial governments and have relatively weak powers. Public policies are rather similar across the nation and distinguish Canada's general approach to social provision from other OECD nations (Bernard & Saint-Arnaud, 2004).

Canada's ruling parties are business sector-oriented, with the Conservative and Liberal parties having exchanged national power with each other since 1867. There have been periods of minority or "hung Parliaments" where the social democratic New Democratic Party held the balance of power. It was during such a period in the 1960s that medicare and public pensions were implemented across Canada. The recent federal election (2011) saw the New Democratic

Party achieve Opposition status in the House of Commons—holding the second largest number of seats to the ruling Conservative Party—for the first time in Canada's history.

Provincial and territorial governments have been led by all three major parties. As of early 2012, four provinces are governed by the Liberal Party, three by the Conservative Party, and two by the New Democratic Party. Saskatchewan is ruled by the conservative Saskatchewan Party. With regard to the territories, Yukon is ruled by the conservative Yukon Party, while the Northwest Territories and Nunavut are governed by consensus among their elected representatives. Canadian political parties are shifted well to the right of their counterparts in Europe, though to the left of the main US political parties.

Key Public Policy Milestones Related to Citizen Support and Benefits up to the Present

Canada's welfare state is undeveloped compared to most other wealthy developed nations (Raphael, 2011e). This is evidenced by meagre government spending on economic and social supports such as old age pensions, unemployment benefits, social assistance, active labour policy, and supports for families and children as compared with most other OECD nations (Raphael, 2011e). Even so, there are a number of Canadian policy milestones whereby Canadian governments instituted supports and benefits for the population. Since these policies address issues of citizen economic and social security, they are relevant to examination of the sources and means of tackling health inequalities. Boychuk (2004) presents four "policy logics" that explain Canadian social provision:

- Universal social provision for the entire population (e.g., universal programs such as health care, pensions, and public education)
- Social insurance against risk to encourage labour market attachment (e.g., workers' compensation for injuries at work, employment insurance, and contributory pensions)
- Social inclusion through the establishment of social minimums to mitigate the effects of marginalization (e.g., refundable tax credits, social assistance, and social housing)
- Social cohesion by fostering social integration in communities, emphasizing "place-based" solutions (e.g., community development programs, programs for at-risk groups such as Aboriginal peoples and immigrants, and industrial adjustment programs)

The beginnings of Canadian governments' social provision included direct aid to the unemployed as a result of the Employment Coordination Act of 1918 (Morel, 2002). In 1920, the federal government introduced unemployment assistance. The assistance provided, however, had to be repaid. In 1940, federal unemployment insurance was established. From these beginnings additional programs were implemented such that the Canadian welfare state reached its zenith during the 1970s (Myles, 1998). Since then there has been a decline in government commitments to provide a range of supports for citizens (Langille, 2009).

Ismael (2006) provides snapshots of social provision policies at differing points in time. By 1965 social insurance programs existed for the unemployed through Unemployment Insurance, created by legislation in 1940 and amended in 1955. Universal programs were available for families with children through Family Allowances (1944), and to the elderly through Old

Age Security (1951). Health insurance for hospital care was created through the Health Insurance and Diagnostic Services Act of 1957. And housing was supported through the National Housing Act of 1938, amended in 1964; the Wartime Housing Corporation; and expansion of the National Housing Act of 1944, subsequently amended in 1964.

The American "War on Poverty" positively influenced Canadian policy developments. By 1973, unemployment insurance had been expanded through 1971 legislation, family allowances through 1973 legislation, and pensions and supports for the elderly by the Canadian Pension Plan (1975) and Guaranteed Income Supplement (1967). The Canada Assistance Plan (1965) supported social assistance benefits and set national standards. Affordable housing was provided through the National Housing Act of 1964, amended in 1973.

By 1989, many of these programs had been significantly scaled back. Reductions in eligibility occurred for Unemployment Insurance (1975, 1977, 1978) and Family Allowances (1979). Interestingly, as a result of political pressure, the Canada Pension Plan for the elderly was actually augmented. Through 2003, all of these programs—except for pensions—were further reduced. As income support and housing programs were reduced, shifts were made to provide service programs to respond to the needs of the most disadvantaged. Even then these programs are meagre when compared to those provided in other OECD nations (see later sections).

In 1999, the OECD described social assistance programs in Canada as follows: "Everywhere the basic social assistance payment is not intended to cover much more than immediate basic needs for housing, clothing, food, and recurring household expenses" (p. 42). Ismael (2006) describes it as follows: "The income maintenance and replacement functions of income security have been pauperized, and income support harmonized with the 'less eligibility' principle that maintains public support below minimum wage standards"(p. 50).

Social assistance payments across Canada keep recipients well below the poverty line (National Council of Welfare, 2010). Additionally, governmental withdrawal from provision of housing programs, employment training, and unemployment supports, combined with very weak labour policy that regulates the employment market—Canada's minimum wages are well below the poverty line—leads to Canada experiencing one of the highest levels of income inequality and poverty rates among wealthy developed nations of the OECD, all important drivers of health inequalities (Bryant et al., 2011).

One important component of Canadian public policy that has prevented the situation from being even worse is the Rand Formula (International Association of Machinists & Aerospace Workers, 2011). The Rand Formula is a labour law tradition—a result of a 1945 arbitration decision—that requires union dues to be paid by all members of a unionized workplace whether one is a member of the union or not. Enshrined in the Canada Labour Code and in most provincial labour laws, it is a strong counterpoint to "right to work" laws in the US that weaken workers' rights. Further details concerning the Canadian welfare state and its effects on the extent of health inequalities are provided in later sections.

Key Milestones Related to Health Policy, Health Promotion, and Reducing Health Inequalities

Canada has achieved an enviable record of contributions to understanding the sources of health inequalities and outlining means of tackling them (Restrepo, 2000). These contributions came by way of Canadian concepts of health promotion and population health. There is more recent concern with the social determinants of health (see Table 5.1). These conceptual contributions have been eclipsed by developments in many other nations, including most of those highlighted in this volume.

The 1974 Lalonde Report introduced the modern era of health promotion by identifying environmental factors as shaping health (Lalonde, 1974). In the early 1980s, the Shifting Medical Paradigm Conference and the Beyond Health Care Conference saw the introduction of a new paradigm of how public policy affected health (Labonte, 1994). The 1986 Epp Report outlined the role governments can play in tackling health inequalities (Epp, 1986).

Since then, numerous federal reports and documents have discussed the importance of the determinants of health and tackling health inequalities, but these concepts gained little, if any, public policy traction. These include the 1994 *Federal/Provincial/Territorial Report on Population Health* (Health Canada, 2001) and Health Canada's *Population Health Template*, among others (Health Canada, 2004). The new millennium saw the *Social Determinants of Health* concept making its way into Public Health Agency of Canada's documents and reports (Public Health Agency of Canada, 2007). The following sections detail these contributions.

Table 5.1
Key Developments in Health Inequalities-Related Concepts in Canada

1974	Lalonde Report
1980	Shifting Medical Paradigm Conference
1984	Beyond Health Care Conference
1986	The Ottawa Charter
1986	The Epp Report
1994	Federal/Provincial/Territorial Report on Population Health
1994	Publication of Why Are Some People Healthy and Others Not?
2000	Health Canada Population Health Template
2002	Social Determinants of Health across the Life-Span Conference
2004	Canada has extensive involvement in the Commission on Social Determinants of Health
2009	Chief public health officer's report on inequalities in health
2011	Canada contributes to Rio de Janeiro Conference on Social Determinants of Health

Note: Expanded from R. Labonte, Death of a program: Birth of a metaphor, in I. Rootman, A. Pederson & M. O'Neill (Eds.), *Health promotion in Canada: Provincial, national, and international perspectives* (Toronto: Saunders, 1994, 72–90). See Labonte (1994), Legowski & McKay (2000), O'Neill et al. (2007), and Raphael (2008) for post-1994 developments.

Canadian Policy Documents and Statements on Health Inequalities

Canada's contributions to tackling health inequalities have influenced developments around the world.

A New Perspective on the Health of Canadians

The 1974 Canadian government report, *A New Perspective on the Health of Canadians* (Lalonde 1974), signalled the beginning of the modern health promotion era (Restrepo, 2000). It outlined four health-influencing fields: human biology, environment, lifestyle, and health care organization. While criticized as overemphasizing individual choice upon lifestyles, the document was important in identifying health determinants other than health care (Labonte & Penfold, 1981).

The report recognized the existence of health inequalities. Although explicit recommendations were limited to assisting the "less privileged" to improve their lifestyle, it stated that "economic circumstances, health education, attitudes, and facility of physical access to health care, as well as improved pre-natal care, are the principal factors to be considered in lowering the rate of infant mortality" (p. 14) and "on the subject of environment, the number of economically deprived Canadians is still high, resulting in lack of adequate housing and insufficient or inadequate housing" (Lalonde, 1974, 18). Nevertheless, governments and the public health and health care sectors chose to focus on the lifestyle field and limited the environmental field to matters of air and water pollution (Legowski & McKay, 2000).

Achieving Health for All: A Framework for Health Promotion

Released simultaneously with the Ottawa Charter in 1986, this report identified reducing health inequalities as a primary goal of health policy: "The first challenge we face is to find ways of reducing inequities in the health of low- versus high-income groups in Canada" (Epp, 1986, 3). Greater health problems among low-income groups were recognized, that "poverty affects over half of single-parent families," and that "more than one million children in Canada are poor" (p. 4). An important means of improving health was through the coordination of healthy public policy. Numerous determinants of health were explicitly mentioned (Epp, 1986):

> All policies which have a direct bearing on health need to be co-ordinated. The list is long and includes, among others, income security, employment, education, housing, business, agriculture, transportation, justice and technology. (p. 12)

Yet, despite extensive distribution, policy development for the most part continued within the lifestyle vein. The lack of explicit governmental activity identifying and tackling health inequalities continued as new documents and statements were created.

Population Health and Health Canada's Determinants of Health

The 1990s saw population health emerge as an alternative approach to health promotion. Population health grew out of efforts by the Canadian Institute for Advanced Research, a government and corporate-funded research institute, to identify the "determinants of health" within an epidemiologically oriented framework (Evans, Barer & Marmor, 1994).

These determinants included: income and social status, social support networks, education, employment/working conditions, social environments, physical environments, personal health practices and coping skills, healthy child development, biology and genetic endowment, and health services. Health Canada—now known as the Public Health Agency of Canada—added determinants of culture and gender and issued a series of documents and reports based on these determinants (Health Canada, 2004). In many of these, the importance of assessing and tackling health inequalities is implied in relation to Canadians experiencing differing quality determinants of health (Health Canada, 1998, 1999, 2000, 2001).

Hancock (2011) argues acceptance of the population health approach was a step backwards as it said little about tackling health inequalities, but rather focused on researching them. The approach also favours traditional epidemiological forms of knowledge over experiential and critical knowledge, and generally neglects the role public policy plays in shaping the quality and distribution of these health determinants (Hancock, 2011; Poland, Coburn, Robertson & Eakin, 1998; Raphael & Bryant, 2002; Robertson, 1998).

Canadian Public Health Association (CPHA)

The CPHA has reported on health inequalities and their determinants since the mid-1970s (Manzano & Raphael, 2010). In 1983, a national conference resolution called for CPHA "to focus attention on the effect on health of external circumstances beyond the individual's control and on fitness in all aspects of well being (including the physical)." Its 1993 *Regina Charter on Reducing Health Inequities* opposed public policies that make the most vulnerable bear the brunt of deficit reduction measures. It supported efforts to improve Aboriginal health by recognizing their alienation from land, culture, and livelihood. Most importantly, it urged the CPHA to take "position of leadership ... as a proponent of public policies to reduce health inequities" and urged provincial, territorial, and local public health associates to do the same.

CPHA's 1986 *Action Statement for Health Promotion in Canada* identified advocating for healthy public policies as the single best strategy to affect the determinants of health (Canadian Public Health Association, 1996). Priority actions included reducing inequalities in income and wealth and strengthening communities through local alliances to change unhealthy living conditions. In 2000, the CPHA endorsed an action plan that recognized poverty's profound influence upon health and identified means to reduce it (Canadian Public Health Association, 2000). Other CPHA reports detail the health effects of unemployment, income insecurity, homelessness, and general economic conditions (Canadian Public Health Association, 2011). These statements have been remarkably advanced for their time in recognizing the importance of identifying and tackling health inequalities (Manzano & Raphael, 2010).

Healthy Cities Conferences

The birth of the Healthy Cities movement took place in Toronto in 1984 (Hancock & Duhl, 1986). The 1980 Shifting Medical Paradigm Conference and the 1984 Beyond Health Care Conference (1980) helped spawn two ideas: healthy public policy and healthy cities. This concept saw its primary realization in the City of Toronto Healthy Cities Office from 1989 to 2001 (City of Vancouver, 2001).

Analysis suggests that in Canada, the Healthy Cities movement evolved into local community-based efforts at poverty reduction, increasing food security, and promoting healthy behaviours (Raphael, 2011a). These activities do not focus explicitly on tackling health inequalities and have little to say about broader public policy that shapes the extent of health inequalities in Canada. Nevertheless, Canadian Healthy Cities activities have influenced developments in Europe and elsewhere (World Health Organization, 2003).

Chief Health Officer of Canada Reports

In 2006, the federal government created the position of Chief Public Health Officer of Canada. His first annual report was entitled *Addressing Health Inequalities* and stated with regard to the social determinants of health (Butler-Jones, 2009):

> How these determinants contribute to the differences in our health matters because some groups of Canadians experience lower life expectancy than others. Some have higher rates of infant mortality, injury, disease and addiction.... These differences in health status are referred to as health inequalities. (p. ii)

Later reports focus on health inequalities among children and seniors (Butler-Jones, 2010, 2011). Nevertheless, the public remains generally unaware of these reports, and there is no evidence they have placed the topic of tackling health inequalities onto the public policy agenda. In addition, these reports have been criticized as neglecting the role that governmental public policy plays in creating and potentially tackling health inequalities (Kirkpatrick & McIntyre, 2009).

Recent Developments

In 2004 the federal government established a series of National Coordinating Centres (NCCs) for promoting health (Government of Canada, 2004). Three of these, the NCC for Determinants of Health, the NCC for Healthy Public Policy, and the NCC for Aboriginal Health have produced reports and analyses of health inequalities-related issues.

In 2006, the federal government organized a federal/territorial/provincial task force on health disparities. At the same time, the newly appointed minister for public health—a ministry since discontinued—carried out consultations to create a set of National Public Health Objectives patterned along developments in other wealthy developed nations. Despite calls for explicit focus on the social determinants of health and tackling health inequalities (see http://www.phac-aspc.gc.ca/hgc-osc/summ-part-1e.html for one example), the resulting objectives said nothing about these issues (Public Health Agency of Canada, 2011) except to call for having a health care system that can respond to "existing health disparities."

The World Health Organization's Commission on the Social Determinants of Health was supported by the Public Health Agency of Canada with two of its knowledge networks (Globalization and Health and Early Childhood Development) centred in Canada, while another (Workplace Health) had significant Canadian representation (World Health Organization, 2008). A Canadian Reference Group was established in conjunction with the commission's activities and provided a response to its final report (Public Health Agency of Canada, 2006).

In 2008, the Canadian Senate's Subcommittee on Population Health concluded that Canada was falling well behind other nations in addressing the social determinants of health (Senate Subcommittee on Population Health, 2008). Reports on poverty by both the Canadian Senate and the House of Commons speak of the importance of tackling health inequalities (Canadian House of Commons, 2010; Canadian Senate, 2009). Nevertheless, the federal government indicated it has no intention of responding with action to these reports (Raphael, 2011a). More recently, it failed to send its minister of health or the parliamentary assistant for health, any Cabinet member, or elected member of its party to the 2011 Rio de Janeiro Conference, which aimed to promote implementation of the commission's recommendations. Instead, a delegation of civil servants, including the chief public health officer, was in attendance.

Finally, the Health Council of Canada recently called for addressing the social determinants of health and reducing health inequalities (Health Council of Canada, 2010), and the Canadian Nurses Association launched a National Expert Commission in May 2011 of which promoting population health is a prominent component (Canadian Nurses Association, 2011). A determinants of health-oriented report, entitled *Health, Not Health Care: Changing the Conversation*, by Ontario's Chief Medical Officer of Health (King, 2011), joins other provincial reports issued in a similar vein (British Columbia Ministry of Health, 2011).

Analysis of These Documents and Their Implications

Despite this history, health inequalities are not placed on any federal, provincial, or territorial public policy agenda. Media coverage of these issues is virtually non-existent (Raphael, 2011c) and the Canadian public remains woefully uninformed as to the presence and extent of health inequalities (Canadian Population Health Initiative, 2004b).

The overall situation is somewhat understated by the Health Council of Canada, an arm's-length, federally funded advisory body to federal, provincial, and territorial ministries of health: "Despite the extent of this cross-Canada activity, our analysis confirms what the literature has already told us: research and analysis about health promotion and the determinants of health are not being translated into public policy and program action in Canada to the degree that was expected" (Health Council of Canada, 2010, 11).

Institutions Responsible for Researching and Tackling Health Inequalities

There is no single governmental institution or agency at the federal or provincial/territorial levels responsible for identifying and tackling health inequalities. This is not to say there are no agencies and organizations concerned with identifying and tackling health inequalities. Since these concerns are not shared by governing authorities, this leads to a situation where federal, provincial, and municipal agencies either support others or carry out inquiries themselves into the extent of health inequalities, but their political masters do little to apply these findings. The following section describes these agencies and institutions and presents some of their findings.

Agencies and Organizations

Agencies and organizations that support or carry out research on health inequalities include government ministries and agencies at all levels, government-funded and independent research and policy institutes, and university-based researchers. There is also research that examines the many determinants of health inequalities, although these activities may not be explicitly identified as being concerned with health.

Statistics Canada is the federal agency mandated by law to provide statistics to governments at all levels. As part of this work, it produces ongoing reports on the presence of health inequalities. Of particular importance is work that reports on the presence of health inequalities among Canadians of differing incomes, different geographical locations, genders, Aboriginal versus non-Aboriginal descent, and immigrants versus those born in Canada. It also reports on determinants of social inequalities such as income, housing, education, and employment among Canadians in general, but also in relation to Aboriginal, immigrant, and disability status, and gender (Analytical Studies Branch, 2011). Statistics Canada manages the extensive Canadian Community Health Survey and the longitudinal Canadian Population Health Survey, which provides a wealth of data for researchers concerned with health inequalities.

The Canadian Institute for Health Information (CIHI) was established in 1994 as an independent, not-for-profit corporation to provide information on Canada's health system and the health of Canadians. It is funded by federal, provincial, and territorial governments. A component of CIHI is the Canadian Population Health Initiative (CPHI), which was established in 1999 to: (1) foster a better understanding of factors that affect the health of individuals and communities; and (2) contribute to the development of policies that reduce inequities and improve the health and well-being of Canadians.

CPHI has produced numerous reports that document the extent of health inequalities by reporting on determinants of health such as income (Canadian Population Health Initiative, 2004a), socio-economic status in urban environments (Canadian Population Health Initiative, 2008), rural location (Canadian Population Health Initiative, 2006), and women's health (Canadian Population Health Initiative, 2003). It also commissions analyses and syntheses of existing literature on income inequality and health (Ross, 2004), poverty and health (Phipps, 2002; Ross, 2002), and other related issues.

The Canadian Institutes for Health Research (CIHR) consists of 13 federally funded research institutes: "The objective of CIHR is to excel, according to internationally accepted standards of scientific excellence, in the creation of new knowledge and its translation into improved health for Canadians, more effective health services and products and a strengthened Canadian health care system" (Government of Canada, 2000). The institutes of greatest relevance to tackling health inequalities are the Institute of Aging; the Institute of Gender and Health; the Institute of Human Development, Child and Youth Health; the Institute of Health Services and Policy Research; and the Institute of Population and Public Health.

Over the years there have been numerous funding calls by these institutes explicitly concerned with health inequalities: *Reducing Health Disparities and Promoting Equity for Vulnerable Populations, Disparities in Dental Health, Reducing Disparities in Health, Population Health Intervention Research: Focus on Health Inequalities*, and *Reducing Social Inequities and Improving Mental Health*, among others. The result has been research that describes the extent of health inequalities in Canada with many of the funded projects producing recommendations for action. As one example, the Institute of Population and Public Health funds the Léa Roback Centre for Research on Social Inequalities in Health in Montreal (Léa Roback Centre for Research on Social Inequalities in Health, 2011). As another, the Institute for Gender and Health funds the Center for the Study of Gender, Social Inequities, and Mental Health at Simon Fraser University (Center for the Study of Gender, Social Inequities, and Mental Health, 2011).

The Social Sciences and Humanities Research Council (SSHRC) used to fund a wide range of health research carried out within social science perspectives. As part of its reorganization, SSHRC stopped funding research concerned with health and health inequalities. This shift has led to a concern that critical studies of health inequalities will suffer as CIHR may not be as receptive to social science analyses of health issues as it operates within traditional epidemiological approaches to understanding health inequalities (Silversides, 2010).

The provinces have established and funded research institutes that consider health inequalities and suggest means of tackling them. One of the most productive has been the Quebec Public Health Institute (Quebec Public Health Institute, 2011), which provides robust examples of health inequalities and their sources (Auger & Alix, 2009). Ontario established the Population Health Improvement Research Network (PHIRN), which funds research into health inequality-related issues (Population Health Improvement Research Network, 2011). Other provincially supported research organizations include the Manitoba Centre for Health Policy (Manitoba Centre for Health Policy, 2011) and the Nova Scotia Health Research Foundation (Nova Scotia Health Research Foundation, 2011), among others.

Local public health units frequently report on the extent of health inequalities. Of particular note are the activities of the City of Montreal Health Department (Direction de santé publique Agence de la santé et des services sociaux de Montréal, 2011), Saskatoon Health Authority (Lemstra & Neudorf, 2008), Vancouver Coastal Health (Vancouver Coastal Health, 2011), and the Toronto Public Health Department (McKeown et al., 2008). Many health units draw upon Statistics Canada data to produce reports documenting the extent of health inequalities in their localities.

There are independent institutes concerned with health inequalities. The Wellesley Institute funded a research project that compiled information on health outcomes related to income differences (Lightman, Mitchell & Wilson, 2008). CERIS–The Ontario Metropolis Centre is a consortium of Toronto-area universities and community partners that focuses on resettlement and integration of immigrants and refugees in Ontario (CERIS–The Ontario Metropolis Centre, 2011). The Institute for Clinical Evaluative Sciences conducts research on health and health services in Ontario and has documented inequalities in cardiovascular disease and type 2 diabetes prevalence and health outcomes among neighbourhoods in Ontario (Basinski, 1999; Glazier & Booth, 2007). The Centre for Inner City Research in Toronto focuses on health inequities among urban populations (St. Michael's Hospital, 2011). There are many others.

These health inequality-related activities are supplemented by research on factors that create health inequalities—i.e., social determinants of health and their distribution—such as income and wealth, poverty, food and housing insecurity, employment security and working conditions, and various identities related to health inequalities such as Aboriginal status, gender, race, immigrant, and disability status (Raphael, 2010).

As one example, the Canadian Centre for Policy Alternatives is an independent, non-partisan research and policy institute that has carried out 33 original studies concerned with growing income and wealth inequality in Canada (Canadian Centre for Policy Alternatives, 2011). Another organization, Campaign 2000, is concerned with reducing child poverty, publishes reports and analyses of the factors driving poverty rates in Canada, and suggests means of reducing it (Campaign 2000, 2011). The Federation of Canadian Municipalities produces reports that document the extent of income inequality and poverty, housing and food insecurity, and other aspects of cities and towns that impact "quality of life" (Federation of Canadian Municipalities, 2011).

The business-oriented Conference Board of Canada (Conference Board of Canada, 2009, 2011b) and the Canadian Labour Congress (Canadian Labour Congress, 2011) both synthesize data to provide reports on how Canada performs in many areas known to be drivers of health inequalities. The work of other non-governmental organizations across Canada, such as United Way, community foundations, various research institutes, and charitable organizations, have all provided evidence on the extent of health inequalities and the importance of tackling them (Raphael, Curry-Stevens & Bryant, 2008).

Much of this research into these social determinants of health and their inequitable distribution that create health inequalities has been compiled in one edited volume (Raphael, 2009b). These contributions provide ample evidence of the extent of health inequalities in Canada, their sources, and the public policy decisions that are driving these health inequalities (Mikkonen & Raphael, 2010).

There is, therefore, ample data on the extent of health inequalities with excellent analyses of how these have come about. However, since the research on health inequalities is not organized under any centrally guided federal or provincial initiative, it has little impact on institutional and public understandings of health inequalities and governmental willingness to address this issue.

Yet even these data sources are under threat. A particularly disturbing trend has been the federal government's elimination of funding for various research and advocacy agencies. The government eliminated the requirement that Canadians respond to Statistics Canada's Long-Form Census, crippling data collection in the country. Its most recent budget ended funding for a network of women's research organizations including the Canadian Women's Health Network and six Centres for Excellence on Women's Health. The federal government has also eliminated funding for The National Council on Welfare which has served as an arm's-length advisory body to the government on issues faced by poor people since 1969. All of these activities served as data sources and provided analyses of issues related to health inequalities.

Much of this is because analyses and activities are inconsistent with the current public policy approaches of governing authorities. The profound lack of media coverage of these activities is also a contributor to governmental neglect (Raphael, 2011c).

Health Inequalities as Manifested in Mortality

A key source for health inequalities-related data is Statistics Canada. Research documents the extent of inequalities in mortality as a function of average urban neighbourhood income across Canada over time. The most definitive work is done by Wilkins and colleagues, who examine the relationship between income, age, and cause of death. Census data are used to classify quintiles such that the first quintile includes areas where the average income is the highest and the fifth quintile includes those where the average income is the lowest (Wilkins et al., 2002; Wilkins, 2007). Then, based on information available from hospital records, life expectancies, mortality rates from various diseases, and infant mortality rates for the areas within each income quintile are calculated.

The overall effect of income differences on premature years of life lost (prior to age 75) is calculated (Wilkins, 2007). In 2001, 20.4 percent of years of life lost for all causes prior to age 75 in Canada could be attributed to income differences. The magnitude of income effects (20.4 percent) approaches or exceeds that associated with the major killers such as cancers (32.6 percent) and heart disease (16.5 percent). Life expectancy is especially shorter for the lowest income quintile of neighbourhoods. Among males in this lowest income quintile, life expectancy was 2.4 years shorter than the next quintile group, and 4.3 years shorter than males in the wealthiest quintile group. Females living in the lowest income quintile had a life expectancy that was 1.4 years less than those in the next group, and 1.9 years shorter than the wealthiest income quintile.

The gap in life expectancy between men and women is 6.2 years in the fifth, or poorest, income quintile group. It is less so in the fourth (5.2 years) and third income quintile (4.8 years), even less in the second income quintile (4.2 years), and least in the wealthiest income quintile (3.9 years). Income interacts with gender, therefore, to predict life expectancy. Poverty seems to be a much stronger threat to life expectancy for men than for women.

These differences in life expectancy reflect findings that Canadians living within the poorest 20 percent of urban neighbourhoods die earlier than other Canadians from a wide range of diseases, such as cardiovascular disease, cancer, diabetes, and respiratory diseases, among others. Excess years of life lost associated with income differences are primarily associated with mortality from circulatory disorders (25.2 percent of total excess), injuries (17 percent of excess), and cancers (13.8 percent).

Wilkins and colleagues (2002) also calculate excess mortality rates due to income differences for specific diseases (overall excess seen in relation to the wealthiest quintile). While overall excess mortality related to income differences is 9.9 percent, excess deaths related to income for diabetes is 27.5 percent; for homicide, 44.1 percent; ill-defined conditions, 26.5 percent; infectious diseases, 35.9 percent; and suicides, 28.6 percent.

A recent analysis identified similar findings for income-related inequalities in life expectancy, health-adjusted life expectancy (an analysis of life expectancy that takes into account health status), and health-related quality of life of adults (an analysis of eight basic measures of health status such as vision, hearing, pain, ambulation, etc.) among Canadians at age 25 who were classified into income deciles using individual-level data (McIntosh, Fines, Wilkins & Wolfson, 2009). A key finding was that health-adjusted life expectancy and health-related quality of life differences were substantially greater between rich and poor than for measures of life expectancy alone. The differences in life expectancy at age 25 between men in the poorest and richest quintile was 7.4 years and for women, 4.5 years. But for health-related life expectancy, the differences between the richest and poorest groups were 11.4 years for men and 9.7 years for women.

Income-related inequalities are seen for infant mortality rates. Infant mortality is an especially sensitive indicator of overall societal health, and the rate in the poorest 20 percent of urban neighbourhoods (7.1/1,000) is 40 percent higher than it is in the wealthiest 20 percent (5.0/1,000) (Wilkins, 2007). Similar findings of income-related health inequalities are available for mortality due to hypertensive and rheumatic heart disease in British Columbia (Wood, Sallar, Schechter & Hogg, 1999), ischemic heart disease in Manitoba (Roos & Mustard, 1997), and suicide rates across Canada (Wilkins, 2007).

The next findings illustrate one situation in which the extent of health inequalities is declining and one in which they are increasing. Figures 5.1 and 5.2 show declining death rates and declining income-related inequalities for cardiovascular disease among urban Canadian men and women (Wilkins, 2007), although it must be noted that the mortality rate among men in the lowest income quintile (145/100,000) is still 44 percent higher than the rate in the richest areas (101/100,000), and the difference for the poorest women (66/100,000) is 22 percent higher than for the richest women (54/100,000). Much of this is a result of improvements in living conditions from the immediate post-World War II period through to the 1980s.

In figures 5.3 and 5.4, however, there is evidence of both increasing death rates and income-related inequalities related to diabetes (Wilkins, 2007). The rate for men in the lowest income quintile (25/100,000) is 92 percent higher than for the richest men (13.2/100,000), and the rate for women in the lowest income quintile (16/100,000) is 78 percent higher than for the richest women (9/100,000). Dying from diabetes may be more sensitive to changes in living conditions than cardiovascular disease, where effects may take decades to manifest (Raphael et al., 2011).

Health Inequalities as Manifested in Morbidity

Health inequalities exist in morbidity. Incidence of low birth weight differs as a function of average neighbourhood income (Wilkins, Houle, Berthelot & Ross, 2000). These data show that rates are 40 percent higher in the poorest 20 percent of neighbourhoods (7.0/100) as compared to what occurs in the wealthiest 20 percent (4.9/100). The magnitudes of income-related health inequalities in low birth weight are also seen at the provincial (Auger & Alix, 2009) and municipal levels (McKeown et al., 2008).

Childhood injury rate differs as a function of average neighbourhood income in Ontario (Faelker, Pickett & Brison, 2000). Children in the poorest neighbourhoods show injury rates that are 67 percent higher than children in the wealthiest neighbourhoods. These differences are apparent for minor, moderate, and extreme injuries. Similar findings are seen in Alberta (Gilbride, Wild, Wilson, Svenson & Spady, 2006).

First-time heart attack admissions in Ontario differ as a function of average neighbourhood income (Alter, Naylor, Austin & Tu, 1999). Admissions in each of the two poorest 20 percent of neighbourhoods are almost three times the admissions for the wealthiest 20 percent. In Ontario, the prevalence rate for diabetes is four times greater among women in low-income communities than among those living in high-income communities (Hux et al., 2002). These kinds of differences are not accounted for by differences in health-related behaviours such as diet, exercise, and smoking (Raphael et al., 2003; Raphael & Farrell, 2002; Xi, 2005). In terms of mental health, the prevalence of depression in 25

Figure 5.1
Ischemic Heart Disease Mortality, Urban Canada, 1971–2001, Males

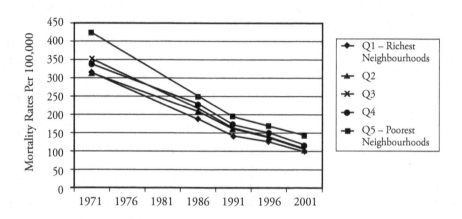

Source: R. Wilkins (2007), *Mortality by neighbourhood income in urban Canada from 1971 to 2001*, Statistics Canada, Health Analysis and Measurement Group (HAMG), HAMG Seminar, and Special Compilations.

Figure 5.2
Ischemic Heart Disease Mortality, Urban Canada, 1971–2001, Females

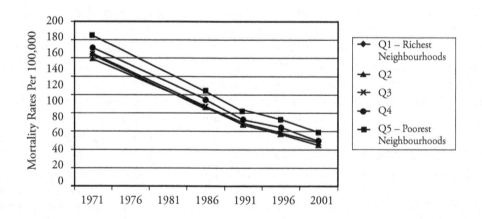

Source: R. Wilkins (2007), *Mortality by neighbourhood income in urban Canada from 1971 to 2001*, Statistics Canada, Health Analysis and Measurement Group (HAMG), HAMG Seminar, and Special Compilations.

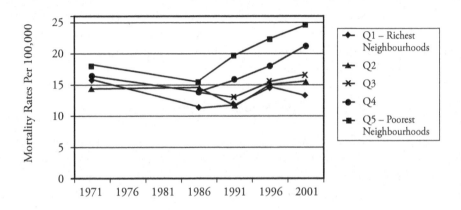

Figure 5.3
Diabetes Mortality, Urban Canada, 1971–2001, Males

Source: R. Wilkins (2007), *Mortality by neighbourhood income in urban Canada from 1971 to 2001*, Statistics Canada, Health Analysis and Measurement Group (HAMG), HAMG Seminar, and Special Compilations.

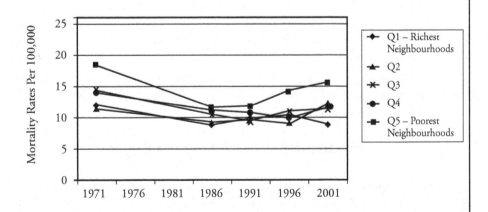

Figure 5.4
Diabetes Mortality, Urban Canada, 1971–2001, Females

Source: R. Wilkins (2007), *Mortality by neighbourhood income in urban Canada from 1971 to 2001*, Statistics Canada, Health Analysis and Measurement Group (HAMG), HAMG Seminar, and Special Compilations.

major Canadian cities is systematically related to income differences (Smith, Matheson, Moineddin & Glazier, 2007).

Income-related differences in type 2 diabetes prevalence across Canada are profound and are not accounted for by differences in physical activity, education, or weight (Dinca-Panaitescu, Dinca-Panaitescu, Bryant, Daiski, Pilkington & Raphael, 2011). Analysis also reveals that living in poverty is an excellent predictor of developing type 2 diabetes over time and is independent of physical activity or weight (Dinca-Panaitescu, Dinca-Panaitescu, Raphael, Bryant, Daiski & Pilkington, 2012).

Aboriginal Health

Aboriginal peoples in Canada show greater incidence of a range of afflictions and premature death from a variety of causes (Health Canada First Nations and Inuit Health Branch, 2003; Smylie, 2009). These health inequalities result from exposures to any number of adverse social determinants of health (e.g., poverty, inadequate housing, food insecurity, low-paid employment and poor working conditions, social exclusion, etc.), and reflect a history of exclusion from Canadian society (Smylie, 2009).

Life expectancies of Aboriginal peoples are five to 14 years less than the Canadian population, and Inuit men and women show the greatest differences (Smylie, 2009). Infant mortality rates—that is, children dying before their first year—are 1.5 to four times greater than the overall Canadian rate.

The rates of numerous infectious and chronic diseases are much higher in the Aboriginal population than in the non-Aboriginal Canadian population. Suicide rates are five to six times higher, and Aboriginal peoples have high rates of major depression (18 percent), problems with alcohol (27 percent), and experience of sexual abuse during childhood (34 percent).

Furthermore, off-reserve Aboriginal peoples rate their health status lower than the overall Canadian population (Tjepkema, 2002). For every age group between 25 and 64, the proportions of Aboriginal peoples reporting fair or poor health are double that of the total population. The effect is more pronounced among Aboriginal women. For example, 41 percent of Aboriginal women aged 55–64 reported fair or poor health, compared with 19 percent of women in the same age group in the total Canadian population. Among those aged 65 and over, 45 percent of Aboriginal women reported fair or poor health, compared with 29 percent in the total female population.

Health Inequalities Related to Gender

Canadians' life expectancy at birth in 2007 was 80.7 years. Women had an average life expectancy of 81.7 years, while men averaged 78.3 (Organisation for Economic Co-operation and Development, 2011b), yet women report more frequent long-term disability and chronic conditions than men (DesMeules, Turner & Cho, 2003). Ruiz and Verbrugge (1997) argue that the higher mortality rate and lower life expectancy of men compared to women can be misinterpreted to imply that women enjoy superior health, but this ignores the higher prevalence of chronic conditions in women, particularly in later life.

Health Inequalities Related to Race and Immigrant Status

Inequalities in health exist between Canadians of European and non-European descent, between white Canadians and Canadians of colour, and between recent and non-recent immigrants. Cross-sectional and longitudinal data from the National Population Health Survey (Ng et al., 2005) provide compelling evidence that the health of immigrants to Canada—especially non-European or non-white immigrants—is twice as likely to show deterioration over time as compared to Canadian-born residents and European immigrants.

Health Inequalities Related to Geographic Location

Canadians living in eastern Canada report generally poorer health than do central Canadians, and western Canadians show the best health status (Statistics Canada, 2001). Canadians living in rural areas show poorer health than do urban dwellers (Mitura & Bollman, 2003, 2004). Statistics Canada examined the predictors of life expectancy, disability-free life expectancy, and the presence of fair or poor health among residents of 136 regions across Canada (Shields & Tremblay, 2002). Behavioural factors were weak predictors of health status as compared to socio-demographic measures. While obesity rate predicted 1 percent of the variation and smoking rate 8 percent of the variation among communities in life expectancy, socio-demographic factors predicted 56 percent of variation in life expectancy.

This study also found that having less than secondary-school education increased the risk of reporting fair or poor health by 44 percent; that being a daily smoker increased the risk by 53 percent; and that being obese did so by 74 percent (Tremblay, Ross & Berthelot, 2002). But being in the lowest income group increased the risk of reporting fair or poor health by more than 307 percent. And being of lower middle income did so by 238 percent. Even middle-income people had a 53 percent greater risk of fair or poor health as compared to the highest income group.

Public Policy and Health Inequalities in Canada

One would expect that given the plethora of findings of health inequalities in Canada, this issue would be on the public policy agenda. But it is not. Public policy in Canada shapes the determinants of health inequalities and these include general labour and employment policy, governmental support to citizens through public spending in a variety of sectors, and public policy approaches that provide citizens with the prerequisites of health that include income, housing, and food if they should become unable to work. Available data indicate that Canada does a poor job in addressing these drivers of health inequalities (Raphael, 2011d, 2011e).

Income and Labour Policy

An important influence of health inequalities is income inequality and Canada has one of the highest rates of income inequality and poverty among wealthy developed nations (Organisation for Economic Co-operation and Development, 2011a). Differences in income inequality are driven by numerous factors, but three key ones are the environments within which employees negotiate their wages and benefits, the levels of benefits provided for those unable to work, and societal tax policy.

Canada has a situation of very low collective agreement coverage, which is related to low union membership (Raphael, 2011e). Not surprisingly, Canada has one of the highest rates of low-income workers, with almost one in four workers identified as being low-wage earners (Jackson, 2010). Canada also has very low levels of benefits for those unable to earn wages (Organisation for Economic Co-operation and Development, 2011d). Canada's rankings, as compared to other wealthy developed member nations of the OECD in a number of health inequalities-related public policy indicators, are presented in Table 5.2.

With regard to tax policy, tax structures that redistribute wealth have changed (Lee, 2007). In 1990 the total tax burden of the bottom 10 percent of Canadian income earners was 25.5 percent of broad income—that is, including market, investments, and benefits—but this increased to 30.7 percent by 2005. In contrast, the top 1 percent of earners' total taxes was reduced from 34.2 percent to 30.5 percent during this period. Similarly, the next highest 4 percent of wage earners had their taxes reduced from 36.5 percent to 33.8 percent, and the next 5 percent (those constituting the 90–95 percentiles of earners) saw reductions from 38.6 percent to 36.9 percent. These shifts represent changes in federal and provincial personal income tax rates, federal and provincial commodity taxes, and property taxes.

Governmental Support to Citizens through Public Spending

Another influence upon health inequalities is welfare state interventions in the form of collecting revenues through taxation and fees, which are then used to provide universal or targeted benefits to the population. In essence, these transfers offer direct support to individuals and provide social infrastructure. These benefits include cash payments and in-kind benefits to families, public pensions, training as part of active labour market policies, and provision of early childhood education recreation and public health care spending (Bryant, 2010). Together these public indicators provide an overall measure of the extent of the welfare state.

Table 5.2 also provides a summary of where Canada stands in relation to other wealthy members of the OECD in public spending in a range of areas. Among the developed nations of the OECD, Canada ranks 26th out of 30. While Canada is among the highest spenders in public expenditure on health care, it is a miserly public spender in the other areas of benefits and supports for citizens (Organisation for Economic Co-operation and Development, 2011b, 2011c, 2011d).

Social Assistance and Unemployment Policy

Canada's approach in this area falls well below standards of most other wealthy developed nations (Raphael, 2011b). Social assistance benefits fall well below poverty lines. Because of strict eligibility requirements, only half of working Canadians are eligible to receive unemployment benefits if their employment is terminated (Raphael, 2011b).

Political and Economic Forces behind These Public Policy Approaches

Numerous writers have examined the factors behind these developments (Langille, 2009; Scarth, 2004). These include the effects of neo-liberal restructuring of government policy involving welfare state retrenchment (Bryant et al., 2011; Raphael, 2011f; Raphael et al.,

Table 5.2
Canada's Relative Rankings among OECD Nations on a Number of
Indicators Driving Health Inequalities (data sources are from 2007 to 2009)

Indicator	Rate (%)	Relative Rank (1 is best or, in the case of spending, the highest)
Inequality in disposable income (Gini)[1]	.33	24th of 34 nations
Poverty rates[1]	11.4	21st of 34 nations
Union membership[2]	27.2	12th of 33 nations
Collective agreement coverage[2]	32.0	26th of 33 nations
Overall social expenditure (% of GDP)[3]	16.9	24th of 34 nations
Public spending on health care[3]	7.0	6th of 34 nations
Public spending on families[3]	1.0	28th of 34 nations
Public spending on elderly[3]	3.8	30th of 34 nations
Public spending on active labour policy[3]	0.3	17th of 34 nations
Public spending on unemployment[3]	0.6	14th of 34 nations
Public spending on incapacity[3]	0.9	28th of 34 nations

Sources: 1 Organisation for Economic Co-operation and Development, *Divided we stand: Why inequality keeps rising* (Paris: Organisation for Economic Co-operation and Development, 2011).

2 Organisation for Economic Co-operation and Development (2010), Trade union density, retrieved from: http://stats.oecd.org/Index.aspx?DataSetCode=UN_DEN; D. Venn, *Legislation, collective bargaining, and enforcement: Updating the OECD employment protection indicators*, OECD Social Employment and Migration Working Papers, no. 89 (Paris: OECD, 2009).

3 Organisation for Economic Co-operation and Development (2011c), Social expenditure database (SOCX), retrieved from: http://www.oecd.org/document/9/0,3746,en_2649_34637_38141385_1_1_1_1,00.html.

2008). These developments are usually justified as necessary to respond to the needs of globalization (Lewchuk, Clarke & de Wolff, 2008), but analysis suggests they result from the business and corporate sector's growing influence, which has degraded the overall quality of the social determinants of life and increased inequities in their distribution (Chernomas & Hudson, 2007; Raphael, 2011e; Scarth, 2004).

Canadian political parties have increasingly adopted pro-business policy approaches and there has been a noticeable shift to the right among the federal Conservative Party and the Liberal Party. Indeed, it has been argued that the strongest attack on the Canadian welfare state came during the 12-year majority rule of the Liberal Party in Ottawa from 1993 to 2004 (Langille, 2009; Scarth, 2004). The impacts upon the social determinants of health inequalities include a hollowing-out of the middle class, increasing precariousness of employment for many Canadians, and growing housing and food insecurity (Raphael, 2009b).

Recommendations for Future Activities

The problematic health inequalities situation in Canada is well documented. The very problem of health inequalities is generally unrecognized by the Canadian public, media, and governmental authorities. There is little evidence of its being placed on the public policy agenda. That said, there are a variety of activities that could help move the issue of tackling health inequalities forward. These issues are further considered in the concluding chapters of this volume.

Research Activities

Raphael and colleagues outlined a number of research activities that, though originally developed to address the issue of income inequality and health, have relevance for tackling health inequalities (Raphael et al., 2006). These include:

- identifying macroeconomic and policy interventions to reduce poverty and income inequality
- establishing data linkages to identify the sources of health inequalities
- creating longitudinal data and systems for collecting and analyzing these data
- creating participatory action research projects
- incorporating measures of socio-economic status into health research data collection
- developing training in advanced conceptualizations, critical perspectives, and interdisciplinary work
- understanding the role of non-income transfers on the poverty/income inequality/health relationship
- investigating the disconnect between research and health policy
- conducting attitudinal research on policy-makers
- developing broader understanding of the structural determinants of health

Public Education

The Canadian public remains woefully unaware of the importance of identifying and tackling health inequalities (Canadian Population Health Initiative, 2004b; Eyles et al., 2001; Frankish et al., 2007). Much of this has to do with media coverage of health inequalities and related issues such as the abysmal state of the social determinants of health in Canada (Raphael, 2011c). While there are efforts to improve media coverage, it has also been suggested that since the media and governmental authorities are not willing to carry out such education, it is up to the public health community to take on this task (Raphael, 2009a, 2011c).

Advocacy Efforts and the Building of Social and Political Movements

Since governments appear unresponsive to tackling health inequalities, efforts to influence public policy have to move beyond advocacy efforts to building social and political movements in support of health. There are supports for such action as well as significant barriers. These issues are considered following presentations of the case studies of the other nations contained in this volume.

Conclusion

In Canada there is a profound gap between governmental and public health agency statements about the importance of tackling health inequalities and actual public policy action that does so. In fact, Canada's leadership role in developing concepts related to tackling health inequalities—much less actually implementing them—has now been eclipsed by developments in many other nations. The results of such neglect, as described by one prominent health promotion authority, includes the following, all of which are drivers of health inequalities (Poland, 2007): (1) a growing gap between the rich and poor; (2) continuing high poverty rates in Canada; (3) dreadful living conditions on Aboriginal reserves; (4) growing numbers of homeless and under-housed Canadians; and (5) a steady erosion of the social safety net.

For decades now, Canadian leaders have reduced the role of government in determining the distribution of economic and social resources among the population. Much of this has involved reducing the size of the Canadian welfare state—that is, the benefits and services that Canadians get as a matter of right. Canada's declining rankings in a number of health and quality of life indicators compared to other nations have been the result.

Canada's health inequalities are being driven by the country's expending fewer resources toward citizen support than most other OECD nations. This trend can be expected to accelerate with the recent election of a majority Conservative government in Ottawa. Continuing evidence of a decline in relative improvement in population health and stagnating or increasing health inequalities as compared to other OECD nations can be expected. The health inequalities that result from Canada's unwillingness to promote citizen economic and social security are clear and troubling, with little sign that this situation will change in the near future.

Critical Thinking Questions

1. What are the key contributions that Canadian thinkers have made to understanding the causes of health inequalities and the means of reducing them?
2. What have been some key research findings concerning health inequalities in Canada?
3. What are the distinctive aspects of Canadian public policy that create health inequalities?
4. How does the political dominance of the Liberal and Conservative parties in Canada and the electoral process contribute to health inequalities in Canada?

Recommended Readings

Bryant, T., Raphael, D., Schrecker, T., & Labonte, R. (2011). Canada: A land of missed opportunities for addressing the social determinants of health. *Health Policy, 101*(1), 44–58.
    The social determinants of health represent the next frontier for reducing health inequalities, yet Canada's recent performance in numerous public policy areas suggests that the nation is failing to address these issues and, in many situations, is creating policies that make the situation worse.

Raphael, D. (2010). *About Canada: Health and illness.* Winnipeg: Fernwood Publishing.
    The author argues that it is the social determinants of health that include such things as income and wealth, employment, quality of education, access to health and social services, and the ability to

obtain food and housing. These issues are placed within a broad public policy perspective that shows how Canada's approach lags behind those of most other wealthy developed nations.

Raphael, D. (2011). *Poverty in Canada: Implications for health and quality of life* (2nd ed.). Toronto: Canadian Scholars' Press Inc.

This volume examines the nature and meaning of poverty in Canada and focuses on how the incidence of poverty—and the health inequalities that result from it—result from governments' public policy decisions. The processes that create poverty are also the ones that create growing social inequality, which manifests in greater health inequalities along all segments of Canadian society.

Rootman, I., Dupéré, S., Pederson, A., & O'Neill, M. (Eds.). (2012). *Health promotion in Canada* (3rd ed.). Toronto: Canadian Scholars' Press Inc.

Adopting a critical/sociological and historical perspective, this book offers an analysis of the health promotion situation in Canada and what the future holds for health promotion worldwide.

Recommended Websites

Canadian Centre for Policy Alternatives Growing Gap Project: www.policyalternatives.ca/projects/growing-gap/about

The Growing Gap project takes an in-depth and sustained look at one of the biggest challenges of our time: worsening income and wealth inequality in Canada. A team of economists and researchers has been tracking household income, wealth, spending, and credit data, unearthing a troubling phenomenon.

Canadian Population Health Initiative: http://tinyurl.com/39e38d9

The Canadian Population Health Initiative (CPHI) aims to expand the public's knowledge of population health. CPHI's mission is to: (1) foster a better understanding of factors that affect the health of individuals and communities; and (2) contribute to the development of policies that reduce inequities and improve the health and well-being of Canadians.

Canadian Public Health Association: www.cpha.ca/en/programs/policy.aspx

The Canadian Public Health Association has issued numerous policy statements and documents about the importance of addressing health inequalities through public policy action. Unfortunately, there has been little, if any, uptake of these concepts into public policy activity by federal or provincial governments.

Federation of Canadian Municipalities: www.fcm.ca

The FCM is carrying out ongoing documentation of the quality of life of Canadian municipalities. It does so by collecting a wide range of indicators that consider income, housing, service, health, and others and placing all of these findings within public policy frameworks. Numerous reports document the decaying public policy environment in Canada and how this is impacting Canadian cities.

References

Analytical Studies Branch. (2011). *Analytical Studies Branch research paper series*. Retrieved from: http://www.statcan.gc.ca/bsolc/olc-cel/olc-cel?catno=11F0019M&lang=eng&chropg=1.

Auger, N., & Alix, C. (2009). Income and health in Canada. In D. Raphael (Ed.), *Social determinants of health: Canadian perspectives* (2nd ed., pp. 61–74). Toronto: Canadian Scholars' Press Inc.

Alter, D.A., Naylor, C.D., Austin, P., & Tu, J. (1999). Effects of socioeconomic status on access to invasive cardiac procedures and on mortality after acute myocardial infarction. *New England Journal of Medicine, 341*(18), 1360–1367.

Basinski, A.S., (1999). Hospitalization for cardiovascular medical diagnoses. In C.D. Naylor & P. Slaughter (Eds.), *Cardiovascular health and services in Ontario: An ICES atlas* (pp. 16–49). Toronto: Institute for Clinical Evaluative Services and Heart and Stroke Foundation (Ontario).

Bernard, P., & Saint-Arnaud, S. (2004). *More of the same: The position of the four largest Canadian provinces in the world of welfare regimes.* Ottawa: Canadian Policy Research Networks.

Boychuk, G. (2004). *The Canadian social model: The logics of policy development,* CPRN Social Architecture Papers, Research Report F|36, Ottawa: Canadian Policy Research Networks.

British Columbia Ministry of Health. (2011). *Provincial health officer's reports.* Retrieved from: http://www.health.gov.bc.ca/pho/reports/annual.html.

Bryant, T. (2009). *An introduction to health policy.* Toronto: Canadian Scholars' Press Inc.

Bryant, T. (2010). Politics, public policy, and health inequalities. In T. Bryant, D. Raphael & M. Rioux (Eds.), *Staying alive: Critical perspectives on health, illness, and health care* (2nd ed., pp. 239–265). Toronto: Canadian Scholars' Press Inc.

Bryant, T., Raphael, D., Schrecker, T., & Labonte, R. (2011). Canada: A land of missed opportunity for addressing the social determinants of health. *Health Policy, 101*(1), 44–58.

Butler-Jones, D. (2009). *Report on the state of public health in Canada 2008: Addressing health inequalities.* Ottawa: Public Health Agency of Canada.

Butler-Jones, D. (2010). *Report on the state of public health in Canada 2009: Growing up well—priorities for a healthy future.* Ottawa: Public Health Agency of Canada.

Butler-Jones, D. (2011). *Report on the state of public health in Canada 2010: Growing older—adding life to years.* Ottawa: Public Health Agency of Canada.

Campaign 2000. (2011). *Current issues.* Retrieved from: http://www.campaign2000.ca/.

Canadian Centre for Policy Alternatives. (2011). *Growing gap updates.* Retrieved from: http://www.policyalternatives.ca/projects/growing-gap.

Canadian House of Commons. (2010). *Federal poverty reduction plan: Working in partnership towards reducing poverty in Canada.* Retrieved from: http://tinyurl.com/5snk45r.

Canadian Institute for Health Information. (2011). *National health expenditure trends, 1975 to 2011.* Retrieved from: http://secure.cihi.ca/cihiweb/products/nhex_trends_report_2011_en.pdf.

Canadian Labour Congress. (2011). *Social and economic issues.* Retrieved from: http://www.canadianlabour.ca/issues/social-and-economic-issues.

Canadian Nurses Association. (2011). *National Expert Commission.* Retrieved from: http://www.cna-aiic.ca/CNA/about/nec/default_e.aspx.

Canadian Population Health Initiative. (2003). *Women's health surveillance report.* Ottawa: Canadian Institute of Health Information.

Canadian Population Health Initiative. (2004a). *Improving the health of Canadians.* Ottawa: CPHI.

Canadian Population Health Initiative. (2004b). *Select highlights on public views of the determinants of health.* Ottawa: CPHI.

Canadian Population Health Initiative. (2006). *How healthy are rural Canadians? An assessment of their health status and health determinants.* Ottawa: CPHI.

Canadian Population Health Initiative. (2008). *Reducing gaps in health: A focus on socio-economic status in urban Canada.* Ottawa: CPHI.

Canadian Public Health Association. (1996). *Action statement for health promotion in Canada.* Retrieved from: http://www.cpha/cpha.docs/ActionStatement.eng.html.

Canadian Public Health Association. (2000). *Reducing poverty and its negative effects on health: Resolution passed at the 2000 CPHA annual meeting.* Retrieved from: http://www.cpha.ca/english/policy/resolu/2000s/2000/page2.htm.

Canadian Public Health Association. (2011). Policy Statements. Available at http://www.cpha.ca/en/programs/policy.aspx.

Canadian Senate. (2009). *In from the margins: A call to action on poverty, housing, and homelessness.* Retrieved from: www.parl.gc.ca/40/2/parlbus/commbus/senate/com-e/citi-e/rep-e/rep02dec09-e.pdf.

Center for the Study of Gender, Social Inequities, and Mental Health. (2011). *Dialogue, research, and action*. Retrieved from: http://www.socialinequities.ca.

CERIS–The Ontario Metropolis Centre. (2011). Retrieved from: http://www.ceris.metropolis.net.

Chernomas, R., & Hudson, I. (2007). *Social murder and other shortcomings of Conservative economics*. Winnipeg: Arbeiter Ring Publishing.

City of Vancouver. (2001). *The Healthy City Office—Toronto, Ontario*. Retrieved from: http://vancouver.ca/ctyclerk/011106/A4-4.htm.

Conference Board of Canada. (2009). *How Canada performs: A report card on Canada*. Ottawa: Conference Board of Canada.

Conference Board of Canada. (2011a). *Economy: Income per capita*. Retrieved from: http://www.conferenceboard.ca/hcp/Details/Economy/income-per-capita.aspx.

Conference Board of Canada. (2011b). *A report card on Canada*. Retrieved from: http://www.conferenceboard.ca/hcp/default.aspx.

DesMeules, M., D. Manuel, and R. Cho. (2003). Health status of Canadian women. In *Women's health surveillance report: a multi-dimensional look at the health of Canadian women* (pp. 17–22). Ottawa: Health Canada, Canadian Population Health Initiative.

Dinca-Panaitescu, S., Dinca-Panaitescu, M., Bryant, T., Daiski, I., Pilkington, B., & Raphael, D. (2011). Diabetes prevalence and income: Results of the Canadian Community Health Survey. *Health Policy, 99*, 116–123.

Dinca-Panaitescu, S., Dinca-Panaitescu, M., Raphael, D., Bryant, T., Daiski, I., & Pilkington, B. (2012). The dynamics of the relationship between diabetes incidence and low income: Longitudinal results from Canada's National Population Health Study. *Maturitas, 72*(3), 229–235.

Direction de santé publique Agence de la santé et des services sociaux de Montréal. (2011). *Social inequalities in health in Montréal: Progress to date*. Montreal: Direction de santé publique Agence de la santé et des services sociaux de Montréal.

Engels, F. (1845/1987). *The condition of the working class in England*. New York: Penguin Classics.

Epp, J. (1986). *Achieving health for all: A framework for health promotion*. Ottawa: Health and Welfare Canada.

Evans, R.G., Barer, M.L., & Marmor, T.R. (1994). *Why are some people healthy and others not? The determinants of health of populations*. New York: Aldine de Gruyter.

Eyles, J., Brimacombe, M., Chaulk, P., Stoddart, G., Pranger, T., & Moase, O. (2001). What determines health? To where should we shift resources? Attitudes towards the determinants of health among multiple stakeholder groups in Prince Edward Island, Canada. *Social Science & Medicine, 53*(12), 1611–1619.

Faelker, T., Pickett, W., & Brison, R.J. (2000). Socioeconomic differences in childhood injury: A population based epidemiologic study in Ontario, Canada. *Injury Prevention, 6*(3), 203–208.

Federation of Canadian Municipalities. (2011). *Quality of life reporting system*. Retrieved from: http://www.fcm.ca/home/programs/quality-of-life-reporting-system.htm.

Forsey, E.A. (2007). *How Canadians govern themselves*. Retrieved from: http://tinyurl.com/25n9xsj.

Frankish, C.J., Moulton, G., Quantz, D., Carson, A., Casebeer, A., Eyles, J., et al. (2007). Addressing the non-medical determinants of health: A survey of Canada's health regions. *Canadian Journal of Public Health, 98*(1), 41–47.

Galabuzi, G.E. (2009). Social exclusion. In D. Raphael (Ed.), *Social determinants of health: Canadian perspectives* (2nd ed., pp. 252–268). Toronto: Canadian Scholars' Press Inc.

Gilbride, S., Wild, C., Wilson, D., Svenson, L., & Spady, D. (2006). Socio-economic status and types of childhood injury in Alberta: A population-based study. *BMC Pediatrics, 6*(30), 1–10.

Glazier, R., & Booth, G. (2007). *Neighbourhood environments and resources for healthy living: A focus on diabetes in Toronto*. Toronto: Institute for Clinical Evaluative Sciences.

Government of Canada. (2000). *Canadian Institutes of Health Research Act*. Retrieved from: http://laws.justice.gc.ca/eng/acts/C-18.1/page-1.html.

Government of Canada. (2004). *Government of Canada announces national collaborating centre for determinants of health*. Retrieved from: http://www.phac-aspc.gc.ca/media/nr-rp/2004/2004_02_e.html.

Hancock, T. (2011). Health promotion in Canada: 25 years of unfulfilled promise. *Health Promotion International, 26*(Suppl. 2), ii263–ii267.

Hancock, T., & Duhl, L. (1986). *Healthy cities: Promoting health in the urban context.* Copenhagen, Denmark: World Health Organization Europe.

Health Canada. (1998). *Taking action on population health: A position paper for health promotion and programs branch staff.* Ottawa: Health Canada.

Health Canada. (1999). *Toward a healthy future: Second report on the health of Canadians.* Retrieved from: http://www.hc-sc.gc.ca/hppb/phdd/report/toward/pdf/english/toward_a_healthy_english.PDF.

Health Canada. (2000). *Reducing health inequalities: Implications for interventions.* Retrieved from: http://www.hc-sc.gc.ca/hppb/phdd/resources/red_inadequecies.htm.

Health Canada. (2001). *The population health template: Key elements and actions that define a population health approach.* Retrieved from: http://www.hc-sc.gc.ca/hppb/phdd/pdf/discussion_paper.pdf.

Health Canada. (2004). *Population health approach.* Retrieved from: http://www.phac-aspc.gc.ca/ph-sp/phdd/approach/approach.html.

Health Canada First Nations and Inuit Health Branch. (2003). *A statistical profile on the health of First Nations in Canada.* Ottawa: Health Canada, First Nations and Inuit Health Branch.

Health Council of Canada. (2010). *Stepping it up: Moving the focus from health care in Canada to a healthier Canada.* Toronto: Health Council of Canada.

Humphries, K., & van Doorslaer, E. (2000). Income-related health inequality in Canada. *Social Science & Medicine, 50*(5), 663–671.

Hux, J., Booth, G., & Laupacis, A. (2002, Sept 18). *The ICES Practice Atlas: Diabetes in Ontario.* Retrieved from http://www.ices.on.ca.

International Association of Machinists & Aerospace Workers. (2011). *Glossary of labour terms.* Retrieved from: http://www.iamaw.ca/publications/labourterms/glossary_e.html.

Ismael, S.T. (2006). *Child poverty and the welfare state: from entitlement to charity.* Edmonton: University of Alberta Press.

Jackson, A. (2010). *Work and labour in Canada: Critical issues* (2nd ed.). Toronto: Canadian Scholars' Press Inc.

King, A. (2011). *Health, not health care: Changing the conversation.* Toronto: Ontario Ministry of Health and Long-Term Care.

Kirkpatrick, S.I., & McIntyre, L. (2009). The chief public health officer's report on health inequalities: What are the implications for public health practitioners and researchers? *Canadian Journal of Public Health, 100*(2), 93–95.

Labonte, R. (1994). Death of a program: Birth of a metaphor. In I. Rootman, A. Pederson & M. O'Neill (Eds.), *Health promotion in Canada: Provincial, national, and international perspectives* (pp. 72–90). Toronto: Saunders.

Labonte, R., & Penfold, S. (1981). Canadian perspectives in health promotion: A critique. *Health Education, 19*, 4–9.

Lalonde, M. (1974). *A new perspective on the health of Canadians: A working document.* Retrieved from: http://www.hc-sc.gc.ca/main/hppb/phdd/resource.htm.

Langille, D. (2009). Follow the money: How business and politics shape our health. In D. Raphael (Ed.), *Social determinants of health: Canadian perspectives* (2nd ed., pp. 305–317). Toronto: Canadian Scholars' Press Inc.

Léa Roback Centre for Research on Social Inequalities in Health. (2011). Retrieved from: http://www.centrelearoback.ca/.

Lee, M. (2007). *Eroding tax fairness: Tax incidence in Canada, 1998 to 2005.* Ottawa: Canadian Centre for Policy Alternatives.

Legowski, B., & McKay, L. (2000). *Health beyond health care: Twenty-five years of federal health policy development.* CPRN Discussion Paper no. H04. Ottawa: Canadian Policy Research Networks.

Lemstra, M., & Neudorf, C. (2008). *Healthy disparity in Saskatoon: Analysis to intervention.* Saskatoon: Saskatoon Health Region.

Lewchuk, W., Clarke, M., & de Wolff, A. (2008). Working without commitments: Precarious employment and health. *Work, Employment and Society, 22*(3), 387–406.

Lightman, E., Mitchell, A., & Wilson, B. (2008). *Poverty is making us sick: A comprehensive survey of income and health in Canada.* Toronto: Wellesley Institute.

Manitoba Centre for Health Policy. (2010). *Study finds growing gaps in wealth and health for Manitobans.* Retrieved from: http://umanitoba.ca/news/blogs/blog/2010/09/30/news-release-gaps-in-weath-and-health-for-manitobans/.

Manitoba Centre for Health Policy. (2011). *Informing health and social policy.* Retrieved from: http://umanitoba.ca/faculties/medicine/units/community_health_sciences/departmental_units/mchp/.

Manzano, A., & Raphael, D. (2010). CPHA and the social determinants of health: An analysis of policy documents and recommendations for future action. *Canadian Journal of Public Health, 101*(5), 399–404.

McIntosh, C., Fines, P., Wilkins, R., & Wolfson, M. (2009). Income disparities in health-adjusted life expectancy for Canadian adults, 1991 to 2001. *Health Reports, 20*(4), 1–11.

McKeown, D., MacCon, K., Day, N., Fleiszer, P., Scott, F., & Wolfe, S. (2008). *The unequal city: Income and health inequalities in Toronto.* Toronto: Toronto Public Health.

Mikkonen, J., & Raphael, D. (2010). *Social determinants of health: The Canadian facts.* Retrieved from: http:/thecanadianfacts.org.

Mitura, V., and Bollman, R. (2003). The health of rural Canadians: A rural-urban comparison of health indicators. *Rural and Small Town Canada Analysis Bulletin.* Ottawa: Statistics Canada, Catalogue no. 21-006-XIE, Vol. 4, No. 6.

Mitura, V., and Bollman, R. (2004). Health status and behaviours of Canada's youth: A rural-urban comparison. *Rural and Small Town Canada Analysis Bulletin*, Vol. 5, No. 3. Ottawa: Statistics Canada, Catalogue no. 21-006-XIE.

Morel, S. (2002). *The insertion model or the workfare model? The transformation of social assistance within Quebec and Canada.* Ottawa: Status of Women Canada.

Myles, J. (1998). How to design a "Liberal" welfare state: A comparison of Canada and the United States. *Social Policy and Administration, 32*(4), 341–364.

National Council of Welfare. (2010). *Welfare incomes 2009.* Ottawa: National Council of Welfare.

National Resources Canada. (2009). *The atlas of Canada: Visible minority population.* Retrieved from: http://atlas.nrcan.gc.ca/site/english/maps/peopleandsociety/population/visible_minority.

Ng, E.Y., Wilkins, R., Gendron, F., & Berthelot, J.-M. (2005). *Dynamics of immigrants' health in Canada: Evidence from the National Population Health Survey.* Ottawa: Statistics Canada.

Nova Scotia Health Research Foundation. (2011). *What's new.* Retrieved from: http://www.nshrf.ca/.

O'Neill, M., Pederson, A., Dupere, S., & Rootman, I. (Eds.). (2007). *Health promotion in Canada: Critical perspectives.* Toronto: Canadian Scholars' Press Inc.

Organisation for Economic Co-operation and Development. (2011a). *Divided we stand: Why inequality keeps rising.* Paris: Organisation for Economic Co-operation and Development.

Organisation for Economic Co-operation and Development. (2011b). *OECD health data 2011: Frequently requested data.* Retrieved from: http://www.oecd.org/document/16/0,3343,en_2649_34631_2085200_1_1_1_1,00.html.

Organisation for Economic Co-operation and Development. (2011c). *Social expenditure database (SOCX).* Retrieved from: http://www.oecd.org/document/9/0,3746,en_2649_34637_38141385_1_1_1_1,00.html.

Organisation for Economic Co-operation and Development. (2011d). *Society at a glance 2011, OECD social indicators.* Paris: Organisation for Economic Co-operation and Development.

Phipps, S. (2002). *The impact of poverty on health.* Ottawa: Canadian Population Health Initiative.

Poland, B. (2007). Health promotion in Canada: Perspectives and future prospects. *Revista Brasileira em Promoção da Saúde, 20*(1), 3–11.

Poland, B., Coburn, D., Robertson, A., & Eakin, J. (1998). Wealth, equity, and health care: A critique of a population health perspective on the determinants of health. *Social Science & Medicine, 46*(7), 785–798.

Population Health Improvement Research Network. (2011). *Welcome to PHIRN!* Retrieved from: http://www.rrasp-phirn.ca/.

Public Health Agency of Canada. (2006). *Canadian reference group on social determinants of health.* Retrieved from: http://www.phac-aspc.gc.ca/media/nr-rp/2006/2006_06bk3-eng.php.

Public Health Agency of Canada. (2007). *Canada's response to WHO Commission on Social Determinants of Health.* Retrieved from: http://www.phac-aspc.gc.ca/sdh-dss/bg-eng.php.

Public Health Agency of Canada. (2011). *Health goals for Canada.* Retrieved from: http://www.phac-aspc.gc.ca/hgc-osc/pdf/goals-e.pdf.

Quebec Public Health Institute. (2011). *Developing knowledge, sharing information.* Retrieved from: www.inspq.qc.ca/english/default.asp?A=7.

Raphael, D. (2007). Addressing health inequalities in Canada: Little attention, inadequate action, limited success. In A. Pederson, I. Rootman, M. O'Neill & S. Dupere (Eds.), *Health promotion in Canada: Critical perspectives* (2nd ed., pp. 106–122). Toronto: Canadian Scholars' Press Inc.

Raphael, D. (2008). Grasping at straws: A recent history of health promotion in Canada. *Critical Public Health, 18*(4), 483–495.

Raphael, D. (2009a). Escaping from the phantom zone: Social determinants of health, public health units, and public policy in Canada. *Health Promotion International, 24*(2), 193–198.

Raphael, D. (Ed.). (2009b). *Social determinants of health: Canadian perspectives* (2nd ed.). Toronto: Canadian Scholars' Press Inc.

Raphael, D. (2010). *About Canada: Health and illness.* Winnipeg: Fernwood Publishing.

Raphael, D. (2011a). Anti-poverty strategies and programs. In D. Raphael (Ed.), *Poverty in Canada: Implications for health and quality of life* (2nd ed., pp. 406–437). Toronto: Canadian Scholars' Press Inc.

Raphael, D. (2011b). Canadian public policy and poverty in international perspective. In D. Raphael (Ed.), *Poverty in Canada: Implications for health and quality of life* (pp. 374–405). Toronto: Canadian Scholars' Press Inc.

Raphael, D. (2011c). Mainstream media and the social determinants of health in Canada: Is it time to call it a day? *Health Promotion International, 26*(2), 220–229.

Raphael, D. (2011d). The political economy of health promotion: Part 1, National commitments to provision of the prerequisites of health. *Health Promotion International.* doi: 10.1093/heapro/dar084.

Raphael, D. (2011e). The political economy of health promotion: Part 2, National provision of the prerequisites of health. *Health Promotion International.* doi: 10.1093/heapro/dar058.

Raphael, D. (2011f). *Poverty in Canada: Implications for health and quality of life* (2nd ed.). Toronto: Canadian Scholars' Press Inc.

Raphael, D., Anstice, S., Raine, K., McGannon, K., Rizvi, S., & Yu, V. (2003). The social determinants of the incidence and management of type 2 diabetes mellitus: Are we prepared to rethink our questions and redirect our research activities? *Leadership in Health Services, 16,* 10–20.

Raphael, D., & Bryant, T. (2002). The limitations of population health as a model for a new public health. *Health Promotion International, 17,* 189–199.

Raphael, D., & Bryant, T. (2006). Maintaining population health in a period of welfare state decline: Political economy as the missing dimension in health promotion theory and practice. *Promotion and Education, 13*(4), 12–18.

Raphael, D., Curry-Stevens, A., & Bryant, T. (2008). Barriers to addressing the social determinants of health: Insights from the Canadian experience. *Health Policy, 88,* 222–235.

Raphael, D., Daiski, I., Pilkington, B., Bryant, T., Dinca-Panaitescu, M., & Dinca-Panaitescu, S. (2011). A toxic combination of poor social policies and programmes, unfair economic arrangements, and bad politics: The experiences of poor Canadians with type 2 diabetes. *Critical Public Health, 22*(2), 127–145.

Raphael, D., & Farrell, E.S. (2002). Beyond medicine and lifestyle: Addressing the societal determinants of cardiovascular disease in North America. *Leadership in Health Services, 15*, 1–5.

Raphael, D., Labonte, R., Colman, R., Torgeson, R., Hayward, K., & Macdonald, J. (2006). Income and health research in Canada: Needs, gaps, and opportunities. *Canadian Journal of Public Health, 97*(Suppl. 3), s16–s23.

Restrepo, H.E. (2000). Introduction. In H.E. Restrepo (Ed.), *Health promotion: An anthology* (pp. ix–xi). Washington: Pan American Health Organization.

Robertson, A. (1998). Shifting discourses on health in Canada: From health promotion to population health. *Health Promotion International, 13*, 155–166.

Roos, N. P., & Mustard, C. A. (1997). Variation in health care use by socioeconomic status in Winnipeg, Canada: Does the system work well? Yes and no. *Milbank Quarterly, 75*(1), 89–111.

Ross, D.P. (2002). *Policy approaches to address the impact of poverty*. Ottawa: Canadian Population Health Initiative.

Ross, N. (2004). *What have we learned studying income inequality and population health?* Ottawa: Canadian Population Health Initiative.

Ruiz, M.T., and L.M. Verbrugge. (1997). A two-way view of gender bias in medicine. *Journal of Epidemiology and Community Health, 51*, 106–109.

Scarth, T. (Ed.). (2004). *Hell and high water: An assessment of Paul Martin's record and implications for the future*. Ottawa: Canadian Centre for Policy Alternatives.

Senate Subcommittee on Population Health. (2008). *A healthy, productive Canada: A determinant of health approach*. Ottawa: Government of Canada.

Shields, M., & Tremblay, S. (2002). The health of Canada's communities. *Health Reports. Supplement, 13*(July), 1–22.

Silversides, A. (2010). Social scientists redirected to CIHR for grants. *Canadian Medical Association Journal, 182*(1), E27–E28.

Smith, K., Matheson, F., Moineddin, R., & Glazier, R. (2007). Gender, income, and immigration differences in depression in Canadian urban centres. *Canadian Journal of Public Health, 98*(2), 149–153.

Smylie, J. (2009). The health of Aboriginal peoples. In D. Raphael (Ed.), *Social determinants of health: Canadian perspectives* (2nd ed., pp. 280–304). Toronto: Canadian Scholars' Press Inc.

Statistics Canada. (2001). How healthy are Canadians? Annual Report. *Health Reports, 12*(3).

St. Michael's Hospital. (2011). *Centre for Research on Inner City Health*. Retrieved from: http://www.stmichaelshospital.com/crich/.

Tjepkema, M. (2002). The health of the off-reserve Aboriginal population. *Health Reports Supplement, 13*, 73–88.

Tremblay, S., Ross, N.A., & Berthelot, J.-M. (2002). Regional socio-economic context and health. *Health Reports Supplement, 13*, 1–12.

Vancouver Coastal Health. (2011). *Population health: What makes our communities healthy?* Retrieved from: http://www.vch.ca/your_health/population_health/.

Virchow, R. (1848/1985). Report on the typhus epidemic in Upper Silesia. In L.J. Rather (Ed.), *Collected essays by Rudolph Virchow on public health and epidemiology* (Vol. 1, pp. 205–319). Canton: Science History Publications.

Wilkins, R. (2007). *Mortality by neighbourhood income in urban Canada from 1971 to 2001*. Ottawa: Statistics Canada, Health Analysis and Measurement Group.

Wilkins, R., Berthelot, J.-M., & Ng, E. (2002). Trends in mortality by neighbourhood income in urban Canada from 1971 to 1996. *Health Reports* (Stats Can), *13*(Supplement), 1–28.

Wilkins, R., Houle, C., Berthelot, J.-M., & Ross, D.P. (2000). The changing health status of Canada's children. *ISUMA, 1*(2), 57–63.

Wood, E., Sallar, A., Schechter, M., & Hogg, R. (1999). Social inequalities in male mortality amenable to medical intervention in British Columbia. *Social Science and Medicine, 49*(12), 1751–1758.

World Health Organization. (2003). *Belfast declaration*. Retrieved from: http://www.who.dk/healthy-cities/CitiesAndNetworks/20040227_3.

World Health Organization. (2008). *Commission on Social Determinants of Health.* Retrieved from: http://www.who.int/social_determinants/en/.

Xi, G. (2005). Income inequality and health in Ontario. *Canadian Journal of Public Health, 96*(3), 206–211.

Chapter 6

Finnish Experiences[1]

Juha Mikkonen

Introduction

Historically, the Finnish welfare state model has been based on the universal provision of equal social rights for all. These rights are clearly defined in the Constitution of Finland (see Box 6.1). Finland belongs to the group of Nordic countries (Finland, Sweden, Norway, Denmark, and Iceland) that all share the same commitment to provide basic security, free education, and social and health services for everyone regardless of income and wealth. These welfare services are equally available to all citizens and funded through relatively high levels of progressive taxation.

In Esping-Andersen's (1990) welfare typology, Finland is identified as a social democratic welfare regime, which generally emphasizes full employment and the role of the state in ensuring adequate income and service provision for citizens (Saint-Arnaud & Bernard, 2003). In international comparison, the Nordic social and economic model has been successful in preventing deep poverty and profound economic inequalities among citizens.

Finnish society has strived to combine social equality with economic competitiveness. According to the Organisation for Economic Co-operation and Development (OECD), Finland is the seventh most equal of 30 most developed OECD countries in terms of income disparities. Poverty rates in Finland are relatively low, but have increased since the recession of the 1990s (OECD, 2008). In terms of economic competitiveness, the World Economic Forum ranks Finland as the sixth most competitive economy in the world (Schwab, 2009).

In Finnish policy-making, health problems have been often seen as socio-political problems rather than as problems that could be solved solely by educating people on healthy lifestyles or by improving health care services. Moreover, Finland has been a strong advocate of the Health in All Policies approach, which emphasizes cross-sectoral actions and broader social and economic factors as the key determinants of health (Puska & Ståhl, 2010; Ståhl, Wismar, Ollila, Lahtinen & Leppo, 2006).

Finnish governments have produced numerous policy papers and strategies that emphasize tackling inequalities in health during the past decades. These health policy strategies have a clear objective of reducing health inequalities (Ministry of Social Affairs and Health, 1987, 1993, 2001, 2008, 2009, 2011). Currently, reducing poverty, inequality, and social exclusion is one of three priority areas of the Finnish government (Prime Minister's Office, 2011a). Although the overall health of Finnish population has improved, relative health inequalities between socio-economic groups have increased despite the policy goals set in public health programs (Rotko, Aho, Mustonen & Linnanmäki, 2011). This may indicate a divergence between strategic policy objectives and the actual implementation of those policies.

National Description and Political Organization and Structure

Finland is the fifth largest country in the European Union with a relatively small population of 5.37 million inhabitants (Statistics Finland, 2011a). A large part of the population (1.5 million) is concentrated in the region of Uusimaa in southern Finland. The most populous city is Helsinki (600,000 inhabitants), which is the capital of Finland. The country is bordered by Russia to the east, Norway to the north, and Sweden to the west. Estonia is situated to the south across the Gulf of Finland.

Nordic countries share the same commitment of providing their citizens with an adequate income and equitable welfare services regardless of socio-economic position. These universal principles see society as providing citizens with a decent standard of living regardless of their social background. For example, Nordic universalism sees many benefits targeted not only to the poor and needy but to the whole population. The main element of income redistribution is a relatively high level of progressive taxation combined with efforts at attaining full employment.

Box 6.1
Social Rights in the Constitution of Finland

Those who cannot obtain the means necessary for a life of dignity have the right to receive indispensable subsistence and care.

Everyone shall be guaranteed by an Act the right to basic subsistence in the event of unemployment, illness, and disability and during old age as well as at the birth of a child or the loss of a provider.

The public authorities shall guarantee for everyone, as provided in more detail by an Act, adequate social, health and medical services and promote the health of the population. Moreover, the public authorities shall support families and others responsible for providing for children so that they have the ability to ensure the wellbeing and personal development of the children.

The public authorities shall promote the right of everyone to housing and the opportunity to arrange their own housing.

Source: Government of Finland, The right to social security: Section 19 of the Constitution of Finland (Helsinki: Government of Finland, 1999).

Finland joined the European Union in 1995 and since 2002, its currency has been the Euro. Finland is a highly industrialized nation with an annual gross domestic product of €180 billion (US$240 billion) (Statistics Finland, 2011a). Finnish trade is largely dependent on foreign exports, which account for over one-third of GDP (Statistics Finland, 2011a). Its main industries are electronics, engineering, forest products, chemicals, and shipbuilding (32 percent of GDP). The service sector has a share of 65 percent of Finnish GDP.

Population Demographics

The population of Finland is rather homogeneous in terms of ethnic origin. Only 4.2 percent of its population (224,388) are foreign-born and only 3.1 percent of those (167,954) living in Finland are foreign citizens (Statistics Finland, 2011a). The largest groups of foreigners are people from Estonia, Russia, and Sweden. Finland has two official languages: Finnish and Swedish. Finland has a rather large bilingual Swedish-speaking minority (5.4 percent of all citizens).

Two notable future challenges for Finnish society will be changing demographics in terms of a growing immigrant population and the aging of its citizens. The beginning of the 2010s is a turning point, with a rapid increase in old age pensioners and a declining tax-paying workforce. Projections indicate that the proportion of Finnish citizens over 65 will increase from 17 percent to 27 percent by 2030 (Blomgren, Mikkola, Hiilamo & Järvisalo, 2011). The challenges of aging populations affect all the European countries, but these changes will be greater in Finland than in other EU countries.

Due to the changing ratio between working and retired citizens, there are pressures to keep aging citizens in the workforce. At the political level, there are numerous debates about how to improve the quality of working life and reduce health inequalities among wage earners. In addition, there have been proposals that the age for old age pension should be raised from 63 to 65 years. However, there are various types of early retirement plans and the expected effective retirement age was 60.4 in 2010 (Finnish Centre for Pensions, 2011; www.etk.fi).

Form of Government and Political Parties

Finland is a democratic republic with a unicameral Parliament of 200 members who are elected for a four-year term on the basis of proportional representation. The president of Finland, who is the head of state, is elected for a six-year term. A decade ago, amendments were passed that reduced the president's governing power by increasing the powers of the prime minister and the Finnish Parliament. The prime minister is the head of the government and appoints other ministers of Cabinet. Finnish politics has a multi-party system and a long tradition of coalition governments. There has not been a one-party majority government during the entire time of Finland's independence. One notable democratic milestone was experienced in 1906, when Finnish women were the first ones in the world to have an unrestricted right to vote and to stand for parliamentary elections. The first female president of Finland was elected in 2000.

During the past 100 years, the Finnish Social Democratic Party and the Agrarian Party (now the Centre Party) have had a significant presence in national governments. Most recently in the 2011 parliamentary elections, six parties formed a coalition government.[2] This kind of wide coalition is unexceptional in Finland and represents a general shift in European politics in which traditional political parties have lost support to nationalist and populist movements.

Municipalities and Regions in Finland

Finland has 336 municipalities that have a high degree of self-governance (Tukia, Lehtinen, Saaristo & Vuori, 2011). Along with maintaining local infrastructure, which includes schools and libraries, municipalities are obliged to provide basic services such as health care and social services. Municipalities are given a right to collect an income tax with marginal rates of between 16 to 21 percent (Finnish Tax Administration, 2011). Currently there are substantial pressures to merge and reform municipalities into larger units to sustain their capability to provide high-quality social and health services in the future. To date, many municipalities work together and have formed social and health care districts to provide legally obligated services such as hospital care for their citizens.

At the regional level, Finland has 19 regions that are governed by regional councils that coordinate co-operation between the municipalities. In 2010, a new regional administration system was established and six regional state agencies were formed to carry out the administrative functions of different ministries at a regional level. These agencies have responsibility for legislative implementation and monitoring regional activity. The state steers municipalities' activities by three means: (1) regulations defined by the law (norm guidance); (2) subsidies (resource guidance); and (3) information to local governments (information guidance) (Ministry of Finance, 2011). Laws and resource provision have been seen as the most effective means of steering municipal activity. In contrast, information guidance has been seen as less effective because it does not provide incentives or sanctions for local governments' activities.

Historical Context

The history of Finland is distinct from that of other Nordic countries because of long periods of Swedish (600 years) and Russian (100 years) rule in the country. From 1809 to 1917, Finland was an autonomous Grand Duchy of the Russian Empire. The Parliament of Finland adopted the Finnish declaration of independence in 1917, with Finland becoming an independent and sovereign nation rather than a part of the Russian Empire.

During the turmoil caused by World War I, Finland experienced a civil war in 1918 that was fought between working-class socialists (commonly called "the Reds") and the ruling conservatives (commonly called "the Whites"). The Russia-leaning Reds lost the battle against the ruling Finnish government, which was better trained and equipped.

Finland fought two wars against the Soviet Union during World War II (1939–1944). These wars united the nation and reduced the social and political divides caused by the Finnish civil war three decades earlier. In 1944, Finland lost its war against the Soviet Union, but the country was able to maintain its independence. After the war, the future of the country was uncertain and social infrastructure was in many ways underdeveloped. The foundations of the Finnish welfare state aimed at social equality were built during the decades following World War II.

Welfare State System Reforms in Finland

The principle of universalism has played an important role in shaping social policies of the Nordic countries. The history of the Nordic welfare state can be divided in two phases. The first phase was accepting the notion of universal social rights and the second phase, starting from the 1960s, was the gradual formation of the institutional base of the welfare state and the introduction of new benefits and services (Kildal & Stein, 2005; Kuusi, 1964).

Postwar social security reforms were seen as a means of supporting Finland's national unity and promoting the sense of shared responsibility among citizens (Niemelä & Salminen, 2006). The improvement of living conditions occurred in tandem with the introduction of many social reforms in the decades following the war. The co-operation of the Social Democrats and the Agrarian Party resulted in the significant socio-political reform of the National Pensions Act (1937), which shifted the trend from employee-based insurance toward national insurance (Kangas & Saari, 2009).

Other major socio-political reforms included the family allowance scheme (1948) and maternity grants (1949), both of which were paid directly to mothers. Another significant socio-political reform of the 1950s was the national pension reform, which increased the overall public pension expenditure 2.5 times between 1956 and 1957 (Niemelä & Salminen, 2006). In 1956, the Social Assistance Act replaced the former Poor Relief Act (1922). The new Act obligated the state to provide necessary maintenance and care for citizens by providing income even when they did not suffer from absolute poverty (Niemelä & Salminen, 2006, 12).

The Era of Health Care Reforms

In the 1940s, the most significant public health innovation was the introduction of publicly run maternity and child health clinics to monitor and promote the health of pregnant women, mothers of young babies, and schoolchildren. A law in 1944 on maternity and child health clinics obligated every municipality to run these clinics free of charge. By 1946 there were 1,500 clinics across the country and the system played a strong role in improving children's health. After the 1940s, child mortality rates began to fall rapidly, and since that time the life expectancy of Finns has increased by 20 years (Teperi & Vuorenkoski, 2006).

The modern and publicly funded hospital system in Finland was built during the 1950s (Kokko, 2000). A nationwide hospital system was a major improvement. At that time, there was an imbalance between hospital and outpatient care, where the latter suffered a shortage of medical doctors (Teperi & Vuorenkoski, 2006). This was especially the case in more rural areas, where citizens did not necessarily receive outpatient care. The next developmental step was to focus on preventive care and outpatient care. In 1963, a national sickness insurance system was introduced that made all permanent residents of Finland eligible for services in outpatient health care. The national sickness insurance compensated for financial losses in case of illness and gave more equal opportunities for different socio-economic groups to access the health care system.

Probably the single most important health care reform in Finland was the Public Health Act (1972), which shifted the health care system to emphasize disease prevention and outpatient care. The reform obliged every municipality to organize a wide range of services accessible in one location. These services included general medical practices, maternity clinics, dental care, and long-term in-patient care. Central and local governments shared the new costs for primary health care services with a state subsidies system.

Workers' trade unions and employers' organizations (labour market organizations) signed an agreement in 1971 that was a starting point for the Occupational Health Care Act (1978).

The Act mandated that employers provide occupation health care services for workers to help prevent health hazards and maintain the population's working capacity (Räsänen, 2006). Currently around 90 percent of wage earners are covered by these occupational health services, and only small-scale employers can have an exemption from providing occupational health care for their employees. Originally, occupational health services had a strong preventive orientation, but later the focus has turned more on general practitioner-level medical services and clinical laboratory testing.

Health in Finland Today

In international comparisons, Finland ranks fairly high on measurements of various health indicators. Due to improved living conditions and healthy behaviours, the life expectancy in Finland has continued to increase, and that for Finnish women is among the highest in Europe. The life expectancy in Finland has doubled during the past 100 years. Currently, the life expectancy for Finnish males is 76.7 years and for females, 83.2 years (Statistics Finland, 2011a). Finland's infant mortality rate in 2010 was 2.3 per 1,000 children, which is very low when placed in international perspective (Statistics Finland, 2011c).

Among Finnish men, cardiovascular disease mortality began to decline from the late 1970s. However, the high prevalence of cardiovascular diseases (CVD) among Finnish men partly explains their elevated CVD mortality rate, which is higher than the OECD average (Blomgren, et al., 2011; OECD, 2011a). In 2009, cardiovascular diseases caused 40 percent of all deaths, neoplasms 22 percent, and dementia 12 percent. The overall cancer mortality is lower in Finland than in many other developed Western countries. Among Finnish males aged 15–64 years, the three most common causes of deaths are alcohol-related deaths, ischemic heart disease, and accidents. The three most common causes of deaths among working-age females are breast cancer, alcohol-related deaths, and accidents. The previously high suicide rate in Finland has recently reached its lowest level since 1967, and the rate of suicides per 100,000 people was 17.78 in 2010 (for men 27.28/100,000 and for women 8.63/100,000) (Statistics Finland, 2011c).

Finnish Policy Documents and Statements on Health Inequalities

Most of the Finnish health policy programs and strategies are published in English for international readers. In addition, there are numerous brief reviews available on the developments of the Finnish health policy (Canada Senate, Subcommittee on Population Health, 2008; Kokko, 2000; Palosuo et al., 2008; WHO, 2002)

The modern foundations of Finnish health policy were laid in a report prepared by the Economic Council (1972). The report defined the equal distribution of health as the general objective of health policy and highlighted how broader social and economic policies have a significant impact on the population health (Palosuo, Koskinen & Sihto, 2008).

Over the past decades, Finnish public policy has been built on governmental programs carried out by governments in power. The single most significant Finnish policy paper is the *Government Programme*, which sets the priorities for the government's four-year term. There are also numerous sectoral programs and strategies that focus on more specific policy goals. In general, many programs recognize the health inequalities among socio-economic groups, but often have a limited set of concrete proposals and actions that would reduce these inequalities. The following section outlines a set of significant Finnish policy programs and their key objectives over the course of the past decades.

Health for All Program (1986/1993)

The Finnish Health for All (HFA) program (Ministry of Social Affairs and Health, 1987) was modelled upon the objectives of the World Health Organization's (WHO) Health for All by the Year 2000 strategy (WHO, 1981). The Finnish HFA program was adopted in 1986 and focused on providing equal access to health care, reducing health-damaging behaviours, and paid less attention to broader socio-economic factors as health determinants. However, the HFA program set the level target to attain the best possible health. Importantly, it emphasized a distribution of health targets focused on reducing health inequalities:

> The aim is to achieve the best possible level of health for the population and the reduction and elimination of differences in health between population groups. Instead of being disease oriented or focusing on the service system, the expression Health for All emphasizes the best possible level of health and functional capacities (the level target). On the other hand the expression emphasizes the goal of social equity and the reduction of inequality; the most even distribution of health possible (the distribution target). (Ministry of Social Affairs and Health, 1987, 46)

Finland revised the HFA program in 1993. The revised version put more attention upon health differences and cross-sectoral co-operation and contained 12 action lines. It called for governmental actors to take responsibility for program implementation (Kokko, 2000; Ministry of Social Affairs and Health, 1993).

On one hand, the revised HFA 1993 program paid more attention to health inequalities, but on the other, it focused less on universal principles and uniform services for the whole population, core foundations of the Nordic welfare states. The revised HFA program outlined an approach that "concentrates heavily on the people worst-off in terms of health and health related lifestyle" (Sihto & Keskimäki, 2000, 280).

Health 2015 Public Health Program (2001)

The Health 2015 public health program set targets for Finland's health policy for 2001–2015 (Ministry of Social Affairs and Health, 2001). The program focuses less on the health service system and more on health promotion. Co-operation between different administrative sectors and actors outside of the government is highlighted as the basis of implementation. The program acknowledges that population health is extensively determined by factors outside of the health care sector.

The Health 2015 program has five objectives that address the health of different age groups and three general objectives that target the whole population (see Table 6.1). Significantly, the program also sets a quantitative target to reduce mortality differences between different vocational and education groups by a fifth by 2015. However, it seems that the target will not be reached by 2015.

Table 6.1
Main Health Policy Targets in Finland up to 2015

Targets for Different Age Groups

1. Child wellbeing and health will increase, and symptoms and diseases caused by insecurity will decrease appreciably.
2. Smoking by young people will decrease to less than 15% of those aged 16–18; health problems associated with alcohol and drug use among the young will be dealt with appropriately and will not exceed the level of the early '90s.
3. Accidental and violent death among young adult men will be cut by a third on the level during the late 1990s.
4. Working and functional capacity among people of working age and workplace conditions will improve, helping people to cope longer in working life; retirement will be about three years later than in 2000.
5. Average functional capacity among people over 75 will continue to improve as it has during the last 20 years.

Targets for Everyone

6. Finns can expect to remain healthy for an average of two years longer than in 2000.
7. Finnish satisfaction with health service availability and functioning, and subjective healthiness and experiences of environment impacts on personal health will remain at least at the present level.
8. In implementing these targets, another aim will be to reduce inequality and increase the welfare and relative status of those population groups in the weakest position. The objective will then be to reduce mortality differences between the genders, groups with different educational backgrounds, and different vocational groupings by a fifth.

Source: Ministry of Social Affairs and Health, *Government resolution on the health 2015 public health programme* (Helsinki: Ministry of Social Affairs and Health, 2001), 6.

An evaluation report published in 2008 (Muurinen, Perttilä & Ståhl, 2008) concluded that Health 2015 was well known in the social and health field, but less familiar to actors from other sectors. Experts and municipal officers who were interviewed indicated that the main obstacles for the program implementation were a lack of financial resources and untrained staff at the local municipal level. A new interim evaluation of the Health 2015 program will be published in the near future by the National Institute for Health and Welfare.

National Action Plan to Reduce Health Inequalities, 2008–2011

The *National Action Plan to Reduce Health Inequalities* (Ministry of Social Affairs and Health, 2008) was prepared by the multi-sectoral National Advisory Board for Public Health in 2008. The Ministry of Social Affairs and Health has the main responsibility for implementing and monitoring of the *Action Plan*. Numerous stakeholders from various governmental research institutes, universities, and civil society organizations were consulted during the document's preparation. The *Action Plan* describes general strategies and specific measures to reduce socio-economic-related health inequalities in Finland.

The main objectives of the plan are to reduce social inequalities in "work ability and functional capacity, self-rated health, morbidity and mortality by levelling up" (Ministry of Social Affairs and Health, 2008, 3). The program aims to ensure the good quality of public services and to increase the employment rate. The *National Action Plan* has three priority areas (Ministry of Social Affairs and Health, 2008, 4):

1. Social policy measures: improving income security and education, and decreasing unemployment and poor housing.
2. Strengthening the prerequisites for healthy lifestyles: measures to promote healthy behaviour of the whole population with special attention to disadvantaged groups where unhealthy behaviour is common.
3. Improving the availability and good quality of social and health care services for everyone.

The *Action Plan* highlights the importance of further developing a reliable knowledge base on health inequalities in Finland. The plan identifies a need for improved monitoring of health inequalities and increased knowledge transfer from researchers to decision-makers on how to reduce health inequalities. The *National Action Plan to Reduce Health Inequalities* contains a list of actions and their responsible actors, but does not include any quantitative targets to measure progress (Ministry of Social Affairs and Health, 2008).

Program for Health Promotion, 2007–2011

The main aims of the Program for Health Promotion are to improve population health and tackle health inequalities by supporting intersectoral co-operation within governmental structures (Finnish Government, 2007). Objectives are to strengthen health promotion structures, support lifestyle changes, improve working and living conditions, strengthen the basic services of social welfare and health care, and reinforce the activities of civil society organizations that provide support for health promotion. In particular, the program highlights the role of municipalities to promote health at a local level.

The policy program was steered and monitored by a ministerial group, with one full-time program director responsible for coordinating its practical implementation. The results of the program were reported in 2011 (Prime Minister's Office, 2011a). The final report of the program emphasizes the positive developments (e.g., increased life expectancy) and cross-sectoral actions that took place during the parliamentary term. In contrast, the National Audit Office's performance report (National Audit Office, 2010) suggested that the Program for Health Promotion lacked clear focus, and that the preparatory resources needed for effective implementation were rather small. Despite the shortcomings and budget constraints, the program was seen as successful in producing new co-operation between different governmental and civil society actors.

National Development Program for Social Welfare and Health Care, 2008–2011 (Kaste Program)

The Kaste Program (Ministry of Social Affairs and Health, 2009) is coordinated by the Ministry of Social Affairs and Health and institutions under the ministry's auspices. The program follows the Finnish government's long-term strategic objectives to improve the population's health and well-being. The focus is on preventive measures and improving the delivery and quality of health care and social services at the local municipal level. The general aims of the program are to: (1) increase municipal inhabitants' social inclusion and reduce levels of social exclusion; (2) increase municipal inhabitants' well-being and health and diminish inequalities in well-being and health; and (3) improve the quality, effectiveness, and availability of services for the municipal inhabitants and reduce regional inequalities (Ministry of Social Affairs and Health, 2009).

The National Advisory Committee on Social Welfare and Health has the main responsibility for monitoring the program's implementation. The monitoring work is divided among consolidation, regional, and civic subcommittees, which have specific responsibilities for supporting local municipalities (consolidation committee), transmitting program proposals from a regional to a municipal level (regional committee), and collecting the views of service clients and individual citizens (civic committee) to support the program implementation.

The Kaste Program, which is funded from the annual state budget, supported development projects in municipal health care and social services with a total amount of €80 million between 2008 and 2011. The program will continue after 2011 and focus particularly on two main actions: (1) reducing inequalities in health and welfare; and (2) restructuring social and health services to increase their efficacy and accessibility.

Finnish Government Programme, 2011–2015

The Finnish *Government Programme* is an action plan that the ruling political parties follow for their parliamentary term. The *Programme* defines the main strategic objectives and sets the priorities for the work of ministers and government bodies. In the past years, the *Government Programme* has been one of the most important government documents. Therefore, many political lobbyists and interest groups have carried out efforts to have their priorities mentioned in the paper.

The current Prime Minister Jyrki Katainen's government (2011) has three priority areas: (1) the reduction of poverty, inequality, and social exclusion; (2) the consolidation of public finances; and (3) the strengthening of sustainable economic growth, employment, and competitiveness (Prime Minister's Office, 2011a). The document presents rising inequality as a threat to Finnish society and highlights the importance of strengthening the basic structures that support citizens' health and welfare. In particular, the *Programme* emphasizes cross-sectoral actions and co-operation to tackle poverty and inequality:

> The promotion of wellbeing and health as well as the reduction of inequality will be taken into account in all societal decision-making, and incorporated into the activities of all administrative sectors and ministries. Poverty and social exclusion cause human suffering, health disparities, and inequality, among other things. (Prime Minister's Office, 2011a, 95, http://www.vn.fi/hallitus/hallitusohjelma/en.jsp)

The Prime Minister's Office and other ministries have a responsibility to monitor and promote the *Programme*. The government holds annual policy review sessions to evaluate whether changes in the economic situation create a need to review the objectives of the *Government Programme*.

Finnish Government Programme, 2007–2011

The *Government Programme* of Prime Minister Matti Vanhanen's second Cabinet (Prime Minister's Office, 2007) emphasized a strong economy and a high employment rate to further health and social welfare. From a welfare perspective, the *Programme* focuses on the sustainable financing of municipal services and reducing the regional differences in access to these services:

> The goal of social and health policy is to promote health, functional capacity and initiative, and diminish the differences in the state of health between the individual segments of population. Additionally, steps must be taken to ensure an adequate level of income security and maintain the work ability of the people and to guarantee the availability of well-functioning primary services to all citizens irrespective of place of residence and wealth. (Prime Minister's Office, 2007, 45–46)

The Vanhanen government set three sub-programs for the parliamentary term 2007–2011 (Prime Minister's Officer, 2011b): (1) the Policy Programme for Health Promotion; (2) the Policy Programme for Employment, Entrepreneurship, and Worklife; and (3) the Policy Programme for the Wellbeing of Children, Youth, and Families. In addition, the government initiated a SATA Committee to restructure and develop the social protection system. Due to conflicting political interests, the committee was not able to produce a comprehensive social security reform that was anticipated, but it succeeded in increasing minimum pensions and proposed approximately 50 smaller reforms to enhance the Finnish social security system.

Socially Sustainable Finland, 2020

The most recent strategy of the Finnish Ministry of Social Affairs and Health states that Finland needs to have a strong foundation for welfare and health in 2020 (Ministry of Social Affairs and Health, 2011). The purpose of the strategy "is to achieve a socially sustainable society in which people are treated equally, everyone has the opportunity to participate, and everyone's health and functional capacity is supported" (Ministry of Social Affairs and Health, 2011, 3).

The strategy aims at a socially sustainable Finland by reducing differentials in health; providing adequate social protection; attaining longer working careers through well-being at work; and achieving a balanced economy and social development, among others (see Box 6.2). The implementation of the strategy requires co-operation of all administrative sectors and knowledge-based decision-making that draws on research and innovations for promoting health and welfare.

Research on Health Inequalities in Finland

For the past three decades, Finnish health policy documents have highlighted the importance of reducing health inequalities as a goal of public policy (see above). Various indicators show that the overall health of the Finnish population has improved from 1980 to 2005, but health

---

Box 6.2
Strategic Choices for Socially Sustainable Finland in 2020

1. A strong foundation for welfare
    *   Health and welfare in all policies
    *   Longer working careers through wellbeing at work
    *   Balancing the various areas of life
    *   Sustainable social protection financing

2. Access to welfare for all
    *   Reduce differentials in welfare and health
    *   Customer-oriented services
    *   New service structures and operating practices
    *   Strong sense of social inclusion

3. A healthy and safe living environment
    *   Strengthen the viability of the environment
    *   Ensure that society can continue to function under exceptional circumstances

Source: Ministry of Social Affairs and Health, *Socially sustainable Finland 2020: Strategy for social and health policy* (Helsinki: Ministry of Social Affairs and Health, 2011), 4.

---

inequalities between socio-economic groups have remained stable and may even have widened (Palosuo et al., 2009). International comparative studies have shown that the level of *relative* mortality differences between socio-economic groups, especially among men, are greater in Finland than in many other western European countries (Mackenbach et al., 2008).

Most of the current Finnish research on public health, health inequalities, and well-being is carried out in governmental research institutions such as the National Institute for Health and Welfare, Statistics Finland, Social Insurance Institution, and the Finnish Institute of Occupational Health. In addition, several universities have programs of research in public health and health sociology. For instance, researchers at the Population Research Unit at the University of Helsinki have produced a large number of studies on socio-economic-related mortality differences in Finland. Civil society activity includes a variety of non-governmental organizations producing research reports and surveys on health and welfare in Finland.

Finnish researchers can access individual-level information from different registers and link the data together to carry out population research (Palosuo et al., 2008). However, Finland does not have a continuing structure for carrying out research on health inequalities, and most of the existing studies have been prepared in the context of short-term projects. An extensive Finnish research bibliography (Forssas et al., 1999) on health inequalities identified 351 studies on health inequalities published between 1966 and 1998. Over 70 percent of these studies were carried out in the 1990s. During the 2000s, the number of publications on health inequalities in Finland has most likely further increased.

Agencies and Organizations Carrying out Research on Health Inequalities

The largest institute that carries out research on health inequalities in Finland is the National Institute for Health and Welfare (THL, www.thl.fi). THL is a research and development institute under the Finnish Ministry of Social Affairs and Health with over 1,000 employees working in seven different cities. THL promotes health and welfare in Finland and works as a statutory statistical authority. The institute was established in 2009 by the merger of the National Research and Development Centre for Welfare and Health (STAKES) and the National Public Health Institute (KTL). THL and its predecessors have produced numerous studies and reports on health inequalities.

The WHO Collaborating Centre on Social Determinants of Health was established at THL in 2011. Ongoing work at the centre includes activities such as evaluating the Finnish Action Plan to reduce health inequalities, operationalization of the WHO's policy recommendations, analyzing policy programs from a social determinants of health perspective, and developing equity focus in public health programs (THL, 2011c). However, the centre does not have resources of its own and its purpose is to collect THL's existing research activities under one umbrella.

A joint project (TEROKA) was started in 2004 to increase knowledge and develop tools to reduce health inequalities in Finland (see Box 6.3). The Ministry of Social Affairs and Health commissioned research institutes to find practical measures to reach the key targets of the national Health 2015 public health program. The TEROKA project group and its steering group consisted of experts from the ministry, research institutes, universities, and non-governmental organizations. The TEROKA group was actively involved in promoting and preparing the *National Action Plan to Reduce Health Inequalities 2008–2011* (Ministry of Social Affairs and Health, 2008) and the report *Health Inequalities in Finland: Trends in Socioeconomic Health Differences 1980–2005* (Palosuo et al., 2009).

The TEROKA project has now ended, but it has generated many new activities such as the website Kaventaja—Reducing Inequalities in Health and Wellbeing, which disseminates accurate and up-to-date information on health inequalities and on ways of reducing them. The website "supports decision-making and planning on the level of municipalities, regions and central government. Key target groups include leading officials and elected officials, together with the specialist staff of the various administrative sectors" (www.kaventaja.thl.fi).

Statistics Finland (www.stat.fi), an agency operating under the Ministry of Finance, is specifically focused on producing statistics and information services. It independently collects and reports the vast majority of official Finnish statistics. The agency has around 1,000 employees with operations in five different cities. The regular production cycle includes over 200 sets of statistics with a wide range of coverage, including statistics on population health and living conditions. Statistics Finland has a good national and international reputation for its high-quality data production and expertise.

The Social Insurance Institution (KELA, www.kela.fi) operates under the Finnish Parliament and has a statutory responsibility to look after the basic security of all residents in Finland. KELA provides public information on social benefits and services, carries out research on

Box 6.3
The TEROKA Project to Reduce Health Inequalities in Finland

TEROKA's main aims:
- Strengthen the knowledge base and follow-up on health inequalities and disseminate information
- Chart and promote co-operation needed for reducing health inequalities
- Encourage policies on tackling health inequalities as well as practical measures
- Advance the use of health impact assessment as a means for health and social policy attempting to reduce health inequalities

TEROKA's action to realize these aims:
- Compile and publish reports on trends in health inequalities
- Maintain and develop Internet services, produce educational material, and provide presentations and lectures
- In co-operation with partners, develop and assess national, regional, and local operation models aiming to reduce health inequalities
- Explore possibilities to reduce heath inequalities by means of health impact assessment
- Gather material for the basis of a strategy and action plan for reducing health inequalities
- Build practical models for regional health inequality follow-ups

Source: Retrieved from: www.teroka.fi.

social security, and collects statistical information on the use of benefits and services. KELA's mission is "to secure the income and promote the health of the entire nation, and to support the capacity of individual citizens to care for themselves" (www.kela.fi).

The Finnish Institute of Occupational Health (FIOH/TTL, www.ttl.fi) has six regional offices around the country and functions under the Ministry of Social Affairs and Health. Its mission is "to promote occupational health and safety as part of good living." The agency has three main areas of activity: (1) to create solutions for well-being at work; (2) to provide client services to serve workplaces and other clients to promote health in working life; and (3) to influence through knowledge, to share information, and to aid decision-making on work and well-being (www.ttl.fi).

Health Inequalities in Finland

The significance of health inequalities to Finnish society is illustrated by estimates of avoidable public health problems. Table 6.2 presents an assessment on which proportion of health problems could be avoided if the prevalence of problems in the lowest socio-economic group were the same as that in the highest socio-economic group (Koskinen & Martelin, 2007).

Table 6.2
Proportion (%) of Avoidable Key Public Health Problems If Their Prevalence in Population Was Similar to the Highly Educated

Health Problem	Proportion (%) of Cases Avoided
Edentulousness (toothlessness)	80
Respiratory deaths	50–75
Alcohol deaths	50–60
Need for daily help due to restrictions in functional capacity	50
Coronary heart disease deaths	30–50
Accidental/violent deaths	20–45
Diabetes	30
Back disorders	30
Osteoarthritis of knee/hip	30
Stroke deaths	20–40
Cancer deaths	20–30
Impaired vision/hearing	20

Source: S. Koskinen & T. Martelin, Nykyiset kansanterveysongelmat ja mahdollisuudet niiden torjumiseen [Current public health problems and opportunities for prevention]. In M. Pekurinen & P. Puska (Eds.), *Terveydenhuollon menojen hillintä* [Reducing health care costs] (pp. 78–92) (Helsinki: Prime Minister's Office, April 2007).

Health Inequalities as Manifested in Mortality

Health inequalities can be observed by analyzing differences in mortality between different groups of occupation, education, and income. Figure 6.1 presents the life expectancies for Finnish females and males aged 35 by occupational group in 1983–2005 (Valkonen, Ahonen, Martikainen & Remes, 2009). The figure illustrates the existence and continuity of mortality differences between occupational groups in Finland. To analyze the results, the researchers used three-year moving averages to reduce random variation that might occur in annual data.

Figure 6.1 shows that the difference in life expectancy between male upper white-collar and blue-collar workers increased by 1.1 years over the course of 20 years. The increase was from 5.0 to 6.1 years between two periods of measurement (1983–1985 and 2003–2005). A similar pattern is seen also among Finnish women whose socio-economic differences in life expectancy increased from 2.3 years in 1983–1985 to 3.3 years in 2003–2005.

Inequalities in mortality between socio-economic groups in the highest and the lowest income quintiles have increased rapidly in Finland. A recent study found that difference in mortality rates of Finnish men was as high as 12.5 years between the highest and the lowest income groups in 2007 (Tarkiainen, Martikainen, Laaksonen & Valkonen, 2011). The increase has been rapid; when measured in 1988, the difference between these groups was only 7.4 years. However, a

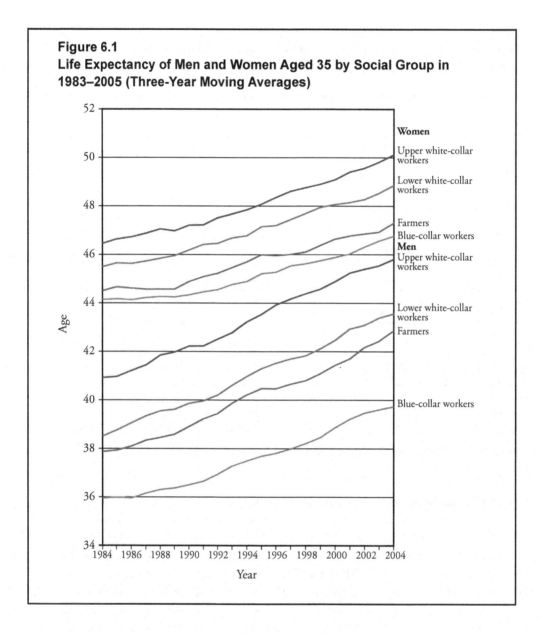

Figure 6.1
Life Expectancy of Men and Women Aged 35 by Social Group in 1983–2005 (Three-Year Moving Averages)

lack of comparable statistical data does not allow these results to be put in an international perspective. The researchers have interpreted these findings to reflect the increased life expectancy among the men in the highest income quintile as well as increased social exclusion and alcohol use among the men in the lowest income quintiles (Tarkiainen et al., 2011).

Health Inequalities as Manifested in Morbidity
Relative socio-economic health differences can be observed in many chronic illnesses, including the prevalence of coronary heart disease, type 2 diabetes, and musculoskeletal disorders (Palosuo et al., 2009). The general pattern is that the overall morbidity is higher in lower socio-economic

groups. For instance, the lowest socio-economic groups are 50 percent more likely than the highest socio-economic groups to experience long-term illnesses (Palosuo et al., 2009).

In Finland, these socio-economic differences in chronic diseases have stayed rather constant from the 1980s to the beginning of the 2000s (Koskinen et al., 2009). Mental health problems seem to be more common among people who experience financial difficulties (Laaksonen et al., 2007). However, the connection between mental health and socio-economic position is complicated and includes selection processes because mental health problems can weaken a person's earning capacity in the job market (Lahelma & Rahkonen, 2011).

Self-rated health is a commonly used indicator that is shown to correlate with mortality rates. Socio-economic differences in self-rated health among Finnish citizens aged 25–64 have stayed stable between 1979 and 2004 (Rahkonen et al., 2009). These findings show that both Finnish men and women in the lower education groups reported poorer self-rated health than in the higher education groups. A similar pattern was also present when health differences were observed by labour market status, and the unemployed consistently reported their health as lower than the employed population. The percentage of people who felt that their health is below the average was 40–50 percent in the lowest education group as compared to 20–30 percent in the highest education group (Rahkonen et al., 2009).

Health inequalities between socio-economic groups are also seen in a range of other issues such as infant mortality and stillbirth, although the number of these incidents is relatively low in Nordic countries (Rom et al., 2010). For instance, a risk for preterm birth was 14 percent higher and low birth weight was 25 percent higher among blue-collar workers when compared to upper white-collar workers in 2003–2006 (Gissler et al., 2009). Socio-economic differences in perinatal health in Finland decreased during the 1990s, but the positive development came to an end in the 2000s (Gissler et al., 2009).

Socio-economic Differences in Alcohol Use and Smoking

From a health equity perspective, alcohol-related problems are significant public health issues affecting disadvantaged populations globally (Babor et al., 2010). Alcohol mortality has increased in Finland during the past decades, especially among men in lower socio-economic groups (Blomgren et al., 2011). The most common cause of death was alcohol related among Finnish men aged 15–64 in 2009 (Statistics Finland, 2011c).

It is likely that the changes in Finnish alcohol policy have played a role in the increase in mortality rates (Herttua, Mäkelä & Martikainen, 2009). In 2004, Finnish import restrictions for alcohol from foreign countries were lessened and the national alcohol tax was decreased. These changes increased the alcohol consumption and alcohol mortality in Finland. However, the alcohol tax was raised again in 2008–2009, which resulted in a decrease in alcohol use and alcohol mortality in Finland. Currently, the total consumption of alcohol is 12.2 L per capita among Finnish citizens aged 15 and over (THL, 2010).

Socio-economic differences in Finland are also significant in terms of smoking prevalence. The number of daily smokers in Finland has sharply decreased in the higher socio-economic groups in the past decades. At the same time, the change has been less rapid in the lowest socio-economic group. In 2009, the proportion of daily smokers in the population over the age of 15 was 22 percent for men and 16 percent for women (Blomgren et al., 2011). Smoking habits are adopted in the early teens and there are significant socio-economic differences in the same age cohorts. For example, the percentage of daily smokers among vocational school students is around 40 percent and only 11 percent in a secondary school, which prepares students for higher education (THL, 2011b).

Recently the Finnish government adopted the Tobacco Act (2010), which aims "to end the use of tobacco products in Finland" (Ministry of Social Affairs and Health, 2010). The new law tightens the restrictions on tobacco marketing and prohibits smoking in most public facilities.

Public Policy and Health Inequalities in Finland

In order for public policies to promote health and welfare, the focus should be not only on at-risk groups and socially excluded people. It is important to prevent social exclusion and other risk conditions before they impact individuals. Numerous macro-level factors such as social safety nets, provision of social and health services, employment policies, taxation and income transfers, and the quality of education system all have an influence on the health of a population. These broader factors that influence daily living conditions and the health of a population are generally known as "social determinants of health" (Mikkonen & Raphael, 2010; WHO, 2008).

In Finland, people in the higher socio-economic groups have benefited the most from the improved living conditions and increased life expectancy produced by the Finnish welfare state (Palosuo et al., 2009). Relative health inequalities in the Finnish population can be partly explained through the good living conditions of the healthiest and most well-off citizens. However, less is known about how the experience of material and social deprivation influences the health of lower socio-economic groups. Public policies have a significant impact on the level of material and social resources that are available to the citizens. The following section briefly summarizes some of the recent public policy developments that might increase, maintain, or reduce health inequalities in Finland.

Income Inequality and Poverty in Finland

One of the central debates during the past few years has been the relation of income inequality to health and well-being (Wilkinson & Pickett, 2006, 2009). Finland has been a very equal country in terms of income distribution, but, as in many Western developed nations, income inequality has risen in Finland. Finnish society began to experience deepening socio-economic differences and income inequality after the recession of the 1990s. During the past few decades, the disposable income of Finnish wage earners has increased, but, at the same time, the level of many minimum social benefits has stagnated (Moisio et al., 2011).

Between 1995 and 2000, Finland experienced the fastest-growing income inequalities among the OECD countries (OECD, 2008). Meanwhile, the incomes of the top income earners more than doubled between 1992 and 2000 (Riihelä, 2009). From 1995 to 2000, the Gini coefficient, which measures income inequality, increased in Finland from 21.7 to 26.7 (Statistics Finland, 2009).[3] During the next decade, the income inequalities among the Finnish population continued to grow, and the Gini coefficient of disposable income was 28.0 in 2007. However, the global financial crisis lowered incomes in the highest income group and the Gini coefficient in Finland fell to 25.9 in 2009 (Statistics Finland, 2011d).

Regardless of these recent changes, income inequality in Finland is still below the average OECD Gini coefficient of .31 in the mid-2000s (OECD, 2008, 51). The growth of Finnish income inequality is caused largely by the fact that minimum social and unemployment benefits in Finland have not been raised since the mid-1990s, and benefits have fallen behind the general wage trend (Moisio, 2006; Moisio et al., 2011). Table 6.3 shows average household disposable income by four specific income deciles between 1995 and 2010. The highest-earning decile has experienced a 66 percent increase in income from €54,751 to €91,115, whereas the lowest-earning decile's increase has been only 12 percent from €9,759 to €10,943 (Statistics Finland, 2011b).

Along with income inequality, the level of relative poverty has risen rapidly in Finland. According to Statistics Finland (2009), in 1996 only 8.5 percent of the Finnish population lived below the at-risk-of-poverty line, which is set at 60 percent of median equivalized income (Eurostat,

Table 6.3
Finnish Household-Dwelling Units' Average Disposable Income in Euros by Income Decile, 1995–2010

Year	1st Income Decile (lowest income)	4th Income Decile	7th Income Decile	10th Income Decile (highest income)
1995	9759	22 007	30 363	54 751
1996	9780	21 937	30 765	55 175
1997	9769	22 481	31 968	60 717
1998	9764	22 667	32 526	64 988
1999	9815	22 991	33 121	72 669
2000	9706	23 132	33 544	78 123
2001	9897	23 600	34 215	73 213
2002	10 072	24 056	34 851	74 312
2003	10 142	24 462	35 653	77 082
2004	10 267	25 301	37 069	83 709
2005	10 310	25 626	37 629	83 962
2006	10 371	26 116	38 539	87 514
2007	10 494	26 921	39 722	94 087
2008	10 663	27 118	40 022	89 564
2009	10 798	27 691	40 480	86 815
2010	10 943	27 822	41 011	91 115

Source: Statistics Finland (2011b), Income distribution statistics, PX-Web databases, retrieved from: http://tilastokeskus.fi/tup/tilastotietokannat/index_en.html.

2009). The percentage of people living at risk of poverty reached 13.3 percent (696,120 citizens) in 2008. The percentage of children aged 0–17 living under the at-risk-of-poverty threshold increased from 6 percent to 13 percent during the period 1996–2008. Finland had 144,782 children living in families under the poverty cut-off line in 2008 (Statistics Finland, 2010).[4]

Labour Policy

The Collective Agreements Act (1946) defines collective bargaining in Finland. The types of collective agreements vary and they can be central, industry-wide, and local agreements, among others. Around 75 percent of Finnish wage earners belong to a trade union (Ministry of Labour, 2006). Unions have had a role in safeguarding workers' rights and benefits, such as wage development, employment security, and the quality of working life. Finland has had a long history of Comprehensive Income Policy Agreements from 1969 to 2007. These agreements were negotiated between trade unions,[5] employers' unions, and the Finnish government (MOL, 2006). These agreements have provided predictability to the Finnish economy and made strikes and other disputes less likely.

However, in 2008, the Confederation of Finnish Industries (EK), an employers' association representing businesses (around 70 percent of the Finnish GDP), announced its unwillingness to make any new national income policy agreements. Comprehensive agreements were argued to be inflexible and unsuitable to new global economy. However, in 2011, trade unions and employers' organizations re-entered into a comprehensive agreement by negotiating the broad-based "framework contract," which included over 90 percent of the members of the Confederation of Finnish Industries and 100 percent of public sectors (HS, 2011; Jokivuori, 2011). The agreement will offer a lump payment of €150 and a 4.3 percent pay increase by the end of the 25-month agreement period. In addition, the Finnish government will support the agreement with tax reliefs worth €400. The future challenges in terms of collective bargaining are related to the potential decrease in union density and to the willingness of unions, employers' organizations, and the government to continue mutual collective agreements in the age of a global economy.

Social Assistance and Unemployment Policy

Studies have indicated that unemployment is strongly associated with health problems and risk of premature death. The recent financial crisis has not increased the unemployment rate in Finland to the extent seen in many southern European countries. In 2011, the seasonally adjusted unemployment rate was 7.3 percent and the labour force participation rate was 69.2 percent among people aged 15–64 years (Statistics Finland, 2011e). However, unemployment is much more common in lower socio-economic groups, though this ratio has remained stable in recent years (Koskinen, 2011). In 2010, the number of people covered by active labour market measures was 118,000, which constituted 4.4 percent of the total labour force (Statistics Finland, 2011e).

Unemployed citizens are eligible for the basic unemployment allowance for a maximum of 500 days if they have been previously employed. If they have not been employed or if they exceed the 500-day limit, they are eligible for the labour market subsidy. This is a means-tested benefit, but it can be paid for an indefinite period. For one adult, the labour market subsidy was on average €553 per month in 2010 (www.kela.fi). In addition, unemployed citizens may be eligible for the general housing allowance for rental costs.

The most important last resort for social security in Finland is social assistance, which is applied through municipal social service centres. Social assistance was a rather marginal benefit until the late 1980s. However, in the past decades the number of recipients has increased. Social assistance is paid to a person who cannot attain an adequate minimum income for living expenses by other means. In 2010, 7 percent of Finnish citizens received social assistance at least once (THL, 2011a). As a recent development, the Finnish government decided to increase the minimum levels of social assistance and unemployment benefits starting in 2012.

In Finland, social expenditure as a share of the GDP was 30.6 percent in 2009, which was 4.3 percent higher than in 2008 (Statistics Finland, 2011c). A large part of social spending in Finland is on old age, health, and disability. In contrast, the average public social expenditure as a share of GDP in OECD countries has been around 20 percent during the past decade (OECD, 2011b).

Health Care System

Finland's health expenditure is 9.2 percent of GDP, which is a bit below the OECD average of 9.6 percent (OECD, 2011a). Finnish municipalities are responsible for organizing health services, but they can decide whether they obtain services from public or private providers. Publicly funded providers produce around 80 percent of health services, private enterprises 17 percent, and non-governmental organizations 3 percent (Kangas & Saari, 2009). According to OECD statistics (OECD, 2011a), public funding covers 75 percent of Finland's health expenditure, which is above the OECD average (72 percent), but less than those of the other Nordic countries (81–84 percent).

Although municipalities are the major funders of Finnish health care provision, Finland also has a mandatory National Health Insurance with universal coverage. Three separate health care systems receive public funding: municipal health care, occupational health care, and private health care. These systems differ significantly in the scope of services provided, in user fees, and in waiting times (Vuorenkoski, Mladovsky & Mossialos, 2008). Currently, Finland has a system of dual public financing for health care. Funding takes place through municipalities, which fund health centres, and through the National Health Insurance, which funds some parts of private health care, occupational health care, outpatient drugs, sickness allowance, and maternity leave allowance (Vuorenkoski et al., 2008).[6] A reform in 1993 placed a responsibility for health care provision more firmly on municipalities and the state control was weakened in terms of reduced requirements for advance and centralized planning (Teperi & Vuorenkoski, 2006).

One challenge in the Finnish health care system is geographical inequities because there are significant differences in the quality and scope of municipal health services. In addition, Finland has relatively large socio-economic differences in the use of health services (Manderbacka et al., 2009). From an equity perspective, another major challenge is municipal health care provided in local health centres, which have increasingly suffered a lack of medical doctors. Municipal health services are used mostly by citizens who are outside the labour market. They are not eligible for occupational health care and often cannot afford private health services. In municipal health care, waiting times are longer than in occupational health care, and the centres are allowed to collect out-of-pocket payments from patients.[7] On average, these patient payments cover around 7 percent of municipal health care expenditure (Teperi, Porter, Vuorenkoski & Baron, 2009, 40).

In contrast to municipal services, the occupational health care in Finland does not have user fees and waiting times are shorter. The situation is problematic because studies have shown that those outside the labour market have more health problems than those who are employed, who are eligible for occupational health care. In addition, the wealthiest citizens can access private health care and still be reimbursed for the fees through the National Health Insurance. In recent years, the structural problems of the Finnish health care systems have received increasing attention, and there have been calls for a comprehensive health care reform (Pekurinen et al., 2010). For example, state subsidy to private health care providers has been under constant debate, but no decisions have been made on radically new reforms that would change the situation. In spite of equity challenges, it can be concluded that the Finnish health care system is still able to provide high-quality services at reasonably low cost (Vuorenkoski et al., 2008).

Child Care and the Education System

In Finland, early childhood education and care (ECEC) is a universal social right, and all children under school age are legally guaranteed a place in municipal daycare. Although municipal daycare is heavily subsided by the state, it is not completely free of charge. For instance, the maximum monthly fee for a full-time daycare was €254 (2010) in the city of Helsinki (www.hel.fi). The fees are earnings-related and adjusted yearly by a local municipality. In addition to municipal services, parents are eligible for governmental and municipal allowances for paying the fees for private daycare or child home care that they have sought themselves (Heinämäki, 2008).

Finland has a nine-year comprehensive school system from the age of seven. However, over 90 percent of children go to a preparatory preschool at the age of six. One noteworthy detail is that during a school day, all the pupils get a free hot meal, which is aimed at providing a base for a healthy and balanced diet. After nine years of basic education, students can choose to continue their education for three years in a vocational school or in a theoretically oriented high school that prepares them for polytechnic or science universities. The basic education and all its materials are free of charge. There are essentially no private schools in the country (Sahlberg, 2011).

Higher education in universities is also free of tuition charges for Finnish citizens and foreign students from the European Economic Area. Financial subsidies are available to students in higher education (i.e., a study allowance and a housing allowance). The amount of monthly subsidies for students varies around €200–€500 per month. In addition, students are eligible for a state-guaranteed study loan, but the majority of students do not use this option (www.kela.fi).

Finnish children have been the top performers in the OECD's international student assessments (PISA). The PISA assessment measures science, math, and reading skills among 15-year-olds in different countries (OECD, 2011c, 117–158). Most Finnish students receive good educational outcomes regardless of their socio-economic background or geographic location. In recent years, the success of the Finnish education system has received increasing international attention (OECD, 2011c; Sahlberg, 2011). From a comparative perspective, Finland has been able to provide relatively equal opportunities for all students to gain knowledge and skills for further development and employment.

Civil Society and NGOs

Finland has a wide array of non-governmental organizations that work in advocacy, health promotion, public education, and as non-profit service providers. These organizations have a significant role in efforts to promote health and social welfare. The stated-owned Finnish Slot Machine Association (RAY) supports approximately 800 Finnish non-governmental organizations by funding them with a share of €291 million in 2012 (www.ray.fi). Moreover, RAY offers support and tools for the management and treatment of gambling problems and, due to the state monopoly, private gambling companies are not permitted to operate in Finland. The strategic aims of the RAY are to: (1) strengthen health and social welfare in Finland; (2) prevent social and health problems; and (3) support citizens in need (www.ray.fi).

Altogether there are around 8,000 social and health organizations in Finland. In addition to advocacy and knowledge translation, these NGOs organize volunteer activities, peer support, various training programs, and service provision. Around 20 percent of municipal social services and 5 percent of health services are provided by Finnish non-governmental organizations (STKL, 2009). Two notable Finnish social and health NGOs were founded at the beginning of 2012 after a merger of smaller non-profit organizations. The Finnish Society for Social and Health (SOSTE), with over 200 member organizations, focuses on social and health policy, and the Finnish Association for Substance Abuse Prevention (EHYT), with approximately 100 member organizations, focuses on substance abuse prevention. Finnish NGOs can have a substantial and fairly independent role in raising themes such as health equity and social determinants of health into the public agenda.

Conclusion

The institutional base of the Finnish welfare state was built gradually after World War II. This process was supported by a strong political commitment to values such as equality and social justice. Finland has been a success story of how an agrarian society was transformed in the course of half a century into a well-developed welfare state with an educated population and high-tech industries. The health of the Finnish population has improved due to improvements in living conditions, education, social safety nets, health care, and individual lifestyles, among others. Public policies promoting shared responsibility and equal opportunities for all citizens, regardless of their economic or social standing, have played a crucial role in Finnish policy-making.

Future challenges of the Finnish welfare state are similar to those of other European nations, including an aging population, economic instability, increased inequality, globalization, and migration. In Finland, the overall health of the population has improved, but health inequalities between socio-economic groups have remained substantially the same despite the equity goals of the Finnish health policy during the past 30 years. This may indicate a lack of efficiency in policy implementation, as well as political decisions that have not been in line with the goals stated in Finnish policy programs. In other words, the aim to reduce health inequalities may have been less a priority than other policy objectives such as market liberalization, economic growth, and short-term financial savings in the government's budget.

Reducing health inequalities requires a strong commitment and political will. In Finland, more focus should be put on the implementation and monitoring of Finnish policy measures and programs that aim to tackle health inequalities. There is a need for a permanent structure with adequate resources to carry out the monitoring of health inequalities in Finland. One important task would be to improve the health impact assessments of different policy initiatives. In particular there is a need to look at the impacts of these policies on the lowest socio-economic groups and a readiness to formulate alternative policy recommendation if required.

In addition to broader public policies promoting health equity, the Finnish challenge is to maintain the quality of social and health services and ensure good access to these services at a municipal level. A high-quality early childhood education, as well as access to educational and employment opportunities, are needed to prevent social exclusion of young people in their later life. The number of old age pensioners is increasing rapidly, and ensuring adequate support and care for an aging population requires a healthy working-age population.

In half a century, Finland was able to rise from a war-ravaged country to one of the most developed welfare states in the world. Now the country is much more prepared to deal with new challenges, and therefore sustaining the Finnish welfare state is chiefly a matter of commitment and determination.

Notes

1. I would like to thank Hannele Palosuo, Marita Sihto, Lauri Vuorenkoski, and Anna-Maria Isola for discussions and providing useful comments on an earlier draft of this chapter.
2. In 2011, the political parties that constitute the Finnish ruling coalition in Parliament are the National Coalition Party (44 seats), the Social Democratic Party (42 seats), the Left Alliance (14 seats), the Green League (10 seats), the Swedish People's Party (10 seats), and the Christian Democrats (six seats). The current opposition parties are the Centre Party (35 seats) and the True Finns (39 seats).
3. The Gini coefficient measures the level of inequality of a distribution. A value of 0 expresses total equality and a value of 1 maximal inequality (values are often multiplied by 100). The Gini coefficient is commonly used as a measure of inequality in income or wealth (see OECD, 2008).
4. Using a poverty line at 50 percent of median, at-risk-of-poverty rates in Finland were 6.7 percent for the total population (352,438 people) and 6.8 percent for children aged 0–17 (74,054 people) in 2008.
5. The most important confederations in Finland are the Central Organisation of Finnish Trade Unions (SAK) (20 affiliated trade unions), the Finnish Confederation of Salaried Employees (STTK) (20 affiliated trade unions), and the Confederation of Unions for Professional and Managerial Staff in Finland (AKAVA) (34 affiliated trade unions).
6. The Social Insurance Institution of Finland reimburses the costs of prescription drugs at three different rates (42 percent, 72 percent, and 100 percent of the price). Full reimbursement is given if out-of-pocket expenses in a calendar year exceed €672.7 (www.kela.fi, February 24, 2011).
7. For instance, the city of Helsinki had the health centre fee of €13.7, the outpatient clinic fee of €27.40, and the hospital day fee of €32.50 in 2011. The maximum payment limit for one person was €633 during the calendar year. If the limit was exceeded, then a resident could apply for an exemption of payment (www.hel.fi, February 24, 2011).

Critical Thinking Questions

1. What are the key social factors that contributed to the development of the Finnish welfare state?
2. What have been the distinctive aspects of the Finnish health policy during the past decades?
3. What kind of political and economic barriers might there be for successful implementation of Finnish health policy programs that promote health equity?
4. How would you explain the factors that contribute to health inequalities among social groups in Finnish society?

Recommended Readings

Ministry of Social Affairs and Health. (2008). *National action plan to reduce health inequalities 2008–2011*. Helsinki: Ministry of Social Affairs and Health. Retrieved from: http://tinyurl.com/c7wxx2r.
  The *Action Plan* outlines strategies and measures to reduce health inequalities in Finland. The publication portrays how the Finnish government can implement and monitor these actions at local and national levels.

Niemelä, H., & Salminen, K. (2006). *Social security in Finland*. Helsinki: Social Insurance Institution (KELA), Finnish Centre for Pensions (ETK), Finnish Pension Alliance (TELA), and Finnish Ministry of Social Affairs and Health. Retrieved from: http://tinyurl.com/cjn7775.
  The report gives a comprehensive overview of the Finnish social security system and its historical origins.

Palosuo, H., Koskinen, S., Lahelma, E., Kostiainen, E., Prättälä, R., Martelin, T., et al. (Eds.). (2009). *Health inequalities in Finland: Trends in socioeconomic health differences 1980–2005*. Helsinki: Ministry of Social Affairs and Health Publications. Retrieved from: http://tinyurl.com/d3324nx.
  The report summarizes the research on socio-economic inequalities in health in Finland during the past 25 years. It covers changes in mortality, self-rated health morbidity, functional capacity, mental health, and healthy life expectancy, among others. In addition, the report provides information for health policy planning and monitoring.

Ståhl, T., Wismar, M., Ollila, E., Lahtinen, E., & Leppo, K. (Eds.). (2006). *Health in all policies: Prospects and potentials*. Helsinki: Ministry of Social Affairs and Health. Retrieved from: http://ec.europa.eu/health/archive/ph_information/documents/health_in_all_policies.pdf.
  The book describes the main tenets of the Health in All Policies (HiAP) approach, which aims to integrate health considerations into other areas of policy-making. The HiAP approach was prepared in the context of the Finnish presidency, to be disseminated to other countries within the European Union.

Recommended Websites

Ministry of Social Affairs and Health (MSAH): www.stm.fi
  Finland's Ministry of Social Affairs and Health is responsible for the planning, guidance, and implementation of social and health policy in Finland. Many of the ministry's reports and strategies are translated in English and are available online.

National Institute for Health and Welfare (THL): www.thl.fi
  The National Institute for Health and Welfare (THL) is a research and development institute under the Finnish Ministry of Social Affairs and Health. Currently, THL is the foremost Finnish institution conducting research on health inequalities and social determinants of health.

Social Insurance Institution of Finland (KELA): www.kela.fi

The institution is responsible for providing basic security to residents of Finland. It also conducts research to develop the Finnish social security system and provides public information on its benefits and services.

Statistics Finland: www.stat.fi

Statistics Finland is the main public authority for statistical data in Finland. It offers many up-to-date statistics and publishes *Finland in Figures*, which contains the key statistical data about Finland.

References

Babor, T., Caetano, R., Casswell, S., Edwards, G., Geisbrecht, N., Graham, K., et al. (2010). *Alcohol: No ordinary commodity. Research and public policy* (2nd ed.). Oxford: Oxford University Press.

Blomgren, J., Mikkola, H., Hiilamo, H., & Järvisalo, J. (2011). *Suomalaisten terveydentila ja terveyteen liittyvät etuudet: Indikaattoriseuranta 1995–2010.* Helsinki: Social Insurance Institution (Kela).

Canada Senate, Subcommittee on Population Health. (2008). *Population health policy: International perspectives.* Ottawa: Standing Senate Committee on Social Affairs, Science, and Technology.

Economic Council (1972). Attachment 1. Section that investigates public policy objectives and their measurement. *Report of the Work Group Investigating Health Policy Objectives.* Helsinki: Economic Council.

Esping-Andersen, G. (1990). *The three worlds of welfare capitalism.* Princeton: Princeton University Press.

Eurostat. (2009). *Europe in figures: Eurostat yearbook 2009.* Luxembourg: Office for Official Publications of the European Communities.

Finnish Centre for Pensions. (2011). *Pocket statistics.* Helsinki: Finnish Centre for Pensions.

Finnish Government. (2007). *Policy programme for health promotion 2007–2011.* Helsinki: Prime Minister's Office, Finnish Government.

Finnish Tax Administration. (2011). *Luettelo kuntien ja seurakuntien tuloveroprosenteista vuonna 2011* [A list of taxes to municipal and parishes in 2011]. Retrieved from: http://www.vero.fi/.

Forssas, E., Keskimäki, I., Koskinen, S., Lahelma, E., Manderbacka, K., Prättälä, R., et al. (1999). *Explaining and reducing socioeconomic health differences—a bibliography of Finnish research publications.* Helsinki: National Research and Development Centre for Welfare and Health (STAKES).

Gissler, M., Rahkonen, O., Arntzen, A., Cnattingius, S., Andersen, A.-M.N., & Hemminki, E. (2009). Trends in socioeconomic differences in Finnish perinatal health 1991–2006. *Journal of Epidemiology and Community Health, 63*(6), 420–425.

Government of Finland. (1999). *The right to social security: Section 19 of the Constitution of Finland.* Helsinki: Government of Finland.

Heinämäki, L. (2008). *Early childhood education in Finland.* Postdam: Liberal Institute & National Research and Development Centre for Welfare and Health (STAKES).

Herttua, K., Mäkelä, P., & Martikainen, P. (2009). An evaluation of the impact of a large reduction in alcohol prices on alcohol-related and all-cause mortality: Time series analysis of a population-based natural experiment. *International Journal of Epidemiology, 40*(2), 441–454.

HS. (2011, November 29). Labour market: Framework contract to be implemented. *Helsingin Sanomat (HS)* [Daily newspaper].

Jokivuori, P. (2011). Social partners agree to national pay settlement. *European Industrial Relations Observatory On-line.* Retrieved from: http://www.eurofound.europa.eu/eiro/2011/10/articles/fi1110011i.htm.

Kangas, O., & Saari, J. (2009). The welfare system of Finland. In K. Schubert, S. Hegelich & U. Bazant (Eds.), *The handbook of European welfare systems* (pp. 189–206). London: Routledge.

Kildal, N., & Stein, K. (2005). The principle of universalism: Tracing a key idea in the Scandinavian welfare model. In N. Kildal & K. Stein (Eds.), *Normative foundations of the welfare state: The Nordic experience* (pp. 13–33). London: Routledge.

Kokko, S. (2000). The process of developing health for all policy in Finland 1981–1995. In A. Ritsatakis, R. Barnes, E. Dekker, P. Harrington, S. Kokko & P. Makara (Eds.), *Exploring health policy development in Europe* (pp. 27–40). Copenhagen: World Health Organization Regional Office for Europe.

Koskinen, S. (2011, November 7). *Why are health inequalities increasing in Finland?* Presented at the Inequality and the Nordic Welfare Model seminar, National Institute for Welfare and Health (THL), Helsinki.

Koskinen, S., Aromaa, A., Huttunen, J., & Teperi, J. (Eds.). (2006). *Health in Finland.* Vammalan kirjapaino Oy: National Public Health Institute KTL, National Research and Development Centre for Welfare and Health STAKES, Ministry of Social Affairs and Health.

Koskinen, S., & Martelin, T. (2007). Nykyiset kansanterveysongelmat ja mahdollisuudet niiden torjumiseen [Current public health problems and opportunities for prevention]. In M. Pekurinen & P. Puska (Eds.), *Terveydenhuollon menojen hillintä* [Reducing health care costs] (pp. 78–92). Helsinki: Prime Minister's Office.

Koskinen, S., Martelin, T., Sainio, P., Heliövaara, M., Reunanen, A., & Lahelma, E. (2009). Chronic morbidity. In H. Palosuo, S. Koskinen, E. Lahelma, E. Kostiainen, R. Prättälä, T. Martelin, A. Ostamo, I. Keskimäki, M. Sihto, E. Linnanmäki & K. Talala (Eds.), *Health inequalities in Finland: Trends in socioeconomic health differences 1980–2005* (pp. 70–82). Helsinki: Ministry of Social Affairs and Health Publications.

Kuusi, P. (1964). *Social policy for the sixties: A plan for Finland.* Kuopio: Finnish Social Policy Association.

Laaksonen, E., Martikainen, P., Lahelma, E., Lallukka, T., Rahkonen, O., Head, J., et al. (2007). Socioeconomic circumstances and common mental disorders among Finnish and British public sector employees: Evidence from the Helsinki Health Study and the Whitehall II Study. *International Journal of Epidemiology, 36*(4), 776–786.

Lahelma, E., & Rahkonen, O. (2011). Sosioekonominen asema [Socio-economic position]. In M. Laaksonen & K. Silventoinen (Eds.), *Sosiaaliepidemiologia: Väestön terveyserot ja terveyteen vaikuttavat sosiaaliset tekijät* [Social epidemiology: Health inequalities and social determinants of health] (pp. 41–59). Helsinki: Gaudeamus Helsinki University Press.

Mackenbach, J.P., Stirbu, I., Roskam, A.-J.R., Schaap, M.M., Menvielle, G., Leinsalu, M., et al. (2008). Socioeconomic inequalities in health in 22 European countries. *New England Journal of Medicine, 358*(23), 2468–2481.

Manderbacka, K., Häkkinen, U., Nguyen, L., Pirkola, S., Ostamo, A., & Keskimäki, I. (2009). Health care services. In H. Palosuo, S. Koskinen, E. Lahelma, E. Kostiainen, R. Prättälä, T. Martelin, A. Ostamo, I. Keskimäki, M. Sihto, E. Linnanmäki & K. Talala (Eds.), *Health inequalities in Finland: Trends in socioeconomic health differences 1980–2005* (pp. 178–194). Helsinki: Ministry of Social Affairs and Health Publications.

Mikkonen, J., & Raphael, D. (2010). *Social determinants of health: The Canadian facts.* Toronto: York University School of Health Policy and Management.

Ministry of Finance. (2011). *Kuntiin kohdistuvan valtionohjauksen periaatteet—normihanketyöryhmän ehdotukset* [Principles on central government steering targeted at local government—project group proposals]. Helsinki: Ministry of Finance.

Ministry of Justice. (1999, June 11). *The constitution of Finland.* Helsinki: Ministry of Justice.

Ministry of Labour. (2006). *Industrial relations and labour legislation in Finland.* Helsinki: Ministry of Labour (MOL).

Ministry of Social Affairs and Health. (1987). *Health for all by the year 2000: The Finnish national strategy.* Helsinki: Ministry of Social Affairs and Health.

Ministry of Social Affairs and Health. (1993). *Health for all by the year 2000: Revised strategy for cooperation.* Helsinki: Ministry of Social Affairs and Health.

Ministry of Social Affairs and Health. (2001). *Government resolution on the Health 2015 Public Health Programme.* Helsinki: Ministry of Social Affairs and Health.

Ministry of Social Affairs and Health. (2008). *National action plan to reduce health inequalities 2008–2011.* Helsinki: Ministry of Social Affairs and Health.

Ministry of Social Affairs and Health. (2009). *National development programme for social welfare and health care (Kaste) 2008–2011*. Retrieved from: http://www.stm.fi/en/strategies_and_programmes/kaste.

Ministry of Social Affairs and Health. (2010). *The aim of the Tobacco Act is to put an end to smoking in Finland*. Press release 224/2010. Retrieved from: http://www.stm.fi/tiedotteet/tiedote/view/1522179.

Ministry of Social Affairs and Health. (2011). *Socially sustainable Finland 2020: Strategy for social and health policy*. Helsinki: Ministry of Social Affairs and Health.

Moisio, P. (2006). Suhteellinen köyhyys Suomessa [Relative poverty in Finland]. *Yhteiskuntapolitiikka, 71*(6), 639–645.

Moisio, P., Honkanen, P., Hänninen, T., Kuivalainen, S., Raijas, A., Sauli, H., et al. (2011). *Perusturvan riittävyyden arviointiraportti* [Evaluation report on basic security in Finland]. Helsinki: National Institute for Health and Welfare.

MOL. (2006). *Industrial relations and labour legislation in Finland*. Helsinki: Ministry of Labour (MOL).

Muurinen, S., Perttilä, K., & Ståhl, T. (2008). *Terveys 2015—kansanterveysohjelman ohjaavuuden, toimeenpanon ja sisällön arviointi 2007* [Evaluation report of the Health 2015 Programme]. Helsinki: National Research and Development Centre for Welfare and Health (STAKES).

National Audit Office. (2010). *Policy programmes as steering instruments: With the policy programme for health promotion as an example*. Retrieved from: http://www.vtv.fi/files/2362/2122010_Policy_programmes_as_steering_instruments.pdf.

Niemelä, H., & Salminen, K. (2006). *Social security in Finland*. Helsinki: Social Insurance Institution (Kela), Finnish Centre for Pensions (ETK), Finnish Pension Alliance (TELA), and Finnish Ministry of Social Affairs and Health.

OECD. (2008). *Growing unequal? Income distribution and poverty in OECD countries*. Paris: Organisation for Economic Co-operation and Development.

OECD. (2011a). *Health at a glance 2011: OECD indicators*. Paris: Organisation for Economic Co-operation and Development.

OECD. (2011b). *OECD Factbook 2011–2012. Economic, environmental, and social statistics*. Paris: Organisation for Economic Co-operation and Development.

OECD. (2011c). *Strong performers and successful reformers in education: Lessons from PISA for the United States*. Paris: Organisation for Economic Co-operation and Development.

Ollila, E., Lahtinen, E., Melkas, T., Wismar, M., Ståhl, T., & Leppo, K. (2006). Towards a healthier future. In T. Ståhl, M. Wismar, E. Ollila, E. Lahtinen & K. Leppo (Eds.), *Health in all policies: Prospects and potentials* (pp. 269–279). Helsinki: Ministry of Social Affairs and Health.

Palosuo, H., Koskinen, S., Lahelma, E., Kostiainen, E., Prättälä, R., Martelin, T., et al. (Eds.). (2009). *Health inequalities in Finland: Trends in socioeconomic health differences 1980–2005*. Helsinki: Ministry of Social Affairs and Health Publications.

Palosuo, H., Koskinen, S., & Sihto, M. (2008). Finland. In C. Hogstedt, H. Moberg, B. Lundgren & M. Backhans (Eds.), *Health for all? A critical analysis of public health policies in eight European countries* (pp.125–159). Östersund: Swedish National Institute of Public Health.

Pekurinen, M., Erhola, M., Häkkinen, U., Jonsson, P.M., Keskimäki, I., Kokko, S., et al. (2010). *Sosiaali—ja terveydenhuollon monikanavaisen rahoituksen edut, haitat ja kehittämistarpeet* [The benefits, problems, and needs for development in dual financed social and health care system]. Helsinki: National Institute for Health and Welfare (THL).

Prime Minister's Office. (2007). *Government programme of Prime Minister Matti Vanhanen's second Cabinet on 19 April 2007*. Helsinki: Prime Minister's Office, Finnish Government.

Prime Minister's Office. (2011a). *Government programme of Prime Minister Jyrki Katainen's Cabinet on 22 June 2011*. Helsinki: Prime Minister's Office, Finnish Government.

Prime Minister's Office. (2011b). *Policy programmes: Parliamentary term 2007–2011*. Helsinki: Prime Minister's Office, Finnish Government.

Puska, P., & Ståhl, T. (2010). Health in all policies. The Finnish initiative: Background, principles, and current issues. *Annual Review of Public Health, 31*(1), 315–328.

Puska, P., Vartiainen, E., Laatikainen, T., Jousilahti, P., & Paavola, M. (2009). *The North Karelia project: From North Karelia to national action.* Helsinki: National Institute for Health and Welfare (THL).

Rahkonen, O., Talala, K., Sulander, T., Laaksonen, M., Lahelma, E., Uutela, A., et al. (2009). Self-rated health. In H. Palosuo, S. Koskinen, E. Lahelma, E. Kostiainen, R. Prättälä, T. Martelin, A. Ostamo, I. Keskimäki, M. Sihto, E. Linnanmäki & K. Talala (Eds.), *Health inequalities in Finland: Trends in socioeconomic health differences 1980–2005* (pp. 61–69). Helsinki: Ministry of Social Affairs and Health Publications.

Räsänen, K. (2006). Occupational health services. In S. Koskinen, A. Aromaa, J. Huttunen & J. Teperi (Eds.), *Health in Finland* (pp. 138–139). Vammalan kirjapaino Oy: National Public Health Institute (KTL), National Research and Development Centre for Welfare and Health (STAKES), Ministry of Social Affairs and Health.

Riihelä, M. (2009). *Essays on income inequality, poverty, and the evolution of top income shares.* Publication 52. Helsinki: Government Institute for Economic Research.

Rom, A.L., Mortensen, L.H., Cnattingius, S., Arntzen, A., Gissler, M., & Nybo Andersen, A.-M. (2010). A comparative study of educational inequality in the risk of stillbirth in Denmark, Finland, Norway, and Sweden 1981–2000. *Journal of Epidemiology and Community Health.* doi: 10.1136/jech.2009.101188.

Rotko, T., Aho, T., Mustonen, N., & Linnanmäki, E. (2011). *Kapeneeko kuilu? Tilannekatsaus terveyserojen kaventamiseen Suomessa 2007–2010* [Bridging the gap? Review into actions to reduce health inequalities in Finland 2007–2010]. Helsinki: National Institute for Health and Welfare (THL).

Sahlberg, P. (2011). *Finnish lessons: What can the world learn from educational change in Finland?* New York: Teachers College.

Saint-Arnaud, S., & Bernard, P. (2003). Convergence or resilience? A hierarchical cluster analysis of the welfare regimes in advanced countries. *Current Sociology, 51*(5), 499–527.

Schwab, K. (2009). *The global competitiveness report 2009–2010.* Geneva: World Economic Forum.

Sihto, M., & Keskimäki, I. (2000). Does a policy matter? Assessing the Finnish health policy in relation to its equity goals. *Critical Public Health, 10*(2), 273–286.

Ståhl, T., Wismar, M., Ollila, E., Lahtinen, E., & Leppo, K. (Eds.). (2006). *Health in all policies: Prospects and potentials.* Helsinki: Ministry of Social Affairs and Health.

Statistics Finland. (2009). *Tulonjakotilasto 2008* [Income distribution statistics 2008]. Helsinki: Statistics Finland.

Statistics Finland. (2010). *Income distribution statistics.* PX-Web databases. Retrieved from: http://tilastokeskus.fi/tup/tilastotietokannat/index_en.html.

Statistics Finland. (2011a). *Finland in figures.* Retrieved from: http://www.stat.fi/tup/suoluk/index_en.html.

Statistics Finland. (2011b). *Income distribution statistics.* PX-Web databases. Retrieved from: http://tilastokeskus.fi/tup/tilastotietokannat/index_en.html.

Statistics Finland. (2011c). *Statistics Finland's PX-Web databases.* Retrieved from: http://tilastokeskus.fi/tup/tilastotietokannat/index_en.html.

Statistics Finland. (2011d). *Tulonjakotilasto 2009* [Income distribution statistics 2009]. Helsinki: Statistics Finland.

Statistics Finland. (2011e). *Työllisyys lisääntyi marraskuussa 2011* [Employment rate increased in November 2011]. Helsinki: Statistics Finland.

STKL. (2009). *Järjestöpokkari. Sosiaali—ja terveysjärjestöt pähkinänkuoressa* [Pocket book on social and health organizations in Finland]. Helsinki: Finnish Federation for Social Welfare and Health (STKL).

Tarkiainen, L., Martikainen, P., Laaksonen, M., & Valkonen, T. (2011). Trends in life expectancy by income from 1988 to 2007: Decomposition by age and cause of death. *Journal of Epidemiology and Community Health.* doi: 10.1136/jech.2010.123182.

Teperi, J., Porter, M.E., Vuorenkoski, L., & Baron, J.F. (2009). *The Finnish health care system: A value-based perspective.* Sitra Reports 82. Helsinki: Sitra.

Teperi, J., & Vuorenkoski, L. (2006). Health and health care in Finland since the Second World War. In S. Koskinen, A. Aromaa, J. Huttunen & J. Teperi (Eds.), *Health in Finland* (pp. 8–12). Vammalan kirjapaino Oy: National Public Health Institute (KTL), National Research and Development Centre for Welfare and Health (STAKES), Ministry of Social Affairs and Health.

THL. (2010). *Yearbook of alcohol and drug statistics 2010*. Helsinki: National Institute for Health and Welfare (THL).

THL. (2011a). *Annual statistics on social assistance 2010*. Helsinki: National Institute for Health and Welfare (THL).

THL. (2011b). *Kouluterveyskysely* [School health promotion study]. Helsinki: National Institute for Health and Welfare (THL).

THL. (2011c). *WHO collaborating centre on social determinants of health*. Helsinki: National Institute for Health and Welfare (THL).

Tukia, H., Lehtinen, N., Saaristo, V., & Vuori, M. (2011). *Väestön hyvinvoinnin ja terveyden edistäminen kunnassa—Perusraportti kuntajohdon tiedonkeruusta 2011* [Promotion of wellbeing and health of the population by local authorities—Basic report on a data collection on municipal management 2011]. Report 55/2011. Helsinki: Finnish National Institute for Health and Welfare.

Valkonen, T., Ahonen, H., Martikainen, P., & Remes, H. (2009). Socio-economic differences in mortality. In H. Palosuo, S. Koskinen, E. Lahelma, E. Kostiainen, R. Prättälä, T. Martelin, A. Ostamo, I. Keskimäki, M. Sihto, E. Linnanmäki & K. Talala (Eds.), *Health inequalities in Finland: Trends in socioeconomic health differences 1980–2005* (pp. 40–60). Helsinki: Ministry of Social Affairs and Health Publications.

Vuorenkoski, L., Mladovsky, P., & Mossialos, E. (2008). Finland: Health system review. *Health Systems in Transition, 10*(4), 1–168.

WHO. (1981). *Global strategy for health for all by the year 2000*. Geneva: World Health Organization.

WHO. (2002). *Review of national Finnish health promotion policies and recommendations for the future*. Copenhagen: World Health Organization, Regional Office for Europe.

WHO. (2008). *Closing the gap in a generation: Health equity through action on the social determinants of health*. Geneva: World Health Organization.

Wilkinson, R.G., & Pickett, K.E. (2006). Income inequality and health: A review and explanation of the evidence. *Social Science and Medicine, 62*(7), 1768–1784.

Wilkinson, R.G., & Pickett, K.E. (2009). *The spirit level: Why more equal societies almost always do better*. London: Allen Lane.

Chapter 7

Norwegian Experiences

Elisabeth Fosse

Introduction

Norway is a Scandinavian nation with a rather small population of 4.9 million. Over the last 30 years the country has become increasingly wealthy as a result of its growing oil economy. Norway is one of the so-called social democratic welfare states, as classified by Esping-Andersen (1990). The "social democratic" regime is characterized by its emphasis on solidarity and universalism, and the redistribution of resources among social groups, mainly through a progressive tax system and entitlements to vulnerable groups. This is a system of emancipation, not only from the market, but also from the family. The result is a welfare regime with direct transfers to children and one that takes direct responsibility for the care of children, providing the conditions for women with families to engage in paid work.

In this welfare state regime, women are encouraged to work and the welfare state is dependent on female participation in the labour market. Norway fits this description very well. There is also a cultural tradition of believing in equality and promoting it in the country. Over several years Norway has been ranked at the top of the UN Health Development Index. Even though the overall picture is positive, the country still has its challenges. Social inequalities in health are increasing and relative health inequalities are not smaller than in other European countries. The government has recently developed policies to reduce health inequalities, but these policies have not yet been fully implemented, and it remains to be seen how effective they will be in reducing health inequalities.

National Description and Political Organization and Structure

Norway has a population of approximately 4.9 million people. The country is quite large, more than 304,000 km², but it has a rather low population density of 15 people per square kilometre. This population density varies significantly among its counties (Statistics Norway, 2011b). After World War II, there was an increased tendency toward urbanization. Life expectancy has gradually improved. In 2009 a newly born girl could expect to reach age 83, while boys could expect to live to 78. The average fertility rate is 1.9 children, which is among the highest in Europe. A large share of the population is employed as compared to other countries. The reason for this is, first and foremost, because so many women are employed. Almost seven out of 10 Norwegian women are gainfully employed.

Norway is a highly developed welfare state with comprehensive welfare provision. It is part of what is often referred to as the Scandinavian welfare state model or, in Esping-Andersen's (1990) terms, the social democratic welfare state regime. This means that the public sector has the dominant position in the provision of social and health services. The welfare state is financed mainly by taxation, duties, and fees. The services are, in principle, universal, i.e., they are not tied to people's positions in the labour market. Everyone has the right to the same services and standard of services.

Norway is a very affluent country; in large part the reason for this is mainly the vast income based on the oil economy. In 2007, GDP per capita was €63,818 (Can$83,090), which was the highest among the Nordic countries (Statistics Norway, 2011b). The total expenditures for health care, social benefits, and social security were 40 percent of GDP in 2008. This is a lower share than in the 1990s, but the reduction is not due to a decrease in spending; rather, it reflects the very large Norwegian GDP (Statistics Norway, 2011b).

Form of Government and Political Parties

Norway is a constitutional monarchy. It has three democratically elected levels of government, all with their own jurisdictions and responsibilities: the Storting (Norwegian Parliament) at the national level; 19 county councils at the regional level; and 430 municipalities at the local level. The Storting passes legislation and decides on state revenues (primarily taxes) and expenditures. The county councils are responsible for county policies within the following areas: secondary education, cultural affairs, communications, dental health, economic development, and regional planning, including the development of the road system. Municipalities have a significant degree of autonomy and are administratively responsible for services such as lower secondary education, preschool, primary health care, care of the elderly, roads, water, waste disposal, and energy.

There are a number of political parties in Norway, and the elective system is based on a party or parties achieving a majority of seats. After World War II and until 1981, the social democratic party, the Labour Party, was in office. Over the last few decades there have mostly been majority coalitions in government. At the moment there is a coalition of the Labour Party, the Socialist Left Party, and the Centre Party; in everyday jargon they are called the red-green coalition. This coalition is now in its second term in government. On the conservative side there are also several parties, the leading one being the Right Party. This is a traditional conservative party, but there is also a far-right party called the Progress Party, which received close to 20 percent of the votes in the last general election in 2007.

Except for the Progress Party, it is fair to say that the other parties support the Norwegian welfare state model. However, it is clear that the parties on the conservative side aim to reduce public spending and increase privatization of public services.

The existence of health inequalities presents a dilemma for Norwegian welfare state ideals of equality. Historically, the problem of health inequality was very much excluded from the political agenda due to a strongly held conviction that Norway had attained a relatively equal society. Voices from outside of Norway, particularly an article by Johann Mackenbach (1997) in *The Lancet*, questioned this conviction by pointing to the existence of significant health gaps among Norwegians. In his article, Mackenbach stated that the relative health inequalities in the Scandinavian countries were just as large as in countries with less developed welfare states.[1] In response to the disconcerting evidence of health inequalities, the centre-left government that took office in 2005 introduced a cross-sector social determinant of health entry point for interventions to tackle social inequalities in health (Strand & Fosse, 2011).

Institutions Responsible for Health Policies and Policies to Reduce Social Inequalities in Health

In Norway, responsibilities for national health policies are shared among different institutions: the Ministry of Health and Care Services, the Norwegian Directorate of Health, and the Norwegian Institute of Public Health.

The Ministry of Health and Care Services' website makes the following statement about the responsibility of the ministry. The concept of equality is part of the statement (Ministry of Health and Care Services, 2011):

> The Ministry of Health and Care Services is responsible for providing good and equal health and care services for the population of Norway. The ministry directs these services by means of a comprehensive legislation, annual budgetary allocations … and through various governmental institutions.

The Norwegian Directorate of Health is a specialist directorate and an administrative body under the Ministry of Health and Care Services and the Ministry of Labour and Social Inclusion. The directorate is administered by the Ministry of Health and Care Services. The Directorate of Health's societal mission, as described on their website, is presented in Box 7.1 (Norwegian Directorate of Health and Social Affairs, 2012).

The third institution with responsibility for health policies is the Norwegian Institute of Public Health (2012). It is a national centre of excellence in the areas of epidemiology, mental health, control of infectious diseases, environmental medicine, forensic toxicology, and drug abuse.

The regional level has an important role in health promotion and public health. Counties coordinate health promotion at the regional and local level. The overall aims are to achieve more healthy life years for the population and to reduce social health inequalities. The regional work in this field is organized as partnerships among counties, local governments, non-governmental organizations, and other relevant partners.

The local level plays an important role in development and implementation of health promotion policies, including policies to reduce social inequalities in health. In Norway, local governments have a strong and independent position. This implies that the central government rarely dictates what municipalities can do. So-called "soft" governing tools are most commonly used to encourage municipalities to implement national policies.

> **Box 7.1**
> **The Role of the Norwegian Directorate of Health**
>
> The Directorate of Health shall improve the whole population's social security and health through comprehensive and targeted efforts across services, sectors, and administrative levels. The directorate shall base these efforts on its role as a specialist body, regulatory administrator, and implementer in the areas of health and care policy.
>
> The Directorate of Health is a specialist body both in the area of public health and living conditions and in the area of health services. This entails being responsible for monitoring the conditions that affect public health and living conditions and monitoring the trends in the health and care services. On this basis, the directorate shall offer advice and guidance about strategies and measures aimed at central government authorities, regional and local authorities, the health enterprises, voluntary organizations, the private sector, and the population. The directorate has a number of important administrative tasks, including authority for applying and interpreting laws and regulations in the health sector. The Directorate of Health shall ensure that approved policies are implemented in the health and care area.

Key Public Policy Milestones Related to Citizen Support and Benefits up to the Present

The Norwegian welfare state model is based on principles of universalism and citizenship (Halvorsen, 2005). This implies that citizenship entitles the citizens to health and welfare services. Like the case in many Western countries, the paths to the present welfare state are diverse. The roots are partly in the humanistic ideas of, and even inspired by, the Bismarckian laws of the 19th century (Halvorsen, 2005). However, it is fair to say that the main advocate for a universal welfare state was the labour movement, which in Norway gained its strength in the first decades of the 20th century. During the 1930s pension reforms were introduced, together with disability pensions and unemployment benefits.

However, it was only after World War II that the development of the welfare state became a main political project. The pension system ensures all citizens above 67 years the right to a retirement pension. This is a basic pension that is supplemented by pensions earned through employment. It is also possible to buy private insurance. There are other publicly funded benefits, disability pensions, unemployment benefits, and benefits for single parents. All families with children receive a monthly allowance.

Norwegian Policy Documents and Statements on Health Inequalities

Reducing inequalities in health was established as a goal with the adoption of the WHO's strategy Health for All 2000 in 1984.

The White Paper of 1987

In Norway a government White Paper was published as a follow-up to the strategies (Ministry of Social Affairs, 1987). In the White Paper, reducing social inequalities in health was a central aim (p. 22; author's translation): "With the adoption of the WHO targets for Health for All in 2000, Norway has made a commitment to reduce social differences by improving health conditions for the most vulnerable."

Suggested public health-related lines of action were to increase the focus on health in policy-making in all public sectors. A second action was to increase activities within disease prevention and health promotion. A third was to stimulate reorganization of health services to give special attention to inequalities in terms of social background and geographic factors and promote equality in the distribution of health services. In this White Paper, the political strategies in particular were highlighted. However, no specific targets or goals were set.

The White Paper on Health Promotion, 1993

In the first governmental White Paper on health promotion (Ministry of Health and Social Affairs, 1993), the Norwegian vision of how health promotion policy should be expressed was based on the Ottawa Charter (World Health Organization, 1986). Health promotion was seen as involving many aspects of municipal activity and involving all sectors, while disease prevention was viewed as primarily a matter for the health services. Health promotion was to focus on improved living conditions, ideally involving a critical focus on policy, communities, and professions. Intersectoral collaboration was to be the hallmark of health promotion. Disease prevention, on the other hand, was to continue managing the traditional prevention tasks of the health services.

Even though the White Paper had a general focus on the broader determinants of health, issues of equity and social inequalities in health were not included. This policy document was followed by a number of action plans in several areas. Even though the rhetoric of the White Paper was inspired by a broad understanding of health, the follow-up policies were more narrow in focus and concentrated mostly on downstream measures in areas like accidents and injuries (Fosse & Røiseland, 1999).

Developments from 1991 to 2002

Dahl (2002) and Fosse (2009) have studied how social inequalities in health have been defined in national policy documents in the period 1991–2001. In these documents, inequality is perceived of mainly in terms of disadvantaged, vulnerable, or marginalized groups and individuals. The *Equitable Redistribution White Paper* (Ministry of Health and Social Affairs, 1999) identified 10 target groups for public intervention: (1) households with long-term low income, (2) disadvantaged immigrants, (3) disadvantaged families with small children, (4) people with psychiatric illnesses, (5) people with long-term illness, (6) the long-term unemployed and occupationally impaired, (7) disadvantaged pensioners, (8) people with disabilities, (9) drug addicts, and (10) homeless people. Inequalities, in terms of social stratification or social class, are hardly mentioned and, if so, they are defined as unimportant.

The follow-up paper to the *Equitable Redistribution White Paper* was the 2002 Government White Paper *Action Plan against Poverty* (Ministry of Health, 2002). The point of departure was that Norway is a good country to live in for the majority of the population (p. 5; author's translation): "The majority in the population have a high standard of living and good living conditions.... In our country there are no larger, easily identifiable groups who are poor, but single people with different backgrounds."

In the paper, the values base of the policy is also outlined (p. 6; author's translation): "Government alone cannot fight poverty. Each person has a responsibility for his or her life. There must be demands placed on everybody, based on each person's abilities and resources."

Like the *Equitable Redistribution White Paper*, the focus is on disadvantaged individuals and groups (p. 6; author's translation): "Intervention will be aimed at people who live in poverty and also at reducing the risk factors for developing poverty. The government's aim is to help people to get out of poverty and prevent it." During this period, neither social inequalities nor the social gradient in health was defined as a problem; the policies were targeted at disadvantaged groups. An interesting point to be made is that at this time, this was an understanding shared by both labour and conservative governments.

Developments since 2003

A government White Paper on public health was published in January 2003 (Ministry of Health, 2003). Entitled *Prescriptions for a Healthier Norway*, it outlined Norway's public health policy for the next decade. In this White Paper the balance between the individual's responsibility for health and society's responsibility is underlined. There is a strong focus on lifestyle factors that may cause disease, and the situation for vulnerable and marginalized groups is the main focus of attention. This paper uses the concept of social inequalities in health. The development of increasing social inequalities is considered a problem, but it is again formulated as a problem for some population groups rather than others (p. 8; author's translation):

> Risk factors are often particularly concentrated in vulnerable parts of the population. There is a need to shed more light on the special health problems of the immigrant population. In general, there is a need for improved adjustment of interventions for the needs of groups at risk for developing health problems.

The government's goals outlined in the paper are (p. 51; author's translation):

- Interventions to influence lifestyles will be assessed in terms of their consequences for social inequalities in health.
- New actions aimed at vulnerable groups or geographic areas will be assessed in terms of the target of reducing social inequalities in health.
- Social inequalities in health will be introduced as an element in health impact assessment (HIA).
- Competence in this policy area will be built up.
- A plan of action will be developed to combat social inequalities in health.

As a follow-up to the *White Paper on Public Health*, an action plan was developed (Directorate of Health and Social Affairs, 2005b). The Ministry of Health and Care Services delegated the responsibility for developing the action plan to the Directorate for Health and Social Affairs,[2] which reports to the ministry. The action plan, published in January 2005, was entitled *The Challenge of the Gradient*. The action plan indicated a shift of focus, compared to former policy documents. One sign of this is that social inequalities in health are now defined in terms of the social gradient. In the plan, it argues against a perspective where the focus is only on the poorest groups (p. 9):

> Working to reduce social inequalities in health means making efforts to ensure that all social groups can achieve the same life expectancy and be equally healthy. Differences in health not only affect specific occupational groups or the poorest people or those with least education. On the contrary, research indicates that we will not address the relation between socio-economic position and health if we base our activities on strategies that focus on "the poor" as an isolated target group.

A government White Paper on social inequalities in health, entitled *National Strategy to Reduce Social Inequalities in Health*, was released in February 2007 (Ministry of Health and Care Services, 2007). It has a 10-year perspective for developing policies and strategies to reduce health inequities.

One main point of the White Paper is that "Equity is good public health policy." This implies a view of public health policies that aim at a more equal distribution of positive factors that influence health. The overall strategy has four goals:

1. to reduce social inequalities that contribute to health differences
2. to reduce social inequalities in health behaviour and use of health services
3. to target efforts for social inclusion
4. to develop increased knowledge and tools for cross-sectoral collaboration and planning

With the release of this government White Paper in 2007, reducing social inequalities in health has become an overall aim in the Norwegian public health policy. Even though it is considered part of Norwegian "health policy," the policy is cross-sectoral and comprehensive and is not limited to the health ministry but includes several ministries.

The New Public Health Act
A new Public Health Act was introduced in Norway beginning January 1, 2012 (Ministry of Health and Care Services, 2011, 1).

> The purpose of the Act is to contribute to societal development that promotes public health and reduces social inequalities in health. Public health work shall promote the population's health, well-being and good social and environmental conditions, and contribute to the prevention of mental and somatic illnesses, disorders or injuries.
>
> The Act establishes a new foundation for strengthening systematic public health work in the development of policies and planning for societal development based on regional and local challenges and needs. The Act provides a broad basis for the coordination of public health work horizontally across various sectors and actors and vertically between authorities at local,

regional and national level. Only by integrating health and its social determinants as an aspect of all social and welfare development through intersectoral action can good and equitable public health be achieved.

The municipalities, county authorities, and central government authorities are all important actors in the efforts to promote public health and reduce social inequalities in health. This Act will ensure that municipalities, county authorities, and central government health authorities implement measures and coordinate their activities in public health work. Promotion of participation and collaboration with stakeholders, such as the voluntary sector, is an important aspect of good public health work. Central government health authorities have a duty to support the public health work of the municipalities, among others, by making available informa-

---

Box 7.2
The Principles of the New Norwegian Public Health Act

- Health equity: Health inequities arise from the societal conditions in which people are born, grow, live, work, and age—the social determinants of health. Social inequities in health form a pattern of a gradient throughout society. Levelling up the gradient by action on the social determinants of health is a core public health objective. A fair distribution of societal resources is good public health policy.
- Health in all policies: Equitable health systems are important to public health, but health inequities arise from societal factors beyond health care. Impact on health must be considered when policies and action are developed and implemented in all sectors. Joined up governance and intersectoral action is key to reduce health inequities.
- Sustainable development: Sustainable development is development that meets the needs of the present without compromising the ability of future generations to meet their own needs. Public health work needs to be based on a long-term perspective.
- Precautionary principle: If an action or policy has a suspected risk of causing harm to the public or to the environment, the absence of scientific consensus that the action or policy is harmful, cannot justify postponed action to prevent such harm.
- Participation: Public health work is about transparent, inclusive processes with participation by multiple stakeholders. Promotion of participation of civil society is key to good public health policy development.

Source: Norwegian Ministry of Health and Care Services (2011), *The Norwegian Public Health Act: A short introduction*, retrieved from: www.regjeringen.no/upload/HOD/Hoeringer%20 FHA_FOS/1234.pdf.

tion and data to monitor public health and health determinants at the local level. The Act aims to facilitate long-term, systematic public health work. The Act is based on five fundamental principles that shall underpin policies and action to improve population health (see Box 7.2).

Analysis of These Documents and Their Implications

Dahl (2002) analyzed Norwegian public health policies from 1991 to 2001 with the objective of reviewing those policies that were explicitly aimed at reducing social inequalities in health. As a point of departure and a theoretical framework, he used Margaret Whitehead's Action Spectrum (Whitehead, 1998). The Action Spectrum outlines actions that reflect various degrees of commitment to reduce social inequalities in health. The most committed of these are comprehensive, coordinated strategies. In the middle of the Action Spectrum, we find the categories "more structured developments" and "isolated initiatives." According to Dahl, Norway has been located at the lower end of the Action Spectrum under the categories "measurement," "awareness raising," and "indifference."

In 2007, five years after this study was published, there seemed to be a movement up the Action Spectrum toward the middle section. The development of the action plan and the action principles is definitely more comprehensive than earlier strategies. On this basis, it seems fair to conclude that Norway has been moving up the Action Spectrum over the last couple of years toward what Whitehead calls comprehensive, coordinated strategies. The new Public Health Act, which is to be implemented in 2012, and its comprehensive, coordinated strategies are at the core of the policies and confirm the Norwegian political development toward comprehensive, coordinated strategies.

Research on Health Inequalities in Norway

The Norwegian Research Council (NFR) is funded mainly by public means, and the ministries are important in defining objectives and targets for research. Research institutions and individual researchers may apply for project funding. The NFR does not have a separate program on social inequalities in health. In terms of research, until 2005, there was little activity in Norway (Dahl, 2000). In 2005 a research program in public health was launched. Social inequality in health was included in this program, but it was not an overarching strategy. There were very few projects that focused on the social determinants of health; the projects funded were mainly on individual lifestyle factors and the distribution of these in different socio-economic groups (Fosse, 2008).

The program has been funded for a second period, from 2011 to 2015. In the new program description, there is an explicit aim to support research that focuses on exploring the social determinants of health (Research Council of Norway, 2012a). Aims and objectives of the program are described in the following way (author's translation): "The overall aim of the program is to contribute to new knowledge on factors influencing population health, on causes for social inequalities in health, and actions to reduce these inequalities and improve population health." Three main areas will be prioritized:

- health behaviours such as physical activity, diet, tobacco; behaviours related to accidents and injuries

- research on life course such as living conditions for children and adolescents, education, work, and income related to health
- promotion of mental health

Social inequalities will have a central focus across these thematic areas. Two of the eight projects that received funding in 2012 included "social determinants" or "socio-economic inequalities" in the project title (Research Council of Norway, 2012b).

Over the last few years, the general interest in social inequalities in health has also led to increased focus on specific aspects of socio-economic status and not only average tendencies or variables. The Norwegian Public Health Institute (2012) funds a number of research projects within the field of social inequalities in health. In Norway there are national databases with information on individuals and households dating back to 1960, employment registries, tax registries, and education registries that can be linked to the cause-of-death register, which provide unique opportunities for population-based studies. There are also registries with more specific data on population groups and geographical areas.

Among the projects at the Norwegian Public Health Institute related to health inequalities are: social inequalities in mortality, longitudinal effects of smoking, blood cholesterol and BMI by education, social status in childhood, and mortality from different causes in a life course perspective. In addition, there are a number of other projects and publications that are reviewed in a report published by the Directorate of Health and Social Welfare (Sund & Krokstad, 2005).

The renewed interest in social inequalities in health provided an increased focus on the significance of socio-economic status in many areas. However, so far most of the data available are on the individual level and focus on risk factors for mortality and morbidity. Another strand of research has been on individual lifestyles in relation to socio-economic status.

The recent Norwegian policy documents also address the structural determinants of health, and the universal welfare state arrangements are regarded as a major vehicle in reducing social inequalities in health. The new Public Health Act embraces the idea of "health for all" policies. A particular focus is on having the local planning system as an important means of ensuring that the overall aims of the policy are being implemented. However, so far there has been little research on structural determinants of health inequalities. Issues of the organization of the welfare state and similar themes have not been an important focus for research funding.

The development of the *White Paper on Social Inequalities in Health* since 2007 coincided with the development of several other policy documents in relevant sectors, and the reciprocal influence between these various processes was profound. The contact and co-operation between various ministries and intra-ministerial departments helped to ensure that health and distribution concerns were addressed in several national strategies on key determinant areas. Indeed, a more fair distribution became a main target in those documents.

Related Documents

Almost at the same time, the Ministry of Labour and Social Inclusion (2006) released a government White Paper titled *Work, Welfare, and Inclusion*. The purpose of this White Paper was to outline strategies and measures aimed at improved inclusion in working life for working-age people who have problems entering the labour market or who are at risk of dropping out of it.

The document states that equality and freedom for all depends on the political will to implement genuine inclusive and redistributive measures.

The policy approach is the so-called "work first approach." This policy approach is the main instrument aimed at reducing economic differences and improving the economic conditions for people who currently live under the poverty threshold. In the White Paper, the government suggests changing the focus from measures based on the individual's limitations to a focus on the person's abilities and opportunities.

Another important paper in the comprehensive strategy to reduce social inequalities was issued by the Ministry of Education and Research (2006) in the report *Early Efforts for Lifelong Learning*. In this White Paper, the government states that it will have an active role in reducing inequalities in society. The aim is to reduce class differences, economic inequalities, and fight poverty and other forms of marginalization. The education system's aim is to contribute to reducing social inequalities and to help more people succeed in reaching their goals. The suggested measures cover several areas and target groups, among them stimulation of language skills in children below school age, increase quality in daycare, provide close follow-up of pupils in primary and secondary schools, and take measures to reduce dropout in upper secondary schools.

These documents introduce numerous measures that address the social determinants of health inequalities. To take one example, an important measure introduced by the *Report on Work, Welfare, and Inclusion* is a NOK250 million (more than €30 million) qualification program and benefit for people with loose or no ties to the labour market. The rationale behind this is that inclusion in the labour market has positive effects on individuals' financial situation, social capital, and health.

In 2006 an action plan to combat poverty was issued (Ministry of Labour and Social Inclusion, 2006b). The government addresses poverty as an issue of equity and fair distribution in society. The aim is a society based on social justice and equal opportunities. The government aims to abolish poverty through universal welfare arrangements, based on the principles of the Norwegian welfare state. The government will prevent poverty by developing welfare systems in relation to work life, the education system, and the health services. A well-developed public welfare state will secure equal opportunities independent of economic and other personal resources for everybody. Still, many disadvantaged groups will need other services in addition to the general welfare services. Therefore, more targeted measures must also be in place to meet the need of these groups. As a part of the action plan, the government will implement measures to:

- provide everybody with an opportunity to join the workforce
- give all children and adolescents the opportunity to develop personally and participate in society
- improve living conditions for the most disadvantaged

In 2007, a *Plan of Action for the Integration and Inclusion of the Immigrant Population* was released (Ministry of Labour and Social Inclusion 2007). The action plan was a follow-up of one from 2006, when the general aims for inclusion of the immigrant population were outlined. There are 17 overall targets, and indicators are developed for all these targets. Different ministries have responsibility for following up. The action plan has a long-term focus, and every year a status report will be presented. The present action plan focuses on four areas vital for successful inclusion of the immigrant population: work, childhood and adolescence, education, and language. The measures following the targets cut across several areas: work, welfare and language, childhood and education, health and care services, police and criminal justice, housing, and a focus on the public sector as employer.

Health Inequalities in Norway

Most groups in society have become healthier in the last 30 years. The health benefits have been greatest for those who already had the best health—those with extensive education, good income, and who are in a relationship. The health benefits have not increased as much for those with lower education and income. Therefore, inequalities in health have increased, particularly in the last decade.

In 2007, the Ministry of Health and Care Services published a national strategy for minimizing social health differences (Ministry of Health and Care Services, 2007). As background information for this parliamentary report, the Norwegian Institute of Public Health compiled a fact report about social inequalities in health (Næss, Rognerud & Strand, 2007). The report contains these main points, among others:

- Norwegian children and adolescents are in good health. However, there are health differences linked to parental income, education, and marital status.
- For adults:
  - There are large differences in self-evaluated health and symptoms of psychological distress.
  - There are large differences in chronic diseases that can increase the risk of a premature death.
  - Single men and women with low income and low education are particularly vulnerable to a premature death.
- Self-evaluated health in the elderly is better than before, but there are clear differences according to education duration. Those with the least education report chronic diseases more often.
- Lifestyle plays a large role in motivation and the ability to maintain positive habits, such as regular physical activity, a healthy diet, and abstinence or limited use of tobacco and other intoxicants.

Almost 10 percent of the population live in households with persistent low income. Among women aged 65 and over, 21 percent fall below the low-income limit. Low income is a risk factor for physical and mental health problems.

Income can be measured in several ways, for example, gross income, household income, or persistent low income. Research on the relation between health and living conditions often uses household income or persistent low income.

Household Income as a Measure of Living Conditions

In studies of health and living conditions, household net income—rather than gross income—is often used as a measure of income. This is because people with the same gross income may have very different living conditions, depending on income from cohabitants, the number of children and adults in the household, and the total household expenditure.

To compare households of different sizes, total household income is divided by an index that accounts for the number of adults and children in the household. The first adult = 1.0, the second adult = 0.5, and each child under 17 years = 0.3. Therefore, a household of two adults and two children must have a household income that is 2.1 times higher than a single-person household to have the same adjusted household income. The calculation is as follows: 1.0 + 0.5 + 0.3 + 0.3 = 2.1.

Persistent Low Income Is a Risk Factor for Health

Adjusted household income is used to calculate persistent low income, which is a risk factor for health. In this case, persistent means over a three-year period, and low income means less than 60 percent of median household income (EU scale). The median is the middle of the income scale; half of the population has a higher income and half has a lower income than the median. The median household income is calculated after tax is deducted.

Almost 10 percent of the population live in households with persistent low income. Over the past 10 years, the proportion has been between 8 and 10 percent. Approximately 2 percent more women than men live in households with persistently low income.

Poverty and Health

Socio-economic status and health are related. Those who are higher up in the social hierarchy have better health than those further down the hierarchy. This is documented in all Western countries.

Statistics Norway's Living Conditions Study from 2005 shows that the poor generally have worse mental health and an unhealthier lifestyle compared with those who are not poor (Myklestad et al., 2008). In this study, the poor were defined as people living in households with a combined income of less than 50 percent of the median of adjusted household income. Adjusted household income is the sum of household income after tax divided by the square root of the number of individuals in the household, and is in line with how the OECD calculates poverty.

Increasing Health Inequalities

In 2010, a report from the Norwegian Institute of Public Health (NIPH) showed that the inequalities continue to increase. Diseases of the heart and lungs create the largest differences in health, probably due to different smoking habits across socio-economic groups (Norwegian Institute of Public Health, 2010).

Key Policy Tools

There are also numerous public policies that support health. These include policies that regulate labour practice, provide family supports, and ensure adequate income and wages. Social assistance and unemployment benefits are supportive of the population and represent the strong emphasis on provision of economic and social security common among social democratic welfare states.

The social democratic welfare state regime is supported by contributions from most citizens in the labour force. Family policy is thus an important part of these regimes. Dual-earner families are the main model, and work life is organized in a way that makes it possible to combine paid work with family life. Full-time daycare at reasonable cost is offered for children from the age of one to six years. Children start school at six, and in the first year, all schools offer daycare in the afternoons. Many women work in the public welfare sector as nurses, teachers, and social workers. Work life is quite flexible, and many women employed in these services work part-time.

A majority of young people take post-graduate education. The Norwegian government provides loans and grants to all students, so they are not dependent on their family's financial situation for their studies. Also, there is no tuition for attending universities and university colleges.

In general, the labour market has been strongly regulated via negotiations between strong trade unions and employers. The Working Environment Act ensures safe working conditions and equal treatment among workers, and ensures that the working environment is a health-promoting and meaningful work situation.

The Working Environment Act applies to all employees, with the exception of seafaring and fisheries, which are regulated by separate regulations. The Act contains provisions about employers' and employees' obligations with respect to ensuring acceptable working environments. Enterprises are required to have safety delegates and working environment committees, and some enterprises are required to have a corporate health service, where necessary.

In annual negotiations, wages, working conditions, and other issues of importance are agreed upon by representatives from different private and public sectors. Even if this system secures decent wages and working conditions for most employees, there are quite large differences between different sectors and education groups. Norway's involvement with EU regulations may also undermine the organized negotiation system. Over the last few years there have been several examples of "social dumping" where immigrant workers in particular are paid wages far below Norwegian standards. Both Norwegian and foreign employers are involved in these contracts.

The Norwegian health care system is mainly public and based on a principle of universality, which implies that all inhabitants are entitled to similar, high-quality health care. People pay an out-of-pocket fee for services provided by primary health care, including general practitioners, up to a fixed limit. When this limit is reached, the services are free. Hospital services are free.

But despite these health-supporting public policies, there is a continuing concern with reducing health inequalities that manifest in a wide range of continuing activities. The policy shift toward an upstream approach to public health and social equity is still quite new, and there are as yet not many results concerning either organizational measures or in terms of reducing social inequalities. Before the publication of the 2007 *White Paper on Health Inequalities*, there were few mechanisms to help implement such considerations in other sectors.

The main mechanism to ensure implementation of health inequality concerns in other sectors laid down in the *Health Inequalities White Paper* is an annual review and reporting system involving more than 10 national ministries and directorates. Through annual reports, all sectors involved, including policy areas such as income and taxes, early childhood, education, labour, social inclusion, public health, and the health system, are to report on achievements (indicators) and policy developments concerning (health) inequalities. The development of the reporting system, which is to be coordinated by the Directorate for Health and Social Affairs, is still in an early phase.

The Directorate for Health and Social Affairs was also assigned the task of establishing a Centre of Competence on social inequalities in health. The *White Paper on Public Health* points out that the important responsibilities of this Centre of Competence are to:

- facilitate co-operation between and coordinate the work of Norwegian experts and institutions working in this field
- systematically collect experiences from international organizations and other countries
- establish a knowledge base
- develop expertise to advise central and local authorities

Financial resources have been allocated to support the health inequalities Resource Unit in the Directorate for Health and Social Affairs as well as a national expert group on social inequalities in health. There are numerous measures intended to reduce social inequalities in various health determinants across government. Indeed, the reduction of social inequalities is a main overall target for the present government (and, one may argue, for the welfare state as such). Such measures are not always explicitly linked to the reduction of health inequalities, but are considered a strengthening of the Norwegian welfare state.

Annual Report from the Directorate of Health on the Efforts to Reduce Social Inequalities in Health

The report details work on establishing a reporting system to monitor the efforts to reduce social differences in health. Establishing the report system is one of the main suggestions in the government report no. 20 (2006–2007), *National Strategy to Reduce Social Inequalities in Health*. Efforts to reduce social inequalities in health will demand an intersectoral approach. Together with a number of important sectors of society, the Directorate of Health will report and follow the development in areas like income, school, work, health behaviour, health services, and social inclusion. By highlighting the social determinants of health, it will be possible to reduce the social inequalities that shape health inequalities. The report will provide feedback on the effect of government policies and will be important for the implementation of new policies to reduce social inequalities in health. The report will be published annually until 2017. The reports will also be used to highlight some issues that are particular challenges.

Norwegian Public Health Act

One of the main features of the new Norwegian Public Health Act is that it places responsibility for public health work on the entire government and an entire municipality rather than only on the health sector. In public health work, the municipalities must involve all sectors, not just the health sector, for the promotion of public health.

The Act builds on a broad determinant perspective on public health work. An overview of public health and health determinants constitutes the starting point for evidence-based public health work. Based on a local assessment of the public health challenges, public health policy development must be an integrated part of ordinary societal and spatial planning and administration processes in counties and municipalities and in other social development strategies.

Instead of detailed requirements, the Act prescribes procedural requirements that will provide the municipalities and counties with a foundation for systematic and long-term public health work across the sectors, based on the municipalities' own planning and administration systems. The municipality will implement the measures that are necessary for meeting its public health challenges. This may, for example, encompass measures relating to childhood environments and living conditions, such as housing, education, employment and income, physical and social environments, physical activity, nutrition, injuries and accidents, tobacco use, alcohol use, and use of other psychoactive substances.

Key Actors

At the turn of the 21st century, dedicated policy entrepreneurs within the government's administration and committed researchers were continuous driving forces in drawing attention to the problem of increasing social inequalities in health (Strand & Fosse, 2011). Following the White Paper (Ministry of Health, 2003), the Directorate of Health was to establish a Resource Unit on social inequalities in health in 2004. Their mandate was to coordinate development of the policy area by collecting evidence and building competence on the subject of social inequalities in health. Their task was to develop concrete measures to reduce social inequalities in health by producing an action plan.

The initial discourse process in the Resource Unit within the Directorate of Health identified a lack of consensus on what constituted the perceived causes of the problem and the policy goals to address these causes. Following the 2003 *White Paper on Public Health*, political guidelines were focused mainly on outlining policy interventions in order to target socially disadvantaged groups.

Research had identified that health inequalities followed a pattern of a gradient throughout the population (Zahl et al., 2003). The gradient approach demands policy options that differ from direct targeting. In order to introduce a new framework, the disadvantaged group focus needed to be amended. As part of this process, a decision was made to investigate European and international evidence, particularly the work by the WHO Commission on Social Determinants of Health. International focus on the social determinants of health and health inequality helped create support for this entry point.

The adoption of a social determinant of health/gradient approach demanded several strategic choices. Accordingly, the Directorate of Health changed the political formulation of the problem of social inequalities to include multi-causal mechanisms, reformulated as a social determinant of health/health inequality entry point for intervention (Strand & Fosse, 2011).

The Resource Unit was originally intended to ensure that inequality considerations were included in health sector planning. Aligned with the underpinning social gradient perspective, the Resource Unit gradually became a driving force for health inequality considerations in all political sectors, thus anchoring a strategy at the ministerial level beyond the political authority of the Directorate of Health.

As such, a strategic option was to have a process-oriented focus by customizing acceptance for a common gradient perspective and creating commitment within the public and professional communities.

In 2005 the Norwegian Directorate of Health established an Expert Group in the field of social inequalities in health. The mandate of the Expert Group was to contribute to further development of national strategies to reduce social inequalities in health. The group members were all highly qualified researchers in the field, representing different backgrounds and approaches to studying social inequalities. The Expert Group would give scientific weight to the reformulation of the problem, and outline principles of action to guide the policy-making process. The bridging of research and policy helped introduce the whole of government/cross-sector policy approach.

To address the different distributional effects of the determinants of health, it was also necessary to include the ministries responsible for a variety of policy areas. A formal outcome of this process was the publication of the report *The Challenge of the Gradient* (Directorate of Health and Social Affairs, 2005b). It explicitly states (p. 31):

> Cross-sectoral challenges require cross-sectoral solutions. The factors that generate and perpetuate social inequalities in health lie far beyond the control of the Directorate for Health and Social Affairs and the health sector alone. If we are to come to grips with the causes of social inequalities in health, we need to agree on comprehensive packages of measures on the national level.

The action plan became an agenda-setting document and constituted a preparatory phase of a comprehensive policy strategy policy that needed to gain support from different political sectors. Scientifically founded theories were applied to the policy-making process, enabling a shift in formulation of the problem. This shift might stimulate the development of different designs of the intervention programs, from a focus on strengthening individuals to more comprehensive strategies, including macro-politics. The delegation of the responsibility to the Directorate of Health for preparing a plan of action raised the opportunity to develop a more comprehensive theoretical framework necessary for the introduction of a structural, coordinated strategy at the government level (Strand & Fosse, 2011).

Principles of Action to Tackle Social Inequalities in Health

In 2005 the national expert group developed a set of *Action Principles to Tackle Social Inequalities in Health* and six general action principles that should be followed to reduce social inequalities in health:

- use explicit objectives
- build on existing knowledge
- emphasize universally oriented population strategies
- combine structural measures with individually oriented health measures
- strategies to reduce social inequalities should be comprehensive and coordinated
- reduce unfortunate social consequences of disease and ill health

In 2005 the government coalition of the Labour Party, the Socialist Left Party, and the Centre Party came into office. This government came into power with promises to fight poverty and work for a more equitable society in terms of fairness in income distribution, education, and health. This rationale fits in with the idea of universalism, and a gradient approach is merging into social democratic rhetoric.

The formal starting point of the development of a strategy to reduce social inequality in health was made by a Cabinet decision in January 2006 and was very much in line with the government's political mandate and priorities (Giæver et al., 2007). The problem had already been investigated and mainstreamed into the bureaucracy through the work with the action plan, and this created the opportunity to draft a government White Paper, which was developed through a 14-month process to February 2007 in co-operation with several ministries. On February 9, 2007, the three-party coalition government launched the White Paper, entitled *National Strategy to Reduce Social Inequalities in Health* (Ministry of Health and Care Services, 2007). The primary objective of the strategy is to reduce social inequalities in health by levelling the social gradient in health.

Recommendations for Future Activities

The Norwegian policy to reduce social inequalities in health is very ambitious. At the national level, the policies include many sectors, and one very interesting research theme could be to study if and how the policies are being integrated in order to provide concerted action to reduce social inequalities in health.

The Public Health Act puts new demands on the local governments in prioritizing comprehensive, intersectoral policies that include reducing social inequalities in health. The Act requires health promotion and public health to be part of the overall local policies and not a concern for the health sector alone. Planning will be the main vehicle in ensuring that the aim of health in all policies is being achieved.

From a research perspective, it would be very interesting to follow the implementation processes from the national level via the regional level to the development at the local level. Some research themes could be to study if the social gradient (in health) is being levelled. Further research themes could focus on how the local governments will tackle new demands for organizing and prioritizing policies to reduce social inequalities.

Based on the fact that the foundation for people's socio-economic position is established in early life, it is also important to include a life course perspective to research, particularly on the importance of equity in the education system.

Supports and Barriers in the Norwegian Context

Of course there are many challenges in the implementation of the policies. Government structures consist of sectors with different interests and agendas, and these may prove difficult to change. Some of the challenges in integrating policies as cross-sectoral responsibility may be the following:

- insufficient anchoring in the sectors involved
- co-operation and coordination problems

- insufficient resources
- insufficient indicator data
- changes in political priorities
- a lack of common concepts and conceptualizations across sectors
- insufficient competence

Still, policies in many areas aim at reducing social inequalities by focusing on the social determinants of health. The policies are mainly upstream and explicitly linked to a political ambition of strengthening redistribution among social groups within the framework of the Norwegian welfare state.

The implementation of the Norwegian Public Health Act will be a test of how the policy will play out in practice. There has to be support from the national level, both economically and otherwise, to facilitate a successful implementation. The Public Health Act is part of a wider reform, the so-called Collaboration Reform. In addition to the Public Health Act, the Collaboration Reform also includes a decentralization of health services from the national to the local level. Traditionally, health services gain more resources and attention than health promotion and public health, and one of the challenges could be that the focus of attention and resources will be on the health service side of the reform, which, in turn, may lead to a neglect of the Public Health Act.

A second threat to the further development of the Norwegian policies to reduce social inequalities in health might materialize if a conservative majority takes over government in the general election in 2013. This might be a coalition that includes the far right-wing party. If this happens, the gradient perspective will surely disappear from the political platform of the government. Traditionally left-wing governments would be expected to focus more on the government's responsibility for the health of the population, while right-wing governments would emphasize individuals' responsibility for their own health.

A third threat is, of course, the global economic crisis. So far, the crisis has not hit Norway very hard due to the country's economic situation. The Norwegian government has also used traditional Keynesian economic tools and increased public spending, which has been possible because of the affluence of the national budgets. However, if the crisis escalates, it will also hit the Norwegian economy and most likely will raise demands for cuts in public spending.

Conclusion

The social gradient perspective with regard to reducing health inequalities demands upstream measures and policies that aim at redistribution among socio-economic groups in line with the ideals of the social democratic welfare state. There are strong arguments that the present Norwegian policy is a product of such social democratic policy implemented by social democratic governments. As shown above, the public health policy from 2003 had a focus on social inequalities in health, but the suggested measures were mainly downstream, aimed at marginalized groups. The present red-green coalition government has followed the principles of strengthening the welfare state and reducing social inequalities in many sectors of society.

The issue of equity is at the core of the social democratic welfare regime ideology (Esping-Andersen, 1990). Graham (2004) argues that targeted, downstream approaches are unlikely to achieve a reduction in health inequalities. On the contrary, such approaches may result in a loss of political commitment to health equity. This assumption is supported by the findings of Navarro and colleagues (2006), who show that a population has better health in states with a social democratic government.

The present Norwegian public health policy approach is radical in its emphasis on upstream measures and intersectoral collaboration to address the social determinants of health. It may be argued that the principles represent a revitalization of universal and structural measures in line with the social democratic welfare state model. In this perspective, universal welfare measures are viewed as more important than contributions from the health sector in reducing social inequalities in health. It also seems to be born from a true conviction that the social democratic welfare state project should be sustained.

Notes

1. The term "relative differences" describe the differences between those in the highest and the lowest socio-economic groups, usually in terms of a ratio. For example, people with high education have better health and live longer than people with low education, and these differences among the groups are increasing (Zahl et al., 2003; Strand et al., 2010). The term "absolute differences" describe these groups in absolute terms such as differences in years of life expectancy or mortality rates. Using absolute measures, Norway is among the top countries regarding health for all social groups.
2. The Directorate for Health and Social Affairs was the former name of the present Directorate for Health.

Critical Thinking Questions

1. Norway is a small Scandinavian country within the social democratic welfare state regime. What are the possibilities for other countries adopting similar policies?
2. "Equity is good public health policy" is a statement in the main Norwegian policy paper. What exactly does this mean in Norway and elsewhere?
3. Research shows that social democratic political parties are more interested than liberal and conservative parties in issues of social equity. What is your experience in your own jurisdiction concerning these issues?
4. Policies targeted at disadvantaged groups or areas will not level the social gradient of health. Why might this be the case?

Recommended Readings

Fosse, E. (2011). Different welfare states, different policies? An analysis of the substance of national health promotion policies in countries representing four European welfare state regimes. *International Journal of Health Services, 41*, 255–271.

This article examines healthy public policy development in four European countries using Esping-Andersen's three types of welfare regimes: liberal, corporatist, and social democratic. Four countries are included in this study, representing different welfare regimes: England, Norway, the Netherlands, and the Czech Republic wherein the directions of welfare state development are not yet totally clear. By analyzing the different policies in the light of Esping-Andersen's typology of welfare state regimes, it is possible to understand the differences among the countries more clearly.

Lundberg, O. (2009). How do welfare policies contribute to the reduction of health inequalities? *Eurohealth, 15*(3), 24–27.

Since a range of social factors and living conditions throughout the life course are important for health and survival, welfare policies that aim at improving such conditions and tackling social problems are important for health. It is important to consider both macro- and micro-level policies when we try to assess what works.

Navarro, V., Whitehead, M., Doran, T., Buström, B., Helmert, U., Costa, G., & Borrell, C. (2003). Special report on the political and social contexts of health: Summary and conclusion of the study. *International Journal of Health Services, 33*(4), 743–749.

This article summarizes the findings of a research project on the political and social contexts of health, which show how societies' socio-economic, political, and cultural variables are the most important factors in explaining their populations' level of health.

Strand, M., & Fosse, E. (2011). Tackling health inequalities in Norway: Applying linear and non-linear models in the policy making process. *Critical Public Health, 121*(2), 1–9.

This article follows the Norwegian policy-making process on social inequalities in health, applying models for policy development with a focus on linear and non-linear movements.

Recommended Websites

European Portal on Action on Health Inequalities: www.health-inequalities.eu/

This website has information about health inequalities in and outside the EU at the national and regional levels. Particularly important are the public policies designed to address these issues.

Norwegian Department of Public Health: http://tinyurl.com/7oclz42

This Norwegian government website provides details related to health promotion and preventive medicine, health surveillance and health registers, nutrition and food safety, and alcohol and drug addiction issues. The "Documents" section contains details on the *National Strategy to Reduce Social Inequalities in Health.*

Norwegian Institute of Public Health: http://tinyurl.com/7zk3lzy

This website gives an overview of research into social inequalities in health in Norway and includes a number of fact sheets focused on identifying and tackling health inequalities in Norway.

Norwegian Ministry of Children, Equality, and Social Inclusion: http://www.regjeringen.no/en/dep/bld.html?id=298

The Ministry of Children, Equality, and Social Inclusion seeks to strengthen the rights of consumers, families, children, and young people, and encourage anti-discrimination and full equality between men and women. The website contains reports, statements, and links to other materials.

References

Dahl, E. (2000). *Social inequalities in health: A review of the Norwegian evidence.* Oslo: Fafo Institute for Applied Social Sciences.

Dahl, E. (2002). Health inequalities and health policy: The Norwegian case. *Norsk Epidemiologi, 12*(1), 69–75.

Directorate for Health and Social Affairs. (2005a). *Principles of action to tackle social inequality in health.* Retrieved from: www.helsedir.no.

Directorate of Health and Social Affairs. (2005b). *The challenge of the gradient action plan against social inequalities in Health.* Oslo: Norwegian Directorate of Health and Social Affairs.

Directorate of Health and Social Affairs. (2012). *About us.* Retrieved from: www.helsedirektoratet.no.

Esping-Andersen, G. (1990). *The three worlds of welfare capitalism.* Cambridge: Polity Press.

Fosse, E. (2008). Comparing policies for reducing social inequities in health—the case of Norway: From indifference to determinants? In C. Hogstedt, H. Moberg, B. Lundgren & M. Backhans (Eds.), *Health for all? A critical analysis of public health policies in eight European countries* (pp. 241–264). Stockholm: Swedish National Institute of Public Health.

Fosse, E. (2009). Norwegian public health policy—revitalisation of the social democratic welfare state? *International Journal of Health Services, 41*(2), 255–272.

Fosse, E., & Røiseland, A. (1999). From vision to reality? The Ottawa Charter in Norwegian health policy. *Internet Journal of Health Promotion, 1.* Retrieved from: http://rhpeo.net/ijhp-articles/1999/1/index.htm.

Giæver, Ø., Torgersen, T., & Stigen, O.T. (2007). *Developing an intersectoral national strategy to reduce social inequalities in health: The Norwegian case.* Retrieved from: http://www.who.int/social_determinants/resources/isa_national_strategy_nor.pdf.

Graham, H. (2004). Tackling inequalities in health in England: Remedying health disadvantages, narrowing health gaps, or reducing health gradients? *Journal of Social Policy, 33*(1), 115–131.

Halvorsen, K. (2005). *Grunnbok i helse—og socialpolitikk* [Basic health and social policy]. Oslo: Universitetsforlaget.

Machenbach, J. (1997). Socioeconomic inequalities in morbidity and mortality in Western Europe. *The Lancet, 349,* 1655–1659.

Ministry of Education and Research. (2006). *Early efforts for lifelong learning.* Report to the Storting, no. 16 (2006–2007). Oslo: Norwegian Ministry of Education and Research.

Ministry of Health. (2002). *Action plan against poverty.* Report to the Storting, no. 6 (2002–2003). Oslo: Norwegian Ministry of Health.

Ministry of Health. (2003). *Prescription for a healthier Norway.* Report to the Storting, no. 16 (2002–2003). Oslo: Norwegian Ministry of Health.

Ministry of Health and Care Services. (2007). *National strategy to reduce social inequalities in health.* Report to the Storting, no. 20 (2006–2007). Oslo: Norwegian Ministry of Health and Care Services.

Ministry of Health and Care Services. (2011). *The Norwegian Public Health Act: Short introduction.* Oslo: Norwegian Ministry of Health and Care Services. Retrieved from: www.regjeringen.no/upload/HOD/Hoeringer%20FHA_FOS/1234.pdf.

Ministry of Health and Care Services. (2012). *About the ministry.* Retrieved from: www.regjeringen.no/en/dep/hod/About-the-Ministry.html?id=426.

Ministry of Health and Social Affairs. (1993). *Challenges in health promotion and health education.* Report to the Storting, no. 37 (1992–1993). Oslo: Norwegian Ministry of Health and Social Affairs.

Ministry of Health and Social Affairs. (1999). *The equitable redistribution White Paper (1999).* Report to the Storting, no. 50 (1998–1999). Oslo: Norwegian Ministry of Health and Social Affairs.

Ministry of Labour and Social Inclusion. (2006a). *Work, welfare, and inclusion.* Report to the Storting, no. 9 (2006–2007). Oslo: Norwegian Ministry of Labour and Social Inclusion.

Ministry of Labour and Social Inclusion. (2006b). *Plan of action to combat poverty.* Attachment to the Proposition to the Parliament (Storting) no. 1 (2006–2007). National budget, 2007. Oslo: Norwegian Ministry of Labour and Social Inclusion.

Ministry of Labour and Social Inclusion. (2007). *Plan of action for the integration and inclusion of the immigrant population: Strengthened efforts 2008.* Attachment to the Proposition to the Parliament (Storting), no. 1 (2007–2008). National budget, 2008. Oslo: Norwegian Ministry of Labour and Social Inclusion.

Ministry of Social Affairs. (1987). *Health policy towards the Year 2000: National health plan.* Report to the Storting, no. 41 (1987–1988). Oslo: Norwegian Ministry of Social Affairs.

Mogstad, M. (2005). *Poverty in greater Oslo: An empirical analysis.* [In Norwegian only.] Report no. 11. Oslo: Statistics Norway.

Myklestad, I., Rognerud, M., & Johansen, R. (2008). *Rapport 2008:8: Vulnerable groups and mental health. Living Conditions Study 2005.* [In Norwegian only.] Oslo: Norwegian Institute of Public Health.

Næss, Ø., Rognerud, M., & Strand, B.H. (2007). *Social inequalities in health: A fact report.* [In Norwegian only.] Report 2007:1. Oslo: Norwegian Institute of Public Health.

Navarro, V., et al. (2006). Politics and health outcomes. *The Lancet, 368*(16), 658–659.

Norwegian Directorate of Health and Social Affairs (2012). *About Us.* Available online at http://www.helsedirektoratet.no.

Norwegian Institute of Public Health. (2008). *News article 2008: Net income 2006.* [In Norwegian only.] Oslo: Norwegian Institute of Public Health.

Norwegian Institute of Public Health. (2010). *The state of public health in Norway: Public health report 2010.* Retrieved from: http://www.fhi.no/eway/default.aspx?pid=233&trg=Area_5774&MainLeft_5669=5774:0:&Area_5774=5544:84298::0:5776:1:::0:0.

Norwegian Institute of Public Health. (2012). *For healthier people.* Retrieved from: www.fhi.no.

Research Council of Norway. (2012a). *Research Programme on Public Health.* Retrieved from: www.forskningsradet.no/servlet/Satellite?c=Page&cid=1222932153156&pagename=folkehelse%2FHovedsidemal.

Research Council of Norway. (2012b). *Årets søknadsresultater for Folkehelseprogrammet.* Retrieved from: www.forskningsradet.no/no/Artikkel/Arets_soknadsresultater_for_Folkehelseprogrammet/1253969811938.

Statistics Norway. (2011a). *More children at risk of poverty.* Retrieved from: http://www.ssb.no/english/subjects/05/01/inntind_en/.

Statistics Norway. (2011b). Website. Retrieved from: www.ssb.no.

Strand, B.H., Grøholt, E.-K., Steingrímsdóttir, Ó.A., Blakely, T., Graff-Iversen, S., & Næss, Ø. (2010). Educational inequalities in mortality over four decades in Norway: Prospective study of middle-aged men and women followed for cause-specific mortality, 1960–2000. *BMJ, 340,* 654–663.

Strand, M., & Fosse, E. (2011). Tackling health inequalities in Norway: Applying linear and non-linear models in the policy making process. *Critical Public Health, 21*(2), 373–381.

Sund, E.R., & Krokstad, S. (2005). *Kunnskapsoversikt over forskning på sosiale ulikheter i helse* [Knowledge base of research on social inequalities in health]. Oslo: Norwegian Directorate of Health and Social Affairs.

Whitehead, M. (1998). Diffusion of ideas on social inequalities in health: A European perspective. *Milbank Quarterly, 76*(3), 469–492.

World Health Organization. (1986). *The Ottawa Charter for health promotion.* Retrieved from: www.who.int/hpr/NPH/docs/ottawa_charter_hp.pdf.

Zahl, P.H., et al. (2003). *Bedre helse—større forskjeller* [Better health—wider differences]. Report 2003:1. Oslo: Norwegian Institute of Public Health.

Chapter 8

Swedish Experiences

Mona C. Backhans and Bo Burström

Introduction

Sweden does very well in terms of population health, with low infant mortality rates and long life expectancy. The extent of health inequalities in Sweden is comparable to other countries when looking at relative figures or comparisons between groups. But absolute levels of health inequalities are clearly lower between groups than is the case in other wealthy developed nations. Much of this has to do with Sweden's all-embracing welfare state, which spends a large part of its gross domestic product (GDP) on citizen supports and public services.

Recently, there has been a change in national government—from the left to the middle-right—with new forms of steering mechanisms called New Public Management. Nevertheless, there remains high confidence in welfare state institutions among the Swedish population. Promoting health equity remains part of the national public health policy, but it has not been prioritized by the current government. The extensive public debate that is now underway regarding the introduction of for-profit organizations in health care may provide new opportunities to put health equity back onto the agenda.

National Description and Political Organization and Structure

Sweden is a large country (four-fifths the size of Spain) with a small population density and just over 9.4 million inhabitants in 2011. The three largest regions of the country (Stockholm, Skåne, and Västra Götaland) account for about 50 percent of the national population. The Swedish birth rate fluctuates considerably with the economic cycle and was 1.94 per woman in 2009. Fourteen percent of the population is foreign-born (Statistics Sweden, 2010).

Sweden—together with Finland, Denmark, Norway, and Iceland—make up the Nordic region in northern Europe. These five countries are commonly perceived as quite similar when viewed from an international perspective. They all more or less share the principle of universalism and achieve broad public participation in various areas of economic and social life via strong political parties, broad interest organizations, a vital civil society, high voting turnout, and open commissions of inquiries as part of the legislative process, which is intended to promote an equality of the highest standards rather than an equality of minimal needs (Lundberg et al., 2008; Trädgårdh, 2007; Einhorn & Logue, 2003).

The key aspects of the welfare systems in these countries are: (1) all-embracing or almost all-embracing social policies; (2) services that are free or subsidized at the point of delivery; (3) a high proportion of GDP spent on health and social services; and (4) an emphasis on full employment. Not surprisingly, Sweden shows evidence of excellent population health and health inequalities that are, in absolute terms, rather smaller than that seen in other wealthy developed nations. The Nordic countries are also characterized by a high degree of gender equality (World Economic Forum, 2011) and low levels of corruption within the public sector (Transparency International, 2011).

Health Situation and Demographics

Sweden usually ranks among the top countries when comparing different health indicators internationally. In 2010 life expectancy at birth was 79.5 for men and 83.5 for women. During the last 10-year period, life expectancy has increased by slightly more than two years for men and 1.5 years for women. In other words, it increased by 2.5 months per year for men and by slightly less than two months per year for women. Since life expectancy increases are larger for men than for women, the gender gap in life expectancy is decreasing.

Differences in life expectancy between educational groups have increased slightly during the last decade. This is true for both men and women. Life expectancy at age 30 is almost five years higher for women and men with tertiary education than for those with only lower secondary education (Figure 8.1). For people with tertiary education, there are no regional differences in life expectancy. On the other hand, among people with lower secondary education, those in the southern part of Sweden have lower mortality rates than those in the northern part (Statistics Sweden, 2010).

There have been attempts to compare health inequalities between countries (NEWS, 2008). One conclusion from these attempts is that comparable data are sparse and available only for a limited number of countries at a few points in time. However, from the data available, it was concluded that relative inequalities in mortality between social groups are not smaller than elsewhere in Europe. In terms of the absolute levels of mortality among manual workers as compared to non-manual workers, Sweden is in a better position than many other countries.

Organization of the Welfare State

As noted above, welfare policy in Sweden is characterized by its universality and relative lack of means-testing and generous benefit levels with a high degree of income replacement. Welfare services are almost solely produced within the public sector, with a small but increasing number of private actors. In both the health care sector and the social sector, the share of care supplied by private actors has risen. However, the majority of care is still financed via taxes through the municipalities or county councils. Public funding finances 82 percent of health care expenditure, and private household out-of-pocket expenditure accounts for 16 percent. Only 0.2 percent of health expenditure in Sweden is financed via private insurance enterprises (European

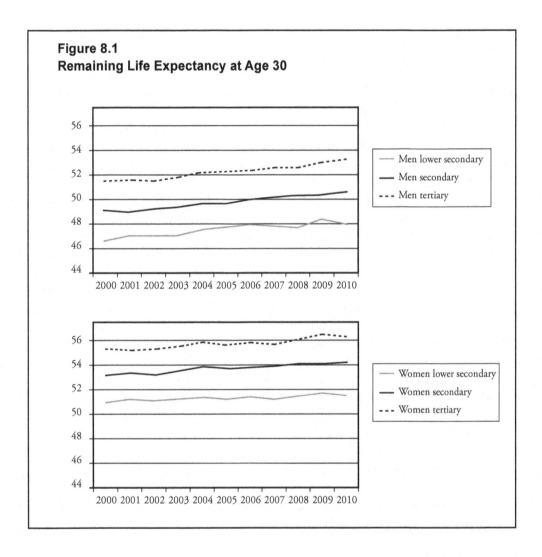

Figure 8.1
Remaining Life Expectancy at Age 30

Commission, 2011). A relatively small share of the population reports that they have refrained from seeking care because of financial problems. In an international survey on health policies conducted by the Commonwealth Fund, 5 percent of Swedes reported that they had not seen a doctor, even though they needed to, because of cost-related problems. This could be compared to Germany or the US, where 16 percent and 22 percent respectively reported that they did not seek care because of cost-related problems (Commonwealth Fund, 2010).

The goal of welfare policy is primarily redistribution, but there are also efficiency aspects (e.g., education and health care are improved) and stability, e.g., countering the negative effects of the economic cycle. General government expenditures as a percentage of GDP (gross domestic product) is one way of measuring the size of the public sector. According to this measurement, the public sector's total share of GDP was 53 percent in 2010, which could be compared to the situation in 1995, when the share was 65 percent (European Central Bank, n.d.). Transfers to households, mainly through social insurance, make up 30 percent of the public sector's expenses. Half of the expenses go to public consumption of goods and services, mainly welfare services—such as social assistance (child care and care of the elderly)—education, and health care. The basic parts of social insurance cover sickness and parental insurance, old age pension, disability pension, and work injury insurance. Social insurance is divided into a residency-based insurance, which provides guaranteed amounts and benefits, and a work-related insurance, which protects against loss of income. Both apply equally to everyone who is habitually resident or who works in Sweden. The large public sector is supported by progressive taxes and the total tax rate as a share of GDP has been around 50 percent of GDP since the early 1980s.

Even though there has been an ongoing discussion of whether the Nordic type of welfare states will persist in the future (Nordic Council of Ministers, 2007), the available evidence—for example, the recent results from Svallfors's (2011) Swedish welfare state studies—indicate that the Swedish system resists, or adapts successfully to, challenges such as changes in demography and the effects of globalization, and at the same time enjoys high confidence among the population. In an article based on surveys of Swedes' attitudes toward the welfare state from 1981 to 2010, Svallfors concludes that overall, there is a large degree of stability in attitudes, and where change is registered, it tends to go in the direction of increasing support.

More people now state their willingness to pay higher taxes for welfare policy purposes; more people want collective financing of welfare policies; and fewer people perceive extensive welfare abuse in 2010 than was the case in previous surveys. At the political level there is also a persistent confidence in the welfare state institutions. In 2010 the Swedish prime minister said in the Statement of Government Policy before Parliament, the Riksdag, that public financing is a central part of the Swedish system (Statement of Government Policy, 2010):

> A well developed welfare system is a matter of social justice. The activities and services offered by the welfare system must be of the highest quality and targeted at individual people according to their needs, irrespective of background, place of residence, gender or financial situation. The basis for achieving this is public financing in a spirit of solidarity. (pp. 12–13)

Political Organization

Sweden has three democratically elected levels of government, each with its own powers and responsibilities: the Riksdag (Swedish Parliament) at the national level, 21 county councils at the regional level, and 290 municipalities at the local level. The Riksdag passes legislation and decides on state revenue (taxes) and expenditure. County councils and municipalities have their own decision-making and tax-levying powers. Municipalities have a significant degree of autonomy and administer local matters such as compulsory and upper secondary education, preschool, elderly care, roads and water, waste and energy. The chief purpose of the county councils is to manage health care. County councils are also responsible for planning dental care and regional public transport.

The Social Democratic Party in Sweden has historically played an important role in the foundations of the Swedish system and is considered the caretakers of the famous cradle-to-grave welfare state. Since the 1930s the party has been in power for the vast majority of the time, but their voter support in the last two elections—in 2006 and 2010—were among the lowest in the entire history of the party. Since 2006 a centre-right alliance—consisting of the Moderate Party, the Liberal Party, the Centre Party, and the Christian Democrats—formed a majority government. The centre-right alliance is still in government after the 2010 parliamentary election, but no longer has a majority in the Riksdag.

Swedish Policy Documents and Statements on Health Inequalities

Even though Sweden did not have a clearly stated public health policy until the beginning of the 1980s, historically the state has made a number of important efforts to improve the health situation for its population in the last few centuries (Sundin & Willner, 2007).

Epidemiological measurement is essential to the assessment of public health practice, and in the 1750s Sweden started to collect annual statistics on population change (mortality tables) and composition (population tables) from all Swedish parishes. To begin with, these data were regarded as so important for state security that they were kept secret. These statistics made it clear to the authorities that Sweden's weak population growth rate was caused primarily by high mortality, especially among young children. In response to this problem, a number of efforts were made to improve the situation, a prime example being the provision of information articles in annual Swedish calendars on how to best treat newborn children.

Even though there is a lack of data from these earlier times that would allow for examination of differences between population groups when it comes to health, we know from early writings that poverty was an important determinant of ill health. For example, the Swedish medical doctor, Abraham Bäck, concluded in the middle of the 18th century that: "The poverty-stricken are ravaged by pestilence while few of the wealthier fall ill" (Lundberg and Fritzell, 2007, 12).

More determined efforts to improve the health situation of the Swedish population can be seen during the latter stages of the 19th century. Examples of this include the introduction of health checks on mothers and children; the creation of school and company health services; and health checks that targeted specific diseases, such as tuberculosis. The development of social medicine as an academic discipline in Sweden also brought with it discussions about topics and issues that today would fall into the domain of public health, such as the impact of living conditions upon health, and the effects and means of preventing alcohol and drug abuse.

However, in the wake of World War II, the focus changed considerably. During this period, the health care sector grew in an unprecedented way. New therapeutic and diagnostic procedures created new subspecialties both among physicians and new hospital structures. As living standards and technology improved, so did the health of the Swedish population. There was also eradication of some diseases, such as tuberculosis. Like the situation of most western European countries during this period, the Swedish health care delivery system became hospital-based (Glenngård et al., 2005).

Public Health Policies at the National Level: Health Inequalities on the Agenda since the 1980s

However, during the 1970s and the 1980s it became clear that the health sector could not expand much further. At the same time, it also became clear that health care alone could not further improve the overall health situation of the Swedish population. This realization occurred simultaneously with the World Health Organization's (WHO) initiative, Health for All by the Year 2000, which began at the end of the 1970s. At the beginning of the 1980s, a number of reports were published showing that even though Sweden had a universal welfare system, there were still health inequalities between social groups. For example, in 1987 the first national public health report presented by the National Board of Health and Welfare showed there were large socio-economic differences in health.

In tandem with the WHO's efforts to develop a strategy to achieve "Health for All" by 2000 and Swedish reports on existing health inequalities, the Swedish government ascertained in its communication, *Developments in Public Health* (Government of Sweden, 1987/1988), that implementing effective measures to equalize health conditions by the year 2000 through a social perspective must be given special consideration. Furthermore, it was emphasized that potential health gains could be achieved through targeted measures, particularly in the area of prevention, aimed at equalizing the health status of various social groups. In its 1991 public health bill, entitled *Some Public Health Issues* (Government of Sweden, 1990/1991), the government referred to the importance of economic and social development for creating good material conditions to ensure that the majority of the population would lead long and healthy lives.

This was a response to findings that for many groups, the trend was toward increased morbidity, social exclusion, and premature death. According to the government, not only did individuals bear a major responsibility for their own health, but all citizens had "a common responsibility to combat the mechanisms in society that lead to inequitable health development."

In 1995, the government appointed a committee tasked to produce national objectives for health development. This committee released a report in 2000 with proposed goals for public health that focused solely on health determinants and not health outcomes. Among other things, it suggested strengthening social capital; providing a satisfactory environment in which children can grow up; improving working conditions and the physical environment; stimulating health-promoting habits; and providing satisfactory infrastructure for health issues.

In response to the committee's suggestions, the Riksdag adopted, in 2003, a bill entitled *Objectives for Public Health* (Government of Sweden, 2002/2003). The bill established a national public health strategy that detailed how the overall aim of Swedish public health policy would be "to create social conditions that will ensure good health on equal terms for the entire population." In addition, 11 objective domains and a large number of policy areas were specified. The 11 objective domains are:

1. participation and influence in society
2. economic and social security
3. secure and favourable conditions during childhood and adolescence
4. healthier working life
5. healthy and safe environments and products
6. health and medical care that more actively promotes good health
7. effective protection against communicable diseases
8. safe sexuality and good reproductive health

9. increased physical activity
10. good eating habits and safe food
11. reduced use of tobacco and alcohol, a society free from illicit drugs, doping, and a reduction in the harmful effects of excessive gambling

Although the main target of the national public health policy continues to stand, it is clear in the updated public health policy from 2008 (Government of Sweden, 2007/2008) that social inequalities as such are now not a priority. The governmental initiatives taken have an emphasis on tobacco and alcohol (especially regarding curtailing adolescents' access to them) and the main target groups for attention are defined as children, young people, and the elderly. The emphasis on supporting parents through educational programs and support groups (Föräldrastöd) has a solid evidence base (Sandler et al., 2011; Bakermans-Kranenburg et al., 2003), and should also have the potential to be empowering and decrease health inequalities over the long term if they are made universally available. A major problem is, of course, the difficulties in reaching those most in need. In 2010–2014, a large intervention project, which will be scientifically evaluated, is being undertaken in a few municipalities.

Policies at the Regional Level: A Growing Concern with Health Inequalities, But No Clear Picture of What Needs to Be Done

As noted earlier, the regional and local levels are fairly autonomous in Sweden. County councils and municipalities have their own political bodies and raise their own taxes. They are also the most important actors when it comes to public health interventions. There is relatively little research on how public health issues are approached in municipalities in Sweden. This could partly be explained by the fact that municipalities differ in many ways when it comes to their geography and demography. There are also differences in the organization and delivery of their services.

However, the National Institute of Public Health has regularly produced surveys or reports on how the 290 municipalities in Sweden work with public health issues. One of the most recent studies on eight municipalities was done within an EU-financed project and showed that good health is generally accepted by municipal representatives as a prerequisite for positive local development (FHI & SoS, 2010). This view is particularly apparent among the local politicians who were interviewed. The interviewed municipalities all have an explicit overall goal of attaining a high and equal level of health in the population as expressed in a Public Health Strategy or the equivalent adopted by the city council. All of the municipalities also have a plan for public health work and how it should be promoted. It is seen as important that the process of developing goals and action plans involve multiple stakeholders. It is also seen as important that the process be integrated with other ongoing municipal developments.

There are also international studies that include Swedish municipalities. For example, the Swedish cities that participate in the WHO Network on Healthy Cities have also been active when it comes to measuring health inequalities. Ritsatakis (2009) noted in her analysis of the work done within the network that cities in countries with a strong tradition of research in equity in health—e.g., the Netherlands, Sweden, and the United Kingdom—reported the most detailed monitoring, including "deprivation indices," which cover a range of indicators of socio-economic determinants of health.

Research on Health Inequalities in Sweden

Research into the existence and causes of health inequalities first took off—or was rediscovered—with the publication of the Lalonde Report in Canada and the Black Report in the United Kingdom. The publication of the first Swedish public health report in 1987 sharpened the focus on health inequities, and research into this area became established by 1990. In 1998, a publication from Socialvetenskapliga forskningsrådet (SFR) collected contributions from Swedish researchers with the aim of establishing a strategy for promoting research on inequality in health. The following section concerns research conducted during the latest 10-year period.

Institutions That Support Research into Health Inequalities

The largest research funder of public health research is the Swedish Council for Working Life and Social Research (FAS), a government agency. Most of the support given is to individual projects, but the FAS also gives strategic support to larger research programs. An overview of research funded since 2001 shows that out of a total of 626 projects in public health, there were 44 projects and 12 research programs explicitly related to health inequalities. Out of the 44 projects, over 60 percent concern etiology, 20 percent explicitly mention the development of theory or methods, and about 15 percent have conducted some type of evaluation of existing policies or concrete measures. No project concerns intervention, however.

Out of the 12 larger research programs (of which many are continuations of earlier research programs), almost 60 percent are directed at the development of theory and/or methods, five concern evaluation, and only three concern etiology (although this is often part of results in projects devoted to theory and/or methods). One of the largest projects/programs is the establishment of the Centre for Health Equity Studies (CHESS) in Stockholm in 2000, whose purpose is to initiate new, and strengthen already established, Swedish research on health inequalities.

Another large research funder is the Swedish Research Council (VR). During the same period, we have been able to identify only four VR-supported projects related to social inequalities in health. Of these, three projects are set in low-income countries (Vietnam and Brazil). The project set in Sweden concerns the social determinants and the polarization of fear of, and exposure to, violence. Riksbankens Jubileumsfond (RJ) is an independent foundation that primarily supports research in the humanities and social sciences. In recent years, it supported two projects that used historical data. One investigated the production of social inequalities during 1650–1900 in nine rural parishes, and one evaluated the importance of sanitary reforms for the reduction in child mortality in Stockholm from 1878 to 1925, and in Mozambique in 1997.

AFA Insurance is jointly owned by employers and unions. In addition to their core insurance activities, they support preventive measures and research grants for improving health in working life. The type of projects normally supported by the AFA concern particular workplaces or professions, so the findings may be used to prevent ill health among exposed groups. However, they tend not to have a broader societal focus and do not compare socio-economic groups. Vinnova is a Swedish government agency whose aim is to increase the competitiveness of Swedish researchers and companies. It has supported several projects regarding gender equity in health care and in working life, but not projects with an explicit social inequalities agenda. However, Vinnova has supported several projects concerning rehabilitation and measures to prevent sickness absence and labour market exclusion.

Research Findings

Few projects during the last 10 years are concerned with providing simple descriptions of the prevalence of health inequalities. This is probably because these inequalities have been fairly well documented in earlier research. Instead, the focus has been on explaining the causes and consequences of these health inequalities. Out of the FAS projects that explicitly mention prevalence of health inequalities, several concern the existence of inequalities in access to and/or the quality of care. Examples of results from such research show that: low education is associated with a 50 percent higher case fatality after myocardial infarction (MI) regardless of sex and birth country (Yang et al., 2011), and most health care provision in Stockholm county council from 1998 to 2005 was equitable in relation to need. But this was not the case for privately provided specialist care (FAS grant no. 2006-0881). Studies regarding management and treatment after cancer diagnosis have found social inequalities in that for some forms of cancer, these social inequalities helped explain the social gradient in survival (Cavalli-Björkman et al., 2011; Berglund et al., 2010; Eaker et al., 2009). Others studies have reported that women, those of non-Swedish origin, the unemployed, and those with a low level of education more often do not seek health care despite a perceived need for it. Stated reasons included a lack of confidence in medical care, and also availability and economic and financial issues (FAS grant no. 2002-0914).

Research into the income gradient in self-rated health (SRH) has shown a threefold (for men) to fivefold (for women) higher prevalence of low SRH among those in the lowest compared to the highest quintile, while the odds ratio for CVD morbidity was 2.6 (men and women combined) for the lowest as compared to the highest quintile (FAS grant no. 2001-2132). Others studies have shown that female low-level manual workers had a risk of myocardial infarction three times higher than that of high-level non-manual women (FAS grant no. 2001-1131). The corresponding figure for men was 2.6.

Another study focusing on road traffic injuries in childhood and adolescence found that the risk of injury for a pedestrian or cyclist was 20–30 percent higher among children of working-class parents, which was further increased when they, as adolescents, began using motor vehicles (FAS grant no. 2001-1190). Intergenerational studies on the Uppsala birth cohort have shown that sons of men born out of wedlock in early 20th-century Sweden, as well as the sons and grandsons of women born out of wedlock, had significantly lower psychological functioning and cognitive abilities (Modin et al., 2009).

Many research projects have examined contributors to health inequalities at the individual, local, and higher levels. Studies of individual risk factors have found that psychosocial and physical work environment factors account for roughly 40–50 percent of the difference in SRH in the lowest as compared to the highest income quintile (FAS grant no. 2001-2132). In this study, income was more important as an explanatory factor for male than female mortality. Studies using a life course approach have found that the relationship between job control and CVD morbidity was almost fully explained by social risk factors during childhood and adolescence (FAS grant no. 2003-0382), and that the longer the experience of social adversity, the greater the risk of MI (FAS grant no. 2002-0551).

Other studies of the same cohort of men have shown that 60–70 percent of socio-economic differences in alcoholism were explained by early risk factors. It was also shown that independent of class of origin, men in manual occupations (as class of destination) had higher mortality rates compared to men in non-manual occupations. When risk indicators at time of conscription to the study were considered, the excess risk in manual occupations was diminished by about 50 percent (FAS grant no. 2001-1057).

Some interesting findings regarding area-level factors are the following: socio-economic composition, but not the ethnic mix, of neighbourhoods has an impact on risk behaviours among young people and pregnant women (FAS grant no. 2007-0898) and there is synergy between exposure at area level (noise) and foreign origin, being marginalized from working life, and financial stress resulting in high blood pressure, stress, and sleep problems (FAS grant no. 2005-1121). One project in the Stockholm area found that the effect of neighbourhood social capital on health and mortality is very weak (FAS grant no. 2004-1757), while another has shown that high residential instability in neighbourhoods in southern Sweden is associated with a higher risk of fatality in cardiovascular disease-related events and a shorter survival after a myocardial infarction (FAS grant no. 2003-0580).

Projects examining income inequality and health at the municipal level have found no support for an association (FAS grant no. 2002-0376 and 2002-0040). One project investigated area effects at parish and neighbourhood level on myocardial infarction, and found that social contexts characterized by social exclusion or poverty/ethnicity had their greatest impact on men (30 percent risk increase), while contexts defined by class structure had most impact on women (70 percent risk increase). Furthermore, both men and women in the most materially deprived or most fragmented areas had similar risk increases after adjustment for individual risk factors (FAS grant no. 2001-1131). Among women, synergy was suggested between a low level of resources in the local area and low individual income.

Studies investigating policy effects have shown that differences in work-life policies and work-related psychosocial factors between Denmark and Sweden did not seem to affect the social gradient in smoking, which is similar in the two countries (FAS grant no. 2004-1075). It was also found that the more active anti-smoking policy in Sweden had decreased the total level of smoking to a greater extent, but, at the same time, it had increased smoking inequalities among women, while for men, the existence of *snus* (smokeless tobacco) had resulted in a low gradient. A project (FAS grant no. 2002-0448) that examined the mechanisms of social differentials in health in Sweden and Great Britain found that socio-economic differences in health were explained by income differences to a greater extent in Great Britain than in Sweden. Comparisons of lone mothers in Britain and Sweden showed a considerably higher poverty rate among British than Swedish lone mothers. Health inequalities between lone and couple mothers were of similar relative magnitude in both countries, but poverty and joblessness explained more of the health disadvantage of British lone mothers than of Swedish lone mothers. The Nordic Experience Public Health and Welfare States project (NEWS) has investigated the importance of social policy for population health (Lundberg et al., 2008). Factors identified as important for health improvements are total social spending, universal access to social insurance, parental leave, and the generosity of basic security pensions. If one should summarize the essence of these projects, the message may be:

- Early risk factors are important predictors of social inequalities in adulthood.
- Social deprivation at the area level can have a large effect on individual health outcomes.
- There are indications of social inequalities in health care.
- Generosity and coverage of social insurance benefits population health, and may buffer against increased health outcome differentials in times of adversity.

Impact of Research on National and Regional Policies and Initiatives

In the updated public health policy, the objectives most connected to socio-structural factors are: (1) participation and influence in society; (2) economic and social security; (3) secure and favourable conditions during childhood and adolescence; and (4) healthier working life. The first objective was inspired by the research on social capital and health. Some of the proposed measures for participation and influence in society are support for volunteer organizations and the Healthy Cities network. The latter has social inequalities as its special focus. There are 16 members, one of which represents an entire region (Skåne). Other mentioned proposals are introducing quasi-markets for health care and elder care; establishing anti-discrimination strategies in government agencies; and supporting measures to include people with functional impairment. Social inequalities in the possibility for economic and social participation—which may be due to poor finances, time constraints, language barriers, or low literacy (in a broad sense)—are, however, not addressed.

In the second dimension, the focus in the public health policy is on maintaining full employment, especially through a decrease in the number of long-term sick leaves. Various active labour market measures directed at immigrants and people with disabilities, as well as rehabilitation programs, are proposed. Such measures are typical of Swedish labour market policy and do not represent a departure from previous policy. Changes in sickness insurance, implying stricter criteria regarding eligibility and lower benefit levels, have possibly led to higher labour force rates, but the consequences for individuals in need of these benefits have been heavily debated.

One proposed measure in line with research findings is local development programs for socially deprived or excluded areas. During 2008–2010, 38 areas in 21 municipalities were granted special funds to develop their own programs, based on local needs. Governmental agencies that collaborate with the municipalities are the police, the social insurance agency, and the public employment service. The FHI has been given the task of establishing indicators for the most important determinants for health improvements in these areas.

For the third objective, supporting parenthood is, as already mentioned, very much a focus. Measures taken in areas other than the family include developing strategies for national child safety; combating bullying at school; preventing the sexual exploitation of children; and developing measures for at-risk youth. Several strategies concern monitoring—for example, mental health in grades 6 and 9, and the prevalence of discriminatory practices in the educational system. As research has shown, child injuries should be a priority for diminishing social inequalities. The national strategy is part of the European Union project, the Child Safety Action Plan, which focuses on preventing drowning among children 0–6 years old and alcohol-related accidents among adolescents. Addressing social inequalities of these outcomes is not an explicit part of the strategy.

One of the first initiatives launched by the recently elected government was to dismantle the National Work Environment Institute (ALI) and redirect funds to research institutions. The remaining governmental agency, the Swedish Work Environment Authority, is an administrative authority that collects statistics, conducts workplace inspections, and issues detailed regulations. The budget for this agency was cut by one-third when ALI was closed. The fourth objective, health in working life, the only concrete measure mentioned, concerns changes in laws regulating temporary employment, which have been simplified. A new national plan for work environment improvements 2010–2015 has, however, been launched, which prioritizes the prevention of injuries and health risks. Among the proposed measures are better ways of enforcing sanctions against employers, supporting occupational health care, and finding good indicators of "healthy work."

At the national level, the Swedish Marmot Commission (FHI, 2010) presented its recommendations in 2010, but has not had much of an impact. The concept of proportionate universalism was borrowed from the English review, and translated to a recommendation to give special support to sparsely populated municipalities and socially deprived suburban areas, as well as specific population groups, such as working-class women and immigrants, young adults with low educational qualifications, and people with functional impairments (Melinder, 2011).

Based on this and the original committee, there have been a number of local and regional initiatives. For example, the southern city of Malmö has formed the Commission for a Socially Sustainable Malmö, with the objective of producing a report with evidence-based recommendations on how to reduce health inequities (Balkfors & Isacsson, 2011). All in all, 21 municipalities and regions that have started working according to the Marmot Commission have come together in a national network (Samling för social hållbarhet), administered by the Swedish Association of Local Authorities and Regions (SKL). The first network conference was given in Malmö in September 2011. Also, Forum folkhälsa, a network of municipalities, regions, and volunteer organizations, has chosen to focus on health inequalities, which has been the theme of its two latest conferences. It is obvious that today, initiatives are being taken at the local and regional level to actively tackle health inequalities.

Public Policy and Health Inequalities in Sweden

In the early 1990s Sweden experienced the most severe economic crisis since the 1930s, with three consecutive years of negative economic growth and high unemployment rates. Subsequently, the economy has recovered and become strengthened, unemployment rates have been reduced, but some features of the Swedish welfare state have substantially changed in recent years.

Labour Market Policy

In the 1980s and early 1990s Sweden had strong regulation and legislation to support individuals in the labour market. The government was also heavily involved in industry, both through its own investments and through subsidies of certain business sectors. Active labour market policies have been a hallmark of Sweden, and include interventions to facilitate reintroduction to the labour market of people who have been laid off because of structural changes by supporting relocation and retraining of individuals in need. In the last 20 years the government has increasingly divested itself of its ownership of industry to private interests.

The economic recession in the early 1990s meant that several hundred thousand jobs were lost in many sectors, especially in the public sector. Female employment in the public sector peaked at the end of the 1980s, and since then many of these jobs have accrued to the private sector, which grew considerably in the second half of the 1990s and the early 2000s. Local government (county councils and municipalities) is a big employer in Sweden, with about one-third of all employees. One response to the economic recession was to reduce the number of public employees and privatize the provision of social, caring, and health care services. Nevertheless, their sources of funding are still public (Palme et al., 2002).

However, in spite of the economy's recovery and increase in employment, the traditionally low unemployment rate of 2–3 percent, which prevailed throughout the 1980s, increased to about 5 percent or higher, and has remained at or above that level since then. The unemployment rate among young adults is one of the highest in Europe, with particularly high rates among certain groups of young adults. The government still pursues active labour market policies, but not as extensively as before the economic recession in the 1990s. The proportion of those who have fixed-term contracts has increased, as have other types of precarious employment (Wikman, 2001).

Family Policy

Sweden has a comprehensive dual-earner family policy that supports the reconciliation of family and work for both parents. Parental leave is extensive (18 months) with high (80 percent) reimbursement rates. Part of the parental leave is intended to be shared between the parents, and apart from the 10 days of leave offered to the father in conjunction with the delivery of the baby, another eight weeks of paid leave are reserved for the father. Social insurance also covers and reimburses absence from work for parents to take care of sick children up to the age of eight. Legislation also allows parents with children younger than eight years to work part-time in their ordinary job. Municipalities must provide child daycare for every child aged 18 months or older. The child care services are generally considered to be of high quality and the fees are heavily subsidized. The number of children per employee has fluctuated between 5.1 and 5.4 during the last 10 years (http://www.skolverket.se/statistik_och_analys/2.1862/2.4317/2.4319).

Income and Wages

Average incomes and wages are comparatively high. Up until recently, Sweden has had a very low Gini coefficient, indicating small income inequalities. However, in recent decades, income inequalities have increased. In 1995 the Gini coefficient was 0.227, increasing to 0.261 in 1999 and to 0.291 in 2009 (Statistics Sweden, 2011). This change is due to many factors, including an increase in wages in the highest income groups, coupled with reductions in taxes. In addition, social transfers have not increased to the same extent as wages and salaries, which contributes to the increased gap. The proportion of the population at risk of poverty (income less than 60 percent of the median income) has increased from 8.4 percent in 1999 to 13.4 percent in 2009. The increase has been steeper in some groups than in others. Among lone parents, the at-risk-of-poverty rate increased from 11 percent in 1999 to 27 percent in 2009.

Social Assistance and Unemployment Policy

With the expansion of social insurance and child benefits, social assistance has been a more marginal component of Swedish welfare policy (Kuvalainen & Nelson, 2012). During and after the economic recession in the 1990s, expenditure for social assistance increased dramatically, primarily due to high unemployment rates. Benefit levels of social assistance, which previously had been comparatively generous, were reduced and eligibility rules were restricted. With higher unemployment levels, an increasing proportion of benefit recipients have long-term social assistance. Recent immigrants are also overrepresented among social assistance recipients (Andrén & Gustafsson, 2004).

A study investigating the development over time in the levels of social assistance benefits in the Nordic countries concluded that since the 1990s, the level of social assistance benefits in Sweden and Finland has declined. In 1990 about 20 percent of social assistance recipients were poor, which was defined as having less than 50 percent of the median income, compared to 36 percent in 2005. The poverty alleviation (the degree to which means-tested benefits succeed in raising a person's income above the poverty threshold) of means-tested benefits was 53 percent in 1990 compared to 41 percent in 2005. The study (Kuvalainen & Nelson, 2012) concluded that social assistance benefits do not provide enough money for families to escape poverty, and that measures need to be taken to increase the adequacy of benefits.

Unemployment insurance has traditionally been managed by trade unions. The fees paid by employees have been comparatively low relative to the benefits received. The centre-right coalition government, elected in 2006, has raised employee fees considerably in recent years, which resulted in an increasing proportion of the working population opting out of the unemployment insurance. When these people are laid off, they must rely on a lower flat-rate unemployment benefit or social assistance benefits for their subsistence (Hort, 2009).

The working imperative is strong in Sweden, and especially so for social assistance recipients and people on sickness benefits. Recent (2008) restrictive changes to the sickness and disability insurance have put a time limit on sick leave and increased the pressure to return to work. People who do not qualify for continued sickness insurance benefits, but cannot return to work, have to rely on social assistance benefits.

Figure 8.2 shows the total number of people on social assistance, sickness insurance, and unemployment insurance from 1999 to 2010. As shown in the figure, the number of people receiving compensation from sickness insurance peaked in 2002 and has since decreased by about two-thirds. Those who are "openly" unemployed—that is, those receiving compensation, but not in training programs—decreased until 2002, then increased until 2004, after which the number dropped, with a small increase again after 2008. The number of people in active labour market training programs has more than doubled since 2008, which attests to the government's attempts to counteract the economic crisis. Also, the number on social assistance has increased by 25 percent since 2007. This may be due to the stricter qualification criteria in unemployment and sickness insurance.

Health Care Policy

Health care in Sweden is part of the comprehensive welfare system. It is tax-funded, covers the whole population, and is generally considered of good quality. The cost of health care

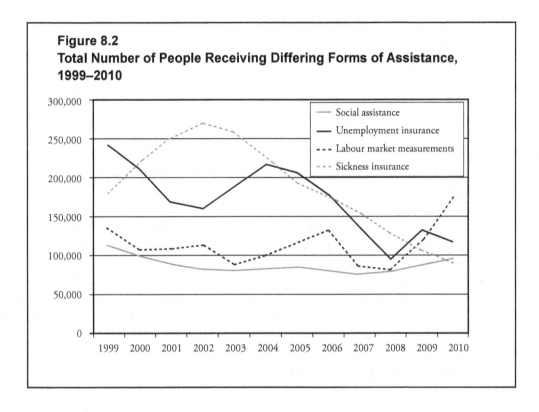

Figure 8.2
Total Number of People Receiving Differing Forms of Assistance,
1999–2010

is in the mid-range of OECD countries despite the high proportion of elderly (aged 80 years or older) in the population. The Swedish Health and Medical Care Act aims at good health for the whole population and emphasizes equitable care for all, based on principles of need. County councils are responsible for the planning and provision of health care for the population. Most of the care is also publicly provided. Patient fees are in the order of €15 (Can$20) for a visit to a general practitioner, €30 to a specialist, and €9 per night in hospital. There are high-cost protection systems both for visits to the doctor and for the cost of pharmaceutical drugs. The proportion of the population with private health insurance has been low (below 5 percent).

In the last 20 years there has been increasing experimentation with market-oriented mechanisms and New Public Management (Bergmark, 2008) in Swedish health care, including a division into purchasers and providers, and opportunities for private entrepreneurs to provide services financed by public funds. The proportion of care provided by such private entrepreneurs has been quite limited, but has increased substantially in recent years. The current government has a stated policy of increasing the number of private providers in health care and strengthening patients' opportunities to choose their care providers. In 2009 a law was enacted to allow private general practitioners to set up clinics, provide health care for patients, and then bill the county council. County councils opposed the law as it would restrict their ability to plan health care and reallocate resources according to need. Nevertheless, the law was passed and more than 200 new primary care clinics have been opened.

In some county councils, not least Stockholm County Council with 20 percent of the national population, the rate of privatization is rapid and is also being extended to other specialties, such as psychiatry. More than half of outpatient services are provided by private entrepreneurs in Stockholm County Council. In Stockholm there is also a privately operated hospital funded by public money. The privatization of health care and care of the elderly has resulted in an increase in the number of for-profit companies that are expanding their work in Sweden.

Examination of Political and Economic Forces behind These Public Policy Approaches

The changes observed in public policy approaches in Sweden have been to a great extent inspired by neo-liberal ideas regarding the role of government, acceptance of growing income inequalities, retrenchment of the welfare state, and an emphasis on the importance of individual choice. Although the long-term social democratic government experimented with privatization and market orientation during its time in power, the pace of the changes have accelerated considerably since 2006, when the current coalition came into its leadership position. The Moderate Party, which is the largest among the coalition partners, has marketed itself as the "new Workers Party," in contrast to the Social Democratic Party.

Recommendations for Future Activities

There have not been any large-scale social or political movements in response to the rapid changes in the provision of health and social care and restrictions in sickness and disability insurance in Sweden. However, some organizations (e.g., Gemensam Välfärd or Common Welfare) have been trying to highlight potential negative effects and to stimulate more debate about these issues. The Swedish Society of Social Medicine has also participated in the debate. Although there is steady and sometimes even increasing support for welfare state interventions, voters are turning away from the Social Democratic Party (Svallfors, 2011), mostly due to an internal crisis in the party that has rendered it basically inept at providing any kind of organized opposition.

In November 2011, there was an ongoing debate in the media and among political circles regarding for-profit enterprises in health care that was stimulated by revelations of maltreatment and tax evasion in one major company in this sector. Similar situations have been exposed in privately run schools and preschools. The growing discontent in the population could well mean that equity in health care will become more prominent on the policy agenda.

While regional and local activity inspired by the WHO's Marmot Commission is growing and is facilitated by the relative autonomy of county councils and municipalities, the same autonomy, coupled with a lack of state support, also means that political support for actions promoting health equity is very unevenly distributed across the country. Whereas both Norway and Denmark have managed to produce concrete national action plans based on their respective commissions, no such initiatives are being taken in Sweden. In Denmark, this work has been undertaken under a Conservative-led government, although the political leadership has recently shifted. Denmark's very poor performance regarding life expectancy since the 1970s may have contributed to a sense of urgency in that country, an urgency that is lacking in Sweden. Instead, a view of health as primarily determined by lifestyle choice has been allowed to take hold in Sweden, while the objectives concerned with structural determinants are simply not prioritized.

Conclusion

What can be done to change this and bring health equity back on the agenda? First, continued monitoring of the size of the health gradient is necessary so that the current state of affairs is made widely known. Second, it is important to evaluate the effects of changes in health and social care as well as social policy, not least the potential effects on equity in health. Both of these concern research efforts. Third, to elicit an appropriate political response, one may consider promoting health as a "special good" (Anand, 2002) to make politicians aware that the general public has a preference for equity in health, which is even stronger than its preference for equality in other outcomes.

A morally just society requires health equity, and good and equal health is an important asset that benefits the whole of society. Health equity should be a goal that most Swedish politicians across the left-right spectrum can endorse, particularly in a country with such a strong egalitarian legacy. There is nothing that leads us to believe that the political majority will change anytime soon. Therefore, it is clear that public health advocates need new strategies to bring politicians on board.

Note

1. The authors would like to thank Henrik Moberg for contributing background information to this chapter.

Critical Thinking Questions

1. Sweden has comparatively good outcomes when it comes to life expectancy, and it has low absolute levels of inequalities between groups, but relative inequality is still high. Which measure is most important or useful to apply when comparing the health situation of different groups in different countries? Single indicators (such as infant mortality or life expectancy), relative measures (i.e., relative risks between different groups), absolute measures (actual differences in rates between groups), or a combination of these three?
2. The Swedish Public Health Policy focuses on health determinants, both distal and proximate. The sub-dimensions are called objectives, but they lack quantifiable targets. What are the benefits and drawbacks to using a determinants rather than an outcome approach? Is it important or superfluous to state targets?
3. In the overview of recent research, it is clear that intervention studies are largely missing in the Swedish context. What is the case in your country? What do you think is the reason for this omission?
4. Previous studies that have evaluated the health effects of recession have found none, and the conclusion has been that the welfare state has buffered against such effects. Recent changes may have altered this picture. How may specific policies act as buffers?

Recommended Readings

Lundberg, O., Åberg Yngwe, M., Kölegård Stjärne, M., Björk, L., & Fritzell, J. (2008). *The Nordic experience: Welfare states and public health.* Final report from the NEWS project. Stockholm: CHESS, 2008.
The NEWS project links research on social policy and public health by highlighting the Nordic experience. The main message is that universal social policies, at least those directed toward children and the old, tend to be positive for population health.

OECD. (2011). *OECD health data 2011: How does Sweden compare?* Retrieved from: http://www.oecd.org/dataoecd/46/6/38980334.pdf.
A good overview of the Swedish health care system (expenditure, private-public spending, etc.).

Sundin, J., & Willner, S. (2007). *Social change and health in Sweden: 250 years of politics and practice.* Östersund: National Institute for Public Health.
This book takes a long look at Sweden's development and tries to draw important lessons from history.

Svallfors, S. (2011). A bedrock of support? Trends in welfare state attitudes in Sweden, 1981–2010. *Social Policy and Administration, 45*(7), 806–825.
Svallfors's research shows that support for public financing of the welfare system has increased during the last decade, as well as the willingness to pay tax to support the general welfare system.

Recommended Websites

Statistics Sweden's English language website: www.scb.se/default____2154.aspx
This website has facts and figures on almost everything you might need to know about Sweden.

Swedish Council for Working Life and Social Research (FAS): www.fas.se/en/
Their grants database provides information on all FAS-supported projects.

Swedish Government website: http://www.sweden.gov.se/sb/d/2197
The government's website has information on health care, health, and social insurance.

Swedish National Institute of Public Health: http://www.fhi.se/en/
The website provides information on Sweden's public health policy and ongoing projects.

References

Anand, S. (2002). The concern for equity in health. *Journal of Epidemiology and Community Health, 56,* 485–487.

Andrén, T., & Gustafsson, B. (2004). Patterns of social assistance receipt in Sweden. *International Journal of Social Welfare, 13,* 55–68.

Bakermans-Kranenburg, M.J., van Ijzendoorn, M., & Juffer, F. (2003). Less is more: Meta-analyses of sensitivity and attachment interventions in early childhood. *Psychological Bulletin, 129*(2), 195–215.

Balkfors, A. & Isacsson, S.-O. (2011). Sveriges första Marmot-kommission i Malmö. *Socialmedicinsk Tidskrift, 88*(4), 299–303.

Berglund, A., Holmberg, L., Tishelman, C., Wagenius, G., Eaker, S., & Lambe, M. (2010). Social inequalities in non-small cell lung cancer management and survival: A population-based study in central Sweden. *Thorax, 65*(4), 327–333.

Bergmark, Å. (2008). Market reforms in Swedish health care: Normative reorientation and welfare state sustainability. *Journal of Medical Philosophy, 33*(3), 241–261.

Cavalli-Björkman, N., Lambe, M., Eaker, S., Sandin, F., & Glimelius, B. (2011). Differences according to educational level in the management and survival of colorectal cancer in Sweden. *European Journal of Cancer, 47*(9), 1398–1406.

Commonwealth Fund. (2010). *Commonwealth Fund International Health Policy Survey.* Retrieved from: http://www.commonwealthfund.org/Surveys/2010/Nov/2010-International-Survey.aspx.

Eaker, S., Halmin, M., Bellocco, R., Bergkvist, L., Ahlgren, J., Holmberg, L., & Lambe, M. (2009). Social differences in breast cancer survival in relation to patient management within a national health care system (Sweden). *International Journal of Cancer, 124*(1), 180–187.

Einhorn, E.S., & Logue, J. (2003). *Modern welfare states: Scandinavian politics and policy in the global age.* Westport CT: Greenwood Publishing Group, 2003.

European Central Bank. n.d. *Statistical data warehouse.* Retrieved from: http://sdw.ecb.europa.eu/reports.do?node=100000314.

European Commission. (2011). *Healthcare statistics.* Retrieved from: http://epp.eurostat.ec.europa.eu/statistics_explained/index.php/Healthcare_statistics.

FHI. (2010). *Kommunalt folkhälsoarbete som kan minska hälsoskillnader.* Östersund: FHI.

FHI (Swedish National Institute of Public Health) & SoS (National Board of Health & Welfare). (2010). *Svenska lärdomar av Marmot-kommissionens rapport* [Closing the gap]. Östersund: FHI.

Glenngård, A.H., Hjalte, F., Svensson, M., Anell, A., & Bankauskaite, V. (2005). *Health systems in transition: Sweden.* Copenhagen: WHO Regional Office for Europe on behalf of the European Observatory on Health Systems and Policies.

Government of Sweden (1987/1988). *Developments in public health.* Government Communication 172. Stockholm: Government of Sweden.

Government of Sweden (1990/1991). *Some public health issues.* Government Bill 1990/91, 175. Stockholm: Government of Sweden.

Government of Sweden (2002/2003). *Objectives for public health.* Government Bill 2002/2003, 35. Stockholm: Government of Sweden.

Government of Sweden (2007/2008). *Objectives for public health.* Proposal 2007/2008. Stockholm: Government of Sweden.

Hort, S.E.O. (2009). The Swedish welfare state: A model in constant flux? In K. Schubert, S. Hegelich & U. Bazant (Eds.), *The handbook of European welfare systems* (pp. 428–443). New York: Routledge.

Kulvalainen, S., & Nelson, K. (2012). Eroding minimum income protection in The Nordic countries? Reassessing the Nordic model of social assistance. In J. Kvist et al. (Eds.), *Changing social inequality: The Nordic welfare model in the 21st century* (pp. 69–88). Bristol: The Policy Press.

Lundberg, O., Åberg Yngwe, M., Kölegård Stjärne, M., Björk, L., & Fritzell, J. (2008). *The Nordic experience: Welfare states and public health. Final re*port from the NEWS project. Stockholm: CHESS.

Lundberg, O., & Fritzell, J. (2007). *Health inequalities and welfare resources: Continuity and change in Sweden.* Bristol: Policy Press.

Melinder, K. (2011). *A Swedish Application of the Marmot Commisson Closing the Gap.* Stockholm: Swedish National Institute of Public Health.

Modin, B., Koupil, I., & Vågerö, D. (2009). The impact of early twentieth-century illegitimacy across three generations: Longevity and intergenerational health correlates. *Social Science & Medicine, 68*(9), 1633–1640.

News. (2008). The Nordic Experience: Welfare states and public health (NEWS). Retrieved from: http://www.chess.su.se/research/projects/past-projects/the-nordic-experience-welfare-states-and-public-health-news-1.54166.

Nordic Council of Ministers. (2007). *What lies ahead for the Nordic model?* Copenhagen: Nordic Council of Ministers.

Palme, J. et al. (2002). *Welfare in Sweden: The Balance sheet for the 1990s.* Stockholm: Fritzes.

Ritsatakis, A. (2009). Equity and social determinants of health at a city level. *Health Promotion International, 24*(Suppl. 1), i81–i90. doi: 10.1093/heapro/dap058.

Sandler, I.N., Schoenfelder, E.N., Wolchik, S.A., & MacKinnon, D.P. (2011). Long-term impact of prevention programs to promote effective parenting: Lasting effects but uncertain processes. *Annual Review of Psychology, 62*, 299–329.

Statement of Government Policy. (2010, October 5). Retrieved from: http://www.regeringen.se/content/1/c6/15/28/42/9a763740.pdf.

Statistics Sweden. (2010). *Statistical yearbook of Sweden 2011*. Örebro: Statistics Sweden.

Statistics Sweden. (2011). *Life expectancy in Sweden 2001–2010*. Life tables for the country and by county. Demographic reports 2011:2. Stockholm: Statistics Sweden.

Sundin, J., & Willner, S. (2007). *Social change and health in Sweden: 250 years of politics and practice*. Östersund: National Institute for Public Health.

Svallfors, S. (2011). A bedrock of support? Trends in welfare state attitudes in Sweden, 1981–2010. *Social Policy and Administration, 45*(7), 806–825.

Trädgårdh, L. (Ed.). (2010). *State and civil society in northern Europe: The Swedish model reconsidered*. Oxford: Berghan Books.

Transparency International. (2011). *Corruption perceptions index 2011*. Retrieved from: http://cpi.transparency.org/cpi2011/results/.

Wikman, A. (2001). *Labour market development in Sweden*. In S. Marklund (Ed.), *Worklife and health in Sweden 2000* (pp. 21–34). Stockholm: Arbetslivsinstitutet.

World Economic Forum. (2011). *The global gender gap report 2011*. Geneva: World Economic Forum.

Yang, D., Dzayee, D.A., Beiki, O., de Faire, U., Alfredsson, L., & Moradi, T. (2011, November 7). Incidence and case fatality after day 28 of first-time myocardial infarction in Sweden 1987–2008. *European Journal of Preventive Cardiology*. doi: 10.1177/1741826711425340.

Chapter 9

An Analysis of International Experiences in Tackling Health Inequalities

Dennis Raphael

Introduction

The previous seven chapters have provided a wealth of details as to how nations are addressing their existing health inequalities. In this chapter, these experiences are analyzed by identifying commonalities and differences among these nations in how they conceptualize the existence of health inequalities, their policy responses to these inequalities, and evidence of their success in tackling them. The chapter then goes beneath these surface realities to consider the societal structures and influences that lead to these distinctive approaches to tackling health inequalities. It attempts to make sense of the stark differences among nations in tackling—or not tackling—their health inequalities in order to identify means of furthering these activities.

Right off it must be acknowledged that there is a remarkable gulf between Europe (and, to some extent, Australia) and North America in putting the health inequalities issue on the public policy agenda. Almost 15 years ago, Whitehead (1998) described how policymakers in the UK, the Netherlands, Sweden, and elsewhere in Europe had taken on the task of tackling health inequalities during the 1980s and 1990s. Indeed, the issue of differences in health between the rich and poor was a matter of intense interest in Sweden as early as the 1930s (Whitehead, 1998). In contrast, health inequalities, as of 2012, have not arisen as serious public policy concerns at the national or provincial/state level anywhere in Canada or the US.

These differences in putting health inequalities on the public policy agenda do not result from nations having differing amounts of evidence or data on the existence of health inequalities in their jurisdictions. Each nation has abundant evidence of the presence of health inequalities. But nations such as Canada and the US, which have generally more adverse health outcomes and greater health inequalities, have governmental authorities that take little notice of them. In contrast, the nations with generally better health outcomes and smaller health inequalities are the ones most committed to tackling them. Is there a link between having economic and political systems that create adverse health outcomes and the unwillingness to tackle health inequalities? Is this why some nations prioritize tackling health inequalities on their public policy agendas while others do not?

If it is the case that tackling—or not tackling—health inequalities is primarily determined by how a society's political and economic structures are organized, then specific analytical tools are needed to help make sense of these processes. To understand how these situations arise requires a critical political economy perspective that sees the existence/tackling of health inequalities as embedded within the operation of a nation's economic and political systems (Coburn, 2010). These societal structures can be further analyzed using what is called a critical realist perspective (Sayer, 2000).

Frameworks for Analysis

A *political economy* framework considers how the interplay of economic and political systems shapes resource distribution among the population.

> Political economy is concerned with the organization of society and how it distributes social and economic resources (Armstrong, Armstrong & Coburn, 2001). This perspective directs attention to the relationship between health and the economic, political and social lives of different people, geographic areas or societies. Political economy is also a materialistic approach because it perceives ideas and institutions as arising from the way in which a society organizes production and considers the distribution of resources. It recognizes politics and economics as fundamentally related. (Bryant, 2005, 70)

An important feature of the political economy approach is the extent to which the economic system—which for all of the nations considered in this volume is capitalist—is managed by governmental authorities (i.e., the political system) with input from various sectors such as the labour movement and civil society organizations and groups. Extensive work has gone into consideration of these issues with one outcome being the concept of varying forms of welfare state regimes (Esping-Andersen, 1990). Three primary forms have been identified: the social democratic, the conservative, and the liberal.[1] A key feature of these differing forms of welfare state regimes is the dominant institution—the *market* or the *state*—within each (Saint-Arnaud & Bernard, 2003).

To what extent is the distribution of economic resources among the population determined by the operation of the economic *market* primarily in terms of wages and investment income as opposed to regulation of the market and benefits provided by the *state*? When the market is the dominant institution, then one's exposure to the social determinants of health is shaped primarily by attachment to the labour market as well as by the state's policy-making. When the state is the dominant institution, then one's exposure to the social determinants of health is shaped primarily by the state's policy-making as well as by one's attachment to the labour market. Of importance also is the reality that when the *market* is the dominant institution, the business and corporate sectors are likely to have greater influence upon public policy-making; when the state is the dominant institution, the labour and civil society sectors will have greater influence (Olsen, 2010). In this inquiry the key contrast is between nations where the *state* is the dominant institution—represented by the social democratic welfare states of Finland, Norway, and Sweden—and those where the *market* is dominant—represented by the liberal welfare states of Australia, Britain and Northern Ireland, Canada, and the US (Saint-Arnaud & Bernard, 2003).

In addition to focusing on the economic and political systems and how these operate, an additional level of analysis involves a *critical realist* perspective to identify what has been termed the real, actual, and empirical levels of reality (Sayer, 2000). The *real* involves an explication of the societal structures and powers that have the capacity to create larger or smaller health inequalities as well as a greater or lesser inclination to tackle them.

> The real is the realm of the objects, their structures and powers. Whether they be physical, like minerals, or social, like bureaucracies, they have certain structures and causal powers, that is capacities to behave in certain ways, and causal liabilities or passive powers, specific susceptibilities to certain kinds of change. (Sayer, 2000, 11)

In our present inquiry, the *real* refers to the societal economic and political structures that have the potential to create larger or smaller health inequalities as well as the response to their presence. Much of this is concerned with the economic and political forces that determine how governmental institutions can organize the distribution of societal resources that shape the extent of health inequalities and responses to these inequalities. One example of the *real* would be workers' ability—through legislation—to form labour unions that would balance the power and influence of the corporate and business sectors in the distribution of economic and other resources and the development of health inequalities-related public policy.

The *actual* is how these societal structures *do* operate within a specific society.

> The actual refers to what happens if and when these powers are activated, to what they do and what eventuates when they do, such as when the bureaucracy's powers are activated and it engages in [specific] activities. (Sayer, 2000, 12)

The *actual* in our present inquiry refers to how these powers and structures operate in each nation to shape the distribution of resources that create health inequalities and the inclination to tackle them. Here the concern is with differences among nations in how these influences and structures create health inequalities-related public policies. Using the example of workers' ability to form labour unions that would balance the power and influence of the corporate and business, the *actual* would be the extent to which unionization actually occurs and its effects upon the societal structures that create public policy.

The *empirical* is the world of experience or the observable with regard to the tackling of health inequalities.

> The empirical is defined as the domain of experience, and insofar as it refers successfully, it can do so with respect to either the real or the actual though it is contingent (neither necessary nor impossible) whether we know the real or actual. (Sayer, 2000, 12)

This is the level of the observable, the actual public policies that shape the distribution of economic and other resources that come to be associated with health inequalities. It is also concerned with governmental authorities' responses to these health inequalities. Again, using the example of workers' ability to form labour unions, the empirical would be concerned with the health inequalities-related public policies that shape the distribution of economic and other resources among the population that are the important drivers of health inequalities. Figure 9.1 illustrates these levels.

The real value of looking at these three levels of reality is that it allows for identification of what is *possible* in addition to what is actually occurring. As Sayer (2000) states:

A crucial implication of this ontology is the recognition of the possibility that powers may exist unexercised, and hence that has happened or been known to have happened does not exhaust

Figure 9.1
Depiction of the Three Levels of Analysis in a Critical Realist Approach to Understanding Health Inequalities-Related Public Policy

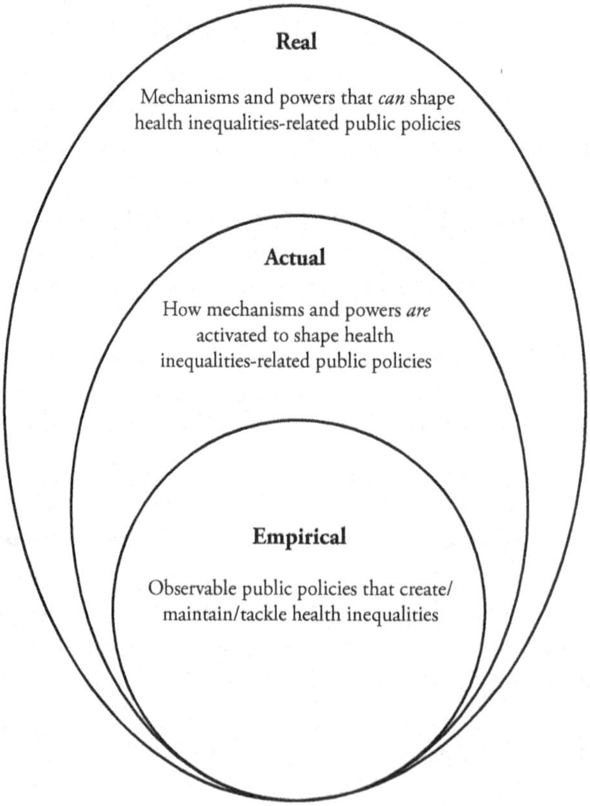

Real
Mechanisms and powers that *can* shape health inequalities-related public policies

Actual
How mechanisms and powers *are* activated to shape health inequalities-related public policies

Empirical
Observable public policies that create/maintain/tackle health inequalities

Source: Adapted from Mingers, J., & Willcocks, L. (2004). *Social theory and philosophy for information systems*. John Wiley series in information systems. Chichester, UK: J. Wiley.

what could happen or have happened. The nature of the real objects present at a given time constrains and enables what can happen but does not pre-determine what will happen. Realist ontology therefore makes it possible to understand how we could be or become many things which currently we are not. (p. 12)

Analysis of the situation at each level allows us, then, to identify what is happening in terms of governmental public policy-making related to health inequalities and efforts to tackle them (*empirical*), consider the structures and powers that underlie these activities (*actual*), and understand the possibilities inherent in having these powers and processes operate in a manner that has not yet occurred (*real*). This introduces a powerful element into the analysis of tackling health inequalities in that it points the way toward potential activities.

Applying a political economy analysis at these three levels recognizes that identifying health inequalities as a public policy issue requiring governmental attention is not simply a matter of researchers collecting data and then seeing governmental public policy-makers act upon these findings. Tackling or not tackling health inequalities is instead embedded within societal structures and power as well as related ideological discourses as to the nature of society, the meaning of health, and the appropriate role that governmental authorities should play in promoting health. This truth is usually ignored by much of the health inequalities-related literature, which sees failure to tackle health inequalities as the result of policy-makers' lack of information or understanding of these issues and/or inefficiencies in bureaucratic organization (Health Council of Canada, 2010). Differences in health inequalities-related public policy are actually a result of powerful economic and social forces that influence governmental authorities' policy-making activities.

Descriptive and Explanatory Frameworks

A variety of frameworks are available for making sense of these issues. There are *descriptive* frameworks that identity how much progress a nation has made in addressing health inequalities and, if so, what approach they are applying. There are also *explanatory* frameworks—political economy and critical realist—that help explain why this is the case and identify means of shifting these activities, if necessary.

Descriptive Analysis

Figure 9.2 provides one influential way of categorizing the progress of a nation's governing authorities in tackling health inequalities through public policy action. In an important 1998 article, Whitehead outlined an Action Spectrum on Social Inequalities along which *policy-makers* of various nations could be positioned. Placing the nations described in this volume on this Action Spectrum as of 2012 is rather easy. The governing authorities of the Scandinavian nations of Finland, Norway, and Sweden are all clearly located in the "Comprehensive coordinated policy" category.

Australia appears to be beyond the "Isolated initiatives" category and at the cusp of the "More structured developments" category primarily because of its national response to Indigenous health. Britain and Northern Ireland appear to be in the "More structured developments" cat-

Figure 9.2
Placement of Nations' Governmental Authorities on the Action Spectrum on Inequalities in Health

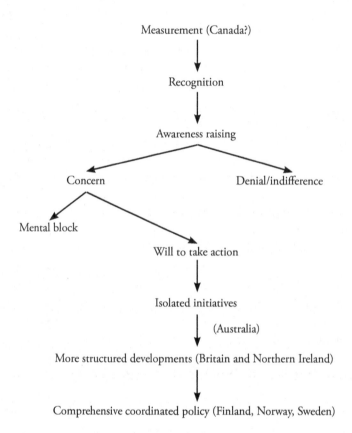

Source: M. Whitehead, Diffusion of ideas on social inequalities in health: A European perspective, *Milbank Quarterly*, 76(3) (1998), 469–492.

egory. One might even reasonably argue that during the initial years of their reducing health inequalities initiatives, England was placed in the "Comprehensive coordinated policy" category. In the case of Canada, governmental authorities have arguably made it to the "Measurement" level, but even then, these measurement activities are not given government sanction, nor are they part of any coordinated Canadian public policy initiative. The US is not even at the "Measurement" level as there is a complete absence of this issue on the country's public policy agenda.

Applying a less stringent criterion of identifying where the Canadian *public health community*—rather than Canadian public policy-makers—is at, we can consider the many policy statements and documents produced by Canadian civil servants and public health authorities as attaining the "Recognition" level. These attempts by civil servants and public health authorities to raise awareness—with some rare local exceptions—have *not* included educating the public on these issues. Therefore, any placement at the edge of the "Awareness raising" level would even then be rather minimal.[2] In fact, there is extensive evidence that the public health community experiences an apparent "Mental block" in that it has been struggling for decades on how to actually move policy-makers to consider the existence of health inequalities as worthy of attention. It is indeed a marvel that a nation that produced so many reports and documents relating the importance of identifying and tackling health inequalities has failed to place these issues on its public policy agenda.

Another valuable descriptive framework for understanding the tackling of health inequalities is that outlined by Graham (2004). Using English policy pronouncements as examples, she makes the distinction between approaches focused on (1) remedying health disadvantages; (2) narrowing health gaps; and (3) reducing health gradients.

Remedying health disadvantages recognizes the important health issues that disadvantaged people experience and aligns activities to reduce these burdens with other policy-making. Graham (2004) notes that it avoids being a population-wide strategy and focuses policy attention on the most disadvantaged, usually those identified as living in poverty. It also does not concern itself with bringing the health of these disadvantaged individuals closer to the national averages. Therefore, in a society where overall health is improving, these efforts may do little to narrow the health gaps between the rich and poor.

Narrowing health gaps recognizes that narrowing the health gaps between groups is as important as reducing the health problems of the most disadvantaged. Success in this endeavour requires achieving greater health improvement among the least well-off than others in order to reduce this gap. But Graham (2004) argues that the general argument in this approach is the same as for the remedying health disadvantages approach:

> The underlying model of health inequalities is the same. The burden of ill health resulting from social inequality is again seen to fall on the poor alone. Like a health-disadvantage approach, a health-gaps perspective conflates inequality with disadvantage, and health inequality with the health deficits of being poor. (p. 122)

Reducing health gradients involves recognizing that health is systematically related to socio-economic positions across the total range. For Graham, this focus widens policy approaches in three ways. First, it directs attention to issues of systematic differences in life chances across the socio-economic spectrum, not just to issues among the most disadvantaged groups. Second, tackling health inequalities becomes a goal that includes everyone across the socio-economic spectrum as health inequalities among all groups are worthy of attention. Third, it suggests that reaching these goals requires that the health of lower and middle groups improve at a faster rate than among the most advantaged of society. This is a very ambitious goal that takes a more sophisticated and mature approach toward understanding the sources of health inequalities and applying the means of tackling them.

Bambra notes the emergence of a new *proportionate universalism* approach in the Marmot Review (Marmot et al., 2010), which proposed combining the *remedying health disadvantages* and *reducing health gradients* by providing universally targeted benefits that are provided more intensively to the most disadvantaged (Bambra, 2011b).

Among the nations in this inquiry, the Scandinavian nations have adopted a reducing health gradients approach. For Norway, this is reflected in its document, *The Challenge of the Gradient*: "[R]esearch indicates that we will not address the relation between socioeconomic position and health if we base our activities on strategies that focus on 'the poor' as an isolated target group." A similar approach is apparent in Sweden, where the 2003 Public Health Bill aims "[T]o create social conditions that will ensure good health on equal terms for the entire population," and for Finland, where, according to the 2007 *Government Programme*, "The goal of social and health policy is to promote health, functional capacity and initiative, and diminish the differences in the state of health between the individual segments of population."

Fosse (2011) argues that both structural and targeted measures are important strategies. The Norwegian national health strategy states: "A fair distribution of resources is good public health policy. The primary goal of future public health work is not to further improve the health of the people that already enjoy good health. The challenge now is to bring the rest of the population up to the same level as the people who have the best health—levelling up. Public health work entails initiatives to ensure a more even social distribution of the factors that affect health" (p. 1). This has elements of the new *proportionate universalism* approach.

The most recent Finnish strategy also appears to be a combination of *reducing health gradients* and *narrowing health gaps* in that it calls for focusing on improving the situation of the most disadvantaged. However, these targeted measures also appear to form the basis of what has been termed "proportionate universalism."

In the UK, policy has historically focused largely on the health of the disadvantaged, i.e., *remedying health disadvantages*. Under New Labour (from 1997 to 2010), there was a shift toward focusing on narrowing health gaps between the worst off and the average across the UK. However, health gaps still tended to be perceived as the result of health disadvantage. Consequently, many of the policy responses focused on trying to improve health in disadvantaged areas (rather than addressing the full societal gradient in health). The Marmot Review (Marmot et al., 2010), a government-commissioned report, proposed combining efforts to address health disadvantage with efforts to reduce health gradients by providing universally targeted benefits more intensively to the most disadvantaged, an approach it called "proportionate universalism" (Bambra, 2011b). However, so far there is little evidence to suggest that any of the UK governments are actively employing this approach.

Australia appears to be a mix, *remedying health disadvantages* and *narrowing health gaps*. Most strategies are about remedying disadvantage (the social inclusion agenda and much of the chronic disease risk factor agenda), but the national Close the Gap strategy is about reducing the gap between Indigenous and non-Indigenous life expectancy. There doesn't appear to be much attention to the gradient in the policies at either a state or federal level.

As noted, for Canada and the US, the issue of tackling health inequalities is not on any public policy agenda. The closest thing to a Canadian strategy is provided in the Canadian document, *Reducing Health Disparities—Roles of the Health Sector: Discussion Paper* (Health Disparities Task Group of the Federal/Provincial/Territorial Advisory Committee on Population Health and Health Security, 2004): "The most appropriate and effective way to improve overall population health status is by improving the health of those in lower SES groups and other disadvantaged populations" (p. v). This would represent the *remedying health disadvantages* approach. In the US there is generally the sense among governmental authorities that giving more people access to medical care will take care of the problem.

Structures and Processes Associated with Governmental Authorities Tackling Health Inequalities

Various structures and processes necessary for tackling health inequalities can be identified based on the experiences of the nations profiled in this volume. It is apparent that any serious tackling of health inequalities would require a government to align the public policy activities of many, if not all, of its ministries and departments toward this objective. The Health Council of Canada and the World Health Organization call this alignment a "whole of government" approach to tackling health inequalities (Health Council of Canada, 2010; World Health Organization, 2008).

There are three aspects—which are all related to each other—associated with a jurisdiction implementing an agenda to tackle health inequalities. The first and apparently the most important is the presence of governmental values consistent with, and committed to, tackling health inequalities. The second is the government having evidence and information about the extent of health inequalities and the assurance that the public both understands and supports the concepts associated with the initiative. The third is establishing governmental structures responsible for implementing and monitoring the effects of these public policy initiatives.

Governmental Authorities' Values and Commitments to Tackling Health Inequalities

Absolutely key is the motivation and willingness of governmental authorities to undertake public policy actions that tackle health inequalities. It is apparent that such motivation is much easier to come by in the social democratic welfare states of Finland, Norway, and Sweden, and much less so in Canada and the US. It is also more present in Australia and Britain and Northern Ireland when a social democratic party of the left is in power.

Jurisdictions that have implemented a tackling health inequalities agenda appear driven by a moral imperative concerned with promoting health equity and reducing inequalities in health. As noted, in Finland, Norway, and Sweden, these commitments fit in rather easily with long-standing ideological commitments to provide economic and social security to its citizens. This has been described as an ideological commitment to promoting equality (Saint-Arnaud & Bernard, 2003). In Australia and the UK, governmental commitments to tackling health inequalities have ebbed and flowed, depending upon which political party is in power. There is little evidence of such commitment among governmental authorities in Canada and the US.

Part and parcel of these activities is the presentation of governmental documents that outline these governmental commitments to tackling health inequalities, such as the Black Report and the Acheson Report in the UK, *In All Fairness: Increasing Equity in Health Across NSW* in the Australian state of New South Wales, and *The Challenge of the Gradient* in Norway, among many others.

As significant as these documents may be, of much greater importance is governmental authorities moving to implement these commitments. Nowhere is the importance of minimizing the gap between words and action more clear than in Canada, where one can point to any number of documents that identify the imperative of addressing health inequalities: the Lalonde Report of 1974 (Lalonde, 1974), the Epp Report of 1986 (Epp, 1986), the Chief Public Health Officer of Canada's report on health inequalities (Butler-Jones, 2008), and others. But what all these documents lacked was a commitment by the governing authorities to implement their recommendations. Therefore, defining documents, while useful, must also reflect governments' commitments to action.

Having Evidence and Information about the Extent of Health Inequalities

Once there is commitment to tackle health inequalities, there is a need for information and evidence that indicate action is necessary. And any government will act upon these issues only when they are assured that the public both understands and supports the concepts associated with the initiative. The nations described in this volume have various sources of information about the extent of health inequalities. For some, there are governmental agencies responsible for providing this information; for others, information is provided by independent agencies or by university researchers.

Unlike some other nations, Canada does not have in place the mechanisms for systematic reporting on the health of Canadians and the presence of health inequalities. Statistics Canada periodically reports on health-related issues, as does the arm's-length Canadian Institute for Health Information, which includes the Canadian Population Health Initiative. The Centers for Disease Control also provide evidence on health inequalities. But these organizations have no specific mandate to report health inequalities-related information on a sustained and comparative basis.

In addition, since Canadian and American governmental authorities have no commitment to tackle health inequalities, there is no imperative for them to respond to health inequalities-related information. In contrast, in the Scandinavian nations and the UK, there are usually official government responses to government-commissioned reports and reviews of policy activities. Evidence, therefore, in support of tackling health inequalities must be collected and reported on a continuing and sustained basis and be combined with explicit governmental commitments to respond to these findings.

There must also be public understanding of these issues such that governments will be willing to act upon available data and information. There is evidence that cultural values of Scandinavians are more consistent with the promotion of redistribution of economic resources—probably a good proxy for support for tackling the sources of health inequalities—than in North America. Kenworthy and McCall examined the extent of support for redistribution of economic resources among citizens of Norway, Sweden, Australia, Canada, the UK, and the US as indicated by response to the question "How much do you agree or disagree with the statement: 'It is the responsibility of the government to reduce the differences in income between people with high incomes and those with low incomes'" (Kenworthy & McCall, 2007, 4). Along a metric of strongly disagree (1), disagree (2), neither agree nor disagree (3), agree (4), and strongly agree (5), the following countries' average scores in 2000 were: the UK (3.7), Norway (3.6), Sweden (3.5), Australia (3.2), Canada (3.2), and the US (2.9).

Another indirect indicator of attitudes toward tackling health inequalities is provided by the proportion of the population who believe that luck determines income (Alesina & Glaeser,

2004). Alesina and Glaeser report the proportions in 1998 as follows: Norway (.50), Sweden (.49), the UK (.49), Finland (.43), Australia (.41), Canada (.39), and the US (.35). These authors report that these attitudes are strongly correlated with the extent of social welfare spending across nations, which is an important driver of health inequalities.

Canada and the US have a formidable task in this regard, and the UK less so. Canadians have little awareness of population health concepts, the importance of health inequalities, and the important role played in these health inequalities by the social determinants of health (Canadian Population Health Initiative, 2004). The situation in the US may be far worse (Robert Wood Johnson Foundation, 2010). This should not be surprising as these issues have not been given prominence by Canadian or American governments whose policy focus and messaging has been limited to health care system reforms and healthy lifestyle choices. As a result, but also contributing to this bad situation, has been the lack of any media coverage of these broader health issues (Raphael, 2011a).

Governmental Structures for Implementing and Monitoring These Initiatives

There is also accumulated evidence that certain governmental structures are required in order for these kinds of activities to occur. In many cases, this may involve setting up an independent authority within government to coordinate tackling health inequalities activity across ministries or departments. It may also involve assigning authority to an existing ministry or department. This authority—with the clear support of the government's leaders—is responsible and accountable for setting policy priorities, assuring efforts to achieve these priorities, and ensuring means of evaluating their attainment. In every jurisdiction where these efforts have been undertaken, this has involved governmental structures and processes that have been termed "whole of government," "intersectoral," or "health in all approaches."

There is also clear evidence that in these active jurisdictions, governments have established close relations with university and health agency researchers who provide guidance and support for the initiatives. There are also explicit efforts to draw support from various organizations that should be responsive to governmental action on these broader issues. In the UK and Australia, for example, there is strong support from the British Medical Association and the Australian Medical Association for a broader approach to population health and reducing health inequalities.

Finally, there are ongoing attempts to either inform or, in some cases, involve the larger civil society in governmental efforts to promote population health and reduce health inequalities. Governmental commitments are explicit, and messaging to the public is consistent. The media are involved in these efforts and the goal of all of these efforts is to promote transparency in governmental efforts. Further details as to what these structures and processes might look like in Canada are provided in Chapter 10.

Explanatory Analysis

As noted, a political economy framework considers how the interplay of economic and political systems shapes the distribution of resources. At the broadest level the political economy approach directs attention to the general form of the welfare state. It was hypothesized that differing forms of the welfare state—i.e., social democratic governance versus liberal governance—would play a strong role in how nations tackle health inequalities. And there is indeed evidence that this is the case.

Clearly, Finland, Norway, and Sweden provide exemplars on how to go about tackling health inequalities through public policy action. They go well beyond establishing "programs" to tackling health inequalities in that social democratic principles of equity drive much of their public policy activity. However, we also have to explain the differences among members of the liberal welfare state group of nations. Australian, and British and Northern Irish experiences— if not their effects—are profoundly different than American and Canadian experiences. To answer these questions, we have to consider the distinctive economic and political organization of each nation.

What is it, then, about the Scandinavian, American, Australian, British and Northern Irish, and Canadian economic and political systems that help to explain their differences in tackling health inequalities? Are there links between these approaches and public policy-making in general? What are the implications of these differences for tackling health inequalities for each of the nations examined in this volume?

Figure 9.3 provides one model that places these potential welfare state differences within a broad political economy context (Coburn, 2004). Though the original model had as its primary outcomes "health and well-being," the terms "extent of health inequalities" and "willingness to tackle them" can meaningfully be substituted.

In this model, Coburn outlines how economic globalization (implemented through free-trade agreements that allow business to quickly move jobs to where wages are lower) is associated with both neo-liberalism and the power of capital (investment monies) to shape public policy (A). These forces interact with a nation's form of the welfare state (i.e., social democratic or liberal in our case) and the market economy of each nation (B) to shape how these forces play out in a variety of indicators known to be drivers of health inequalities (C). The end result of these differences is both the extent of health inequalities and the willingness to tackle them (Coburn's original model also had the nation's overall economic wealth as an outcome) (D). This analysis would suggest that differing forms of the welfare state determine the extent of health inequalities within a nation and the willingness to tackle them through public policy activity.

The implications of these regimes for addressing health inequalities are obvious and are explicitly outlined in the Finnish, Norwegian, and Swedish case studies: The social democratic welfare states emphasize universal welfare rights, regulate the employment market, and provide generous benefits and entitlements on a universal basis. The opposite is the case in the American and Canadian case studies: These liberal welfare states provide very modest benefits and entitlements, the employment market is generally unregulated, and the state usually steps in with assistance only when the market fails to provide for the most basic needs. These liberal states have means-tested benefits targeted to the least well-off.

There are clear affinities, then, between health inequality issues and aspects of these clear exemplars of social democratic and liberal welfare states. The American and Canadian liberal welfare states, with their emphasis on minimizing state intervention in the operation of the marketplace and provision of minimal benefits, produce both health inequalities and an unwillingness to address them. The Scandinavian social democratic welfare states, with their

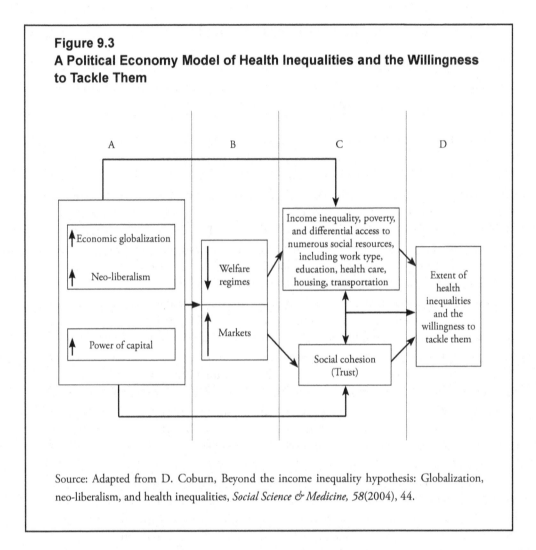

Figure 9.3
A Political Economy Model of Health Inequalities and the Willingness to Tackle Them

Source: Adapted from D. Coburn, Beyond the income inequality hypothesis: Globalization, neo-liberalism, and health inequalities, *Social Science & Medicine, 58*(2004), 44.

emphasis on promoting equity, are more likely to implement public policies that reduce and respond to health inequalities.

What about the Australian, and British and Northern Irish situations? The most striking aspect of these nations' situations is the presence of a social democratic party of the left—the Labor and Labour Party respectively—that has attained power at the national and, in the case of Australia, at the federal and state levels. Attention to addressing health inequalities is closely related to the ascendance of these parties to governance. But these parties have gained power that is embedded within liberal welfare states where long-standing public policy directions make the creation of health inequalities more likely than in the Scandinavian case. It can be expected, then, that public policy that drives health inequalities in Australia and Britain and Northern Ireland will fall midway between those of the Scandinavian nations and the liberal American and Canadian ones. This appears to be the case and further evidence of this is provided in later sections.

Critical Realist Analysis

With the political economy framework directing attention to the operation of the economic and political systems of each nation, a critical realist analysis uncovers the means by which these systems create health inequalities as well as public policy responses to these inequalities.

The Real, the Actual, and the Empirical

The key question is how do the economic and political systems of a nation manage the distribution of the social determinants of health inequalities? An ever-growing literature concerning these activities is accumulating (Navarro, 2002, 2007; Navarro & Muntaner, 2004; Olsen, 2002, 2010), but one clear finding is that much of this has to do with the extent to which a nation's economy is managed by governmental authorities (Pontusson, 2005). This is related to the politics of a nation, specifically the power balances and imbalances among differing sectors within a society, most notably between the labour and the business sectors. Also of importance are electoral behaviour and the strength of various political parties.

A variety of models aim to depict the means by which these economic and political structures operate to shape the extent of health inequalities. The Commission on the Social Determinants of Health, for example, identifies the socio-economic and political context, governance, public policy (macroeconomic, social, and health), and cultural and societal norms of a nation as driving the extent of health inequalities (World Health Organization, 2008, 43).

Figure 9.4 expands upon work by Navarro and colleagues (2004), Brady (2009), and Coburn (2004) to recognize some of the more specific structures and forces that shape the extent of health inequalities in a nation as well as the inclination to tackle them. Each component is subjected to a critical realist analysis in which the *real* identifies the structures and powers that have the *potential* to shape health inequalities and responses to them, the *actual* is how these powers and structures *play out*, and the *empirical* are the observable results among our nations.

The components of Figure 9.4 concerned with "The State" and "Power Relations" are primarily about societal structures and powers (real) and how they are activated (actual) to create "SDOH-Related Public Policies" (empirical). These public policies then determine the extent of "Social Inequalities" and resultant "Health Inequalities." Each component is considered in turn.

The Real and Actual

This is the level of structures and powers. It describes what is possible and sets the stage for examination of the actual, which is the situation of how these structures and powers play out in each nation.

Form of the Welfare State

The current form of the welfare state is important in at least three ways. First and most importantly, it represents a nation's distinctive manner of dealing with a range of public policy issues. Esping-Andersen (1990) describes the liberal and social democratic welfare states as follows:

> In one cluster we find the "liberal" welfare state, in which means-tested assistance, modest universal transfers, or modest social-insurance plans predominate. Benefits cater mainly to a clientele of

Figure 9.4
Factors Contributing to the Extent of Health Inequalities and the
Willingness to Tackle Them

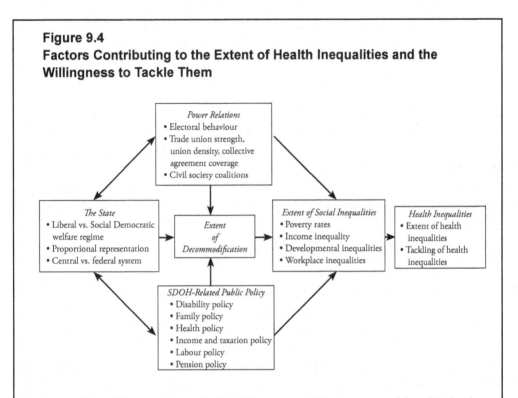

Source: Adapted from models provided by V. Navarro et al., The importance of the political and the social in explaining mortality differentials among the countries of the OECD, 1950–1998, in V. Navarro (Ed.), *The political and social contexts of health* (pp. 11–86) (Amityville: Baywood Press, 2004), and informed by the work of D. Brady, *Rich democracies, poor people: How politics explain poverty* (New York: Oxford University Press, 2009) and D. Coburn, Beyond the income inequality hypothesis: Globalization, neo-liberalism, and health inequalities, *Social Science & Medicine, 58*(2004), 41–56.

low-income, usually working-class, state dependents. In this model, the progress of social reform has been severely circumscribed by traditional, liberal work-ethic norms: it is one where the limits of welfare equal the marginal propensity to opt for welfare instead of work. Entitlement rules are therefore strict and often associated with stigma; benefits are typically modest. In turn, the state encourages the market, either passively—by guaranteeing only a minimum—or actively—by subsidizing private welfare schemes.

The third, and clearly smallest, regime cluster is composed of those countries in which the principles of universalism and decommodification of social rights were extended also to the new middle classes. We may call it the "social democratic" regime type since, in these nations, social democracy was clearly the dominant force behind social reform. Rather than tolerate a dualism between state and market, between working class and middle class, the social democrats pursued a welfare state that would promote an equality of the highest standards, not an equality of minimal needs as was pursued elsewhere. This implied, first, that services and benefits should be upgraded to levels commensurate with even the most discriminating tastes of the new middle classes; and, second, that equality be furnished by guaranteeing workers full participation in the quality of rights enjoyed by the better-off. (pp. 26–27)

These ways of dealing with public policy issues are important drivers of the extent of health inequalities and the willingness to tackle them. They help explain why some nations—i.e., the Scandinavian ones—find it so easy to tackle health inequalities through public policy activities while others—the liberal ones—find it so difficult (Raphael, 2011b).

Second, in addition to providing a shorthand means of describing the general approach to public policy, the form of the welfare state shapes the making of future public policy through what political economists call "path dependency." Put simply, a nation will—all things being equal—continue along a particular ideological path in its development of public policy. This is a result of a self-reinforcing process by which positive feedback from previously made decisions direct future actions (Pierson, 2000).

Third, the form of welfare state shapes citizens' understandings of the nature of society such that even if governing authorities undertake to tackle health inequalities, their ability to do so will be constrained by these public understandings (Coburn, 2010). Excellent examples are the cases of Canada and the US, where citizens' knowledge of the social determinants of health and the existence of health inequalities is primitive at best, and where there is increasing commitment to individualist approaches of personal responsibility for health and well-being that makes the creation of health equity-related public policy difficult.

How do these structures play out among our seven case-study nations? The Scandinavian nations are clear representatives of the social democratic welfare state. The state is the primary institution shaping the distribution of the social determinants of health. Britain and Northern Ireland, and Australia are liberal welfare states whose policies have been influenced by the presence of a social democratic party of the left that has governed at the federal and, in the case of Australia, at state levels for significant periods of time.

Canada has a social democratic party of the left that has governed at the provincial level, while the US does not have any such viable party. The ordering along this important dimension would be (from "left" to "right") Group A: Finland, Norway, and Sweden; Group B: Australia and Britain and Northern Ireland; Group C: Canada; and Group D: the US. This order clearly corresponds to the placement of nations along the Action Spectrum presented in Figure 9.2. Figure 9.4 indicates that the form of the welfare state both influences and, in return, is influenced by a society's power relations and social determinants of health-related public policy. The form of the welfare state is also influenced by its electoral process and political organization.

Proportional Representation vs. First-Past-the-Post (FPTP) Electoral Process
There is evidence that the presence of proportional representation increases the likelihood of health inequalities-reducing public policy within jurisdictions. In the "first-past-the post" system, a party must come in first in order to win the local seat. These won local seats constitute a party's presence in the legislature. In the system called proportional representation, a party is awarded

seats on the basis of the percentage of total votes cast. Thus, a party that garners 20 percent of the votes across every district would receive 20 percent of the seats in the legislature. In the first-past-the-post system, this party could not receive any seats. There is evidence that the "first-past-the-post" electoral system common in Australia, Britain and Northern Ireland, Canada, and the US minimizes the influence of progressive political parties, thereby increasing health inequalities. The Scandinavian nations operate under systems of proportional representation.

Proportional representation strengthens the influence of left political parties, which are more likely to support redistribution of wealth and advocate for universal social and health programs. Esping-Andersen (1985) argues that the early imposition of proportional representation in the Scandinavian nations was integral to the development of their welfare states. Alesina and Glaeser (2004) show how proportional representation enhances the growth and influence of left political parties, thereby strengthening the welfare state.

Such political systems enable political parties that are pro-redistribution to gain representation in fragmented legislatures. And proportional representation systems buffer welfare programs from spending cuts if the governments of the day attempt to turn back the clock on equity-oriented public policies. Again, a correspondence is noted among the presence of electoral systems and placement on the Action Spectrum for Addressing Health Inequalities.

Unitary (Central) vs. Federal System of Governance
It appears that having a federal versus a unitary or central structure of governance plays an important role in the strength of the welfare state and the amount of redistribution of economic and other resources among the population. Banting and Corbett's (2002) description of the effects of a federal system on the strength of the welfare state suggests that, all things being equal, a federal system is less likely to develop public policies that will minimize the extent of health inequalities.

> This pattern is consistent with a substantial body of research that concludes that federalism and decentralization tended to constrain the expansion of the welfare state during the twentieth century. A large number of studies have concluded that federalism and decentralization create several types of barriers that constrain an expansive and redistributive welfare state: by increasing the number of sites of political representation, federalism multiplies the number of veto points at which action can be delayed, diluted, or defeated; by creating separate regional jurisdictions, federalism generates interregional economic competition as state/provincial governments compete for private capital, which can exit for other regions with more hospitable fiscal regimes. (Banting & Corbett, 2002, 5)

Canada, the US, and Australia are federal jurisdictions, while the Scandinavian nations have strong central governments that direct regional and municipal activity. The situation in the UK involves more of a devolution of powers to the components of the UK, rather than the development of a federal system, and may lead to greater variation in approach rather than a general weakening of commitments to tackling health inequalities. Of particular note, however, is that the Scandinavian nations delegate responsibility to local governments to implement activities directed by the central government.

Power Relations

The form of the welfare state is both a result and contributor to existing power relations within a nation. Esping-Andersen (1985) provides an illuminating portrait of how the welfare state and social democratic parties arose to power in tandem in Scandinavia through an alliance of industrial workers and farmers. In Australia, Britain and Northern Ireland, and Canada, social democratic parties were formed with support from the labour sector. The strength of political parties and their ability to gain power shape public policy. The strength of civil society coalitions also reinforces the form of the welfare state and helps shape public policy-making.

Electoral Behaviour

Citizens' electoral behaviour places political parties in a position to shape the distribution of economic and other resources among the population—primary drivers of health inequalities within nations. Nations with stronger support for social democratic parties have stronger welfare states, lower poverty rates, and better health—due in large part to lesser health inequalities (Brady, 2009; Navarro et al., 2004; Rainwater & Smeeding, 2003). The ranking of nations that were governed by social democratic parties of the left from 1946 to the 1990s is as follows: Norway and Sweden (32 percent), Finland (20 percent), Britain and Northern Ireland (15 percent), Australia (12 percent), and Canada and the US (0 percent) (Rainwater & Smeeding, 2003), showing perfect correspondence with placement on the Action Spectrum for Addressing Health Inequalities.

Trade Union Strength

The strength of trade unions has an indirect and direct role in the extent of health inequalities. Indirectly, nations with stronger trade unions have stronger and more extensive welfare states—an important determinant of the extent of health inequalities (Swank, 2005). This comes about through greater influence of the working class upon public policy development. The strength of trade unions directly leads to provision of higher wages and better benefits. Collective bargaining agreements are associated with lower rates of poverty and income inequality, and generally stronger forms of the welfare state (Swank, 2005), all of which have been found to be strongly related to health outcomes (Innocenti Research Centre, 2005, 2007; Navarro et al., 2004). Figure 9.5 shows union density and collective bargaining coverage for the seven nations in this inquiry. While the strongest correspondence is between collective bargaining coverage and placement on the Action Spectrum, outside of Australia, with its relatively high collective agreement coverage, there is also a perfect correspondence between trade union density and such placement.

Civil Society Organizations

It has been argued that civil society can play an important role in tackling health inequalities.

> Civil society actors can be powerful drivers for positive social, political, and economic changes that affect health equity. These actions include those of informal community groups, formal civil society organisations such as labour unions, and large-scale social movements such as the anti-apartheid movement in South Africa. (Blas et al., 2008, 1686)

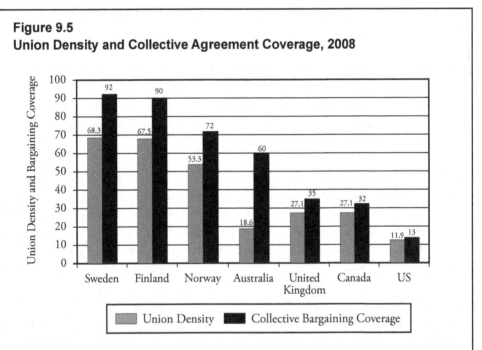

Figure 9.5
Union Density and Collective Agreement Coverage, 2008

Sources: Organisation for Economic Co-operation and Development (2010), *Trade union density*, retrieved from: http://stats.oecd.org/Index.aspx?DataSetCode=UN_DEN; D. Venn, Legislation, collective bargaining, and enforcement: Updating the OECD employment protection indicators, OECD Social Employment and Migration Working Papers, no. 89 (Paris: OECD, 2009).

There is no explicit literature, however, on how the strength of civil society organization in wealthy developed nations shapes health inequalities-related public policy. In his analysis of factors shaping the strength of the welfare state, Brady (2009) applies the term "latent coalitions for egalitarianism" to refer to groups of citizens who may come together under differing circumstances in support of a more generous welfare state. These latent coalitions could become organized around a variety of issues. One possible taxonomy is organizing around specific social determinants of health.

In Canada, there are organizations concerned with issues related to Aboriginal peoples, women, people with disabilities, as well as specific public policy sectors such as housing, early life, income and income distribution, education, employment and working conditions, food insecurity and hunger, and unemployment and job security. To date, these groups have not come together under a unified umbrella in any form, much less tackled health inequalities. Nor do they generally receive government support.

Civil society influence would seem to depend on governmental support for such activity. In the case of Sweden, for example, it has been suggested that: "The new public health policy came to fruition through a consultative political process in which representatives of all Sweden's major political parties and of civil society were engaged" (Irwin & Scali, 2005, 25). For a more relevant exemplar of what could be done in this area, consider what Mikkonen describes in the Finnish case study:

> Finland has a wide array of non-governmental organizations that work in advocacy, health promotion, public education, and as non-profit service providers. These organizations have a significant role in efforts to promote health and social welfare. The state-owned Finnish Slot Machine Association (RAY) supports approximately 800 Finnish non-governmental organizations by funding them with a share of €291 million in 2012 (www.ray.fi).

Wijkström (2004) provides evidence on the extent of civil society activity in Sweden and places it in a comparative analysis with a number of other nations. With regard to Sweden, he states: "Civil society organizations are found in all possible parts of Swedish society, conducting a multitude of different tasks, involving all types of people in a rainbow-like organizational plethora" (p. 2). He provides some intriguing data on the percentage of non-profit sector work that is unpaid voluntary activity. The available figures for the nations in this inquiry during the mid-1990s are Sweden (76 percent), Norway (61 percent), the UK (50 percent), Finland (49 percent), the US (39 percent), and Australia (32 percent) (Canada n/a).

Another indicator is whether civil society—as indicated by non-profit sector work—in a country has an advocacy or what Wijkström calls a "voice" focus, or a welfare or "service" focus. The voice/service ratio during the mid-1990s was a striking 107 percent in Sweden, indicating an equal balance between these two activities. Figures for the other nations are 63 percent in Norway, 58 percent in the UK, 30 percent in Finland, 21 percent in Australia, and 11 percent in the US (indicating very little voice or advocacy work in relation to welfare work in the US). Sweden—and, to some extent, the other Scandinavian countries—shows strong involvement of civil society in advocacy work. Wijkström (2004) concludes—and his comments are especially relevant in terms of tackling health inequalities—that:

> [W]e can see that civil society and its organizations in Sweden, but also in the other Scandinavian countries, seem to differ quite remarkably in a number of interesting dimensions. As already noticed, the case of Sweden is found at the extreme end in all of these tables, which at least calls for some more in-depth comparative research or studies, focusing in closer on these particular issues or special dimensions. (p. 19)

SDOH-Related Public Policy (Empirical Level)

Nations differ in the extent to which they invest societal resources in providing benefits and supports for citizens in a variety of public policy areas. It appears that these investments are closely related to the provision of the prerequisites of health and spending on universal programs that benefit virtually all citizens, such as early child education and care, employment training, pensions, and provision of community-based health care and social services (Hemrijck, 2002). At other times, this spending involves provision of adequate benefits to those who are unable to work because of illness, disability, or unemployment due to the loss of jobs in a changing economy (Organisation for Economic Co-operation and Development, 2003, 2011a). These expenditures are especially important with regard to families with children (Esping-Andersen, 2002; Innocenti Research Centre, 2005, 2007).

Overall Public Social Spending

Figure 9.6 provides the percentage of gross domestic product that our seven nations allocate in the form of overall public expenditure. This includes spending on pensions, health, working-aged income support, and other social expenditures. This indicator provides a good measure of welfare state development related to provision of the social determinants of health (Raphael, 2011b). Sweden allocates the highest percentage of GDP, followed by Finland, Norway, the UK, Canada, the US, and Australia.

Disability Policy

Strong differences exist among our nations in disability-related policy. An extensive policy analysis by the Organisation for Economic Co-operation and Development ranked nations in their generosity of payments (Compensation Policy) and efforts at involving those with disabilities (Integration Policy) (Organisation for Economic Co-operation and Development, 2003). Rankings (from strong to weak) were for *Compensation*: Sweden and Norway, Australia, the US, the UK, and Canada. For *Integration*, it was Sweden, Norway, Australia, the UK, the US, and Canada. Rankings for Finland were not available.

Family Policy

The case studies detail the differences among our nations in family-related policy. The most obvious difference is in the provision of child care and early education services. As noted in the case studies, the Scandinavian nations stand out in terms of their provision of benefits and supports to citizens. Raphael (2011b) shows the familiar relative rankings of nations on public expenditure as a percentage of GDP on child care and early education services (from the greatest to the least) of Sweden (1.0 percent), Finland (.9 percent), Norway (.8 percent), the UK (.6 percent), Australia (.4 percent), the US (.35 percent), and Canada (.2 percent).

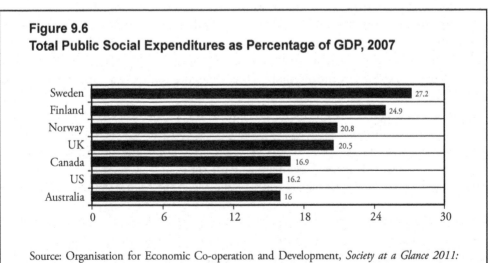

Figure 9.6
Total Public Social Expenditures as Percentage of GDP, 2007

Source: Organisation for Economic Co-operation and Development, *Society at a Glance 2011: OECD social indicators* (Paris: Organisation for Economic Co-operation and Development, 2011).

Health Care Policy

All nations, except the US, provide some form of universal health care for citizens. The Scandinavian nations, like Canada, provide care primarily through a public system. Australia and Britain and Northern Ireland have two-tier systems in which individuals can opt out of the public system and received care in the private sector. Public expenditures on health care have been related to health outcomes (Navarro et al., 2004). Ranking nations on public spending on health care as a percentage of GDP in 2009 results in the following order: the US (8.3 percent), Sweden (8.2 percent), the UK (8.2 percent), Norway (8.1 percent), Canada (8.1 percent), Finland (6.8 percent), and Australia (5.9 percent), a rather weak correspondence to the Action Spectrum (Organisation for Economic Co-operation and Development, 2011b). The US score is not really a positive indicator as its system has extensive extra costs associated with its disorganized and profit-driven system.

A somewhat stronger correspondence is seen when looking at public spending on health care as a percentage of total health care spending—a measure of depth of public coverage— which finds an order of Norway (84 percent), the UK (84 percent), Sweden (81 percent), Finland (75 percent), Canada (71 percent), Australia (68 percent), and the US (48 percent).

Income and Taxation Policy

It is well documented that progressivity of taxation differs between the social democratic and liberal nations. Brooks and Hwong (2006) describe how the high-taxation nations of Scandinavia appear to produce a variety of superior societal outcomes as compared to the low taxation liberal nations. Two measures are possible. The top marginal tax rate is the rate at which the wealthiest are taxed and serves as one measure of progressivity of income taxes. The second is the overall level of taxation in a nation as a percentage of GDP.

The top marginal tax rate of a nation can be supplemented by examining the threshold at which it kicks in. The OECD provides both the highest marginal tax rate of a nation as well as the threshold expressed as a multiple of the average wage (Organisation for Economic Co-operation and Development, 2012b). Table 9.1 provides these data for our nations. What is of particular interest is the wide range of the highest income tax rate thresholds. In the Scandinavian nations, those earning twice the average income are paying at the highest tax rates. In contrast, in the UK the threshold is four times the average wage and in the US it is almost nine times.

The OECD also provides data on the total tax revenue as a percentage of GDP for 2009 (Organisation for Economic Co-operation and Development, 2012a). Sweden collects 46.7 percent of overall GDP through taxation, followed by Norway (42.9 percent), Finland (42.6 percent), the UK (34.3 percent), Canada (32 percent), Australia (25.9 percent), and the US (24.1 percent). The correspondence between these levels and placement on the Action Spectrum is almost perfect.

Active Labour Policy

Active labour policy consists of a variety of programs that nations use to eradicate high and persistent unemployment and reduce low pay and poverty among the working-age population (Organisation for Economic Co-operation and Development, 2004). These may include formal classroom training, on-the-job training programs, subsidies to private-sector employ-

Table 9.1
Highest Marginal Income Tax Rate and Threshold Level as a Multiple of Average Income

	Sweden	Norway	Finland	UK	Australia	Canada	US
Highest marginal rate	56.5%	40.4%	48.2%	50%	46.5%	46.4%	41.7%
Threshold level	1.5	1.6	1.9	4.3	2.9	2.9	8.9

Source: Organisation for Economic Co-operation and Development (2012a), OECD tax database, retrieved from: www.oecd.org/document/60/0,3746,en_2649_34533_1942460_1_1_1_1,00.html#A_RevenueStatistics.

ers, job-search assistance, training programs for youth, and direct job creation for adult workers. The ranking from the greatest to the least spending is Sweden (1.3 percent), Finland (.9 percent), Norway (.8 percent), the UK (.5 percent), Australia (.4 percent), Canada (.4 percent), and the US (.1 percent). The correspondence between these levels and placement on the Action Spectrum is perfect.

Old Age Spending
The OECD provides a measure of public spending on old age—most of which is concerned with pensions—as a percentage of GDP. The rankings from the greatest to the least spending in 2007 is Sweden (9 percent), Finland (8.4 percent), Norway (6.2 percent), the UK (5.8 percent), the US (5.3 percent), Australia (4.3 percent), and Canada (3.8 percent), again illustrating the differences between the Scandinavian and other nations.

Decommodification
A key concept that underlies many or all of the components of Figure 9.4 is that of decommodification. According to Eikemo and Bambra: "Essentially, it is the extent to which individuals and families can maintain a normal and socially acceptable standard of living regardless of their market performance (Eikemo & Bambra, 2008, 4). Generally, social democratic welfare state nations have exhibited the greatest extent of decommodification, the liberal nations the least. To illustrate the concept's relevance to inequalities in health, Bambra (2005) created two indices of decommodifcation and examined scores of 18 OECD nations for 1998: cash benefits (e.g., replacement rates during illness and unemployment, duration of unemployment illness and benefits, pension generosity, etc.) and health care services (e.g., public health care coverage and public versus private expenditure). The social democratic welfare state nations of Finland, Norway, and Sweden were clearly placed in the quadrant reflecting a greater extent of decommodification for both cash benefits and health care services. Interestingly, Canada just made it into this quadrant as well. The US and Australia were in the quadrant representing a lesser extent of decommodification for both domains, while the UK was low for cash benefits, but high for health care services.

A more recent report and reconceptualization by Menahem (2010) creates an index of decommodified security that is closely related to the issue of health inequalities. He assessed the approaches of OECD nations toward provision of three types of income: (1) replacement income for the risks of old age, unemployment, sickness, and disability, plus survivors' pensions; (2) reimbursements and benefits in kind: costs of health care, family allowances, housing benefits; and (3) allowances and benefits in kind paid as a part of measures to combat social exclusion (income support, etc.). These are the rankings of the nations included in the study reported in this inquiry from the highest to the lowest on his decommodified security index: Sweden, Finland, Norway, Canada, the UK, Australia, and the US. The contrast between the social democratic and liberal nations is clear.

Extent of Social Inequalities

The form of the welfare state, trade union density, and strength of the welfare state feed into the extent of social inequalities. Data are available on two broad indicators of social inequalities: poverty rates and income inequality. Data are also available on developmental indicators and workplace inequalities.

Poverty Rates and Income Inequality

During the mid-2000s, the ranking of nations' poverty rates for families with children (from the lowest to the highest) are: Sweden (4 percent), Finland (4 percent), Norway (5 percent), the UK (10 percent), Australia (12 percent), Canada (15 percent), and the US (21 percent) (Organisation for Economic Co-operation and Development, 2008). For income inequality, the ranking, using the Gini coefficient, is: Sweden (.23), Finland (.27), Norway (.28), Australia (.30), Canada (.32), the UK (.34), and the US (.38). Again, a very close correspondence is seen with these rankings and placement on the Action Spectrum.

Developmental Inequalities

The Innocenti Research Centre ranks nations in terms of the extent of inequality among children in *material well-being, education well-being*, and *health well-being* (Innocenti Research Centre, 2010). Rankings from less inequality to more equality are: Finland, Norway, Sweden, Canada, the UK, and the US (Australia n/a).

Workplace Inequalities

The OECD calculates an employment protection index of rules and regulations that protects employment and provides benefits to temporary workers (Organisation for Economic Co-operation and Development, 2011c). This can serve as an indirect measure of workplace inequalities. The relative rankings of our nations on this indicator in 2008 are: Norway, Finland, Sweden, Australia, Canada, the UK, and the US.

Health Inequalities

More is known about national differences in health outcomes than is known about differences in the extent of health inequalities. In terms of overall life expectancies, nations rank as follows: Australia (81.4 years), Sweden (81.0), Norway (80.8), Canada (80.7), Finland (79.5), the UK (79.5), and the US (78.1) (Organisation for Economic Co-operation and Development, 2011b). In terms of infant mortality rates, the correspondence with placement on the Action Spectrum is much closer: Sweden (2.8/1,000), Finland (2.8), Norway (3.2), Australia (4.7), the UK (5.0), Canada (5.4), and the US (6.9).

Extent of Health Inequalities

Obtaining and analyzing comparable data across wealthy developed nations is a difficult task, but some evidence is available (Brennenstuhl, Quesnel-Vallee & McDonough, 2012). While there is extensive evidence that health—as measured by life expectancy and the infant mortality rate—is generally better in the social democratic nations than in the liberal ones, there is also evidence that health inequalities in the social democratic nations are usually, but not always, as great or even greater than in other wealthy developed nations (Bambra, 2011a). Bambra (2011a) argues that much of this may have to do with the use of relative rather than absolute measures of inequality. She notes that:

> This has meant [high inequality scores in Scandinavian nations] that the Scandinavian countries are effectively victims of their own success, as while they have substantially improved the health of all, the high level of health of the middle classes has meant that relative social inequalities remain. This, it could be argued, is the real issue in terms of why the Scandinavian countries perform comparatively poorly in terms of relative health inequalities, and, as Lundberg has pointed out, *this is an achievement, not something to be criticised.* (emphasis added; p. 743)

Bambra (2011a) also points out that in addition to the lowest socio-economic groups in Scandinavia being better off in absolute health terms than those in other welfare type nations, "[T]he absolute mortality risk difference between manual and non-manual is lowest in Sweden and Norway" (p. 743). She also notes that the most vulnerable in Scandinavia, such as the elderly, the ill, and children, show smaller socio-economic health inequalities than elsewhere. This leads to the general finding that relative measures of inequalities are inversely related to overall population health: "Countries with lower overall mortality tend to experience larger inequalities in mortality" (p. 743).

Two examples of health inequalities within nations are provided here. The Innocenti Research Centre (2010) provides a measure of inequality using an aggregate of self-reported health, healthy eating, and vigorous physical activity. Inequality is calculated as the gap between the median score and the average of those below the median. The ranking from least inequality to the most is Norway, Canada, the UK, Sweden, Finland, and the US (Australia n/a).

The OECD provides an indicator of health inequalities in reporting the variation (in standard deviations) in national age of mortality for those older than 10 years (Organisation for Economic Co-operation and Development, 2010). The range in standard deviations was from 15.4 years for the US to 12.7 years for Sweden. The order from least inequality to greatest is Sweden, Norway, Australia, the UK, Canada, Finland, and the US. The only anomaly in terms of general findings to date is the rank for Finland. The most distinctive findings are the poor US rankings.

Tackling Health Inequalities

Table 9.2 summarizes how these various components of Figure 9.4 correspond with placement on the Action Spectrum for Addressing Health Inequalities. The most striking aspect of the content of Table 9.2 is the contrast between the profiles of Sweden and the US. Sweden dominates the number 1 rankings, while the US dominates the number 7 rankings. Also striking is the dominance of the Scandinavian nations in the top ratings and Canada and the US in the bottom ones. The UK and Australia provided a middle-ground portrait. Distinctive differences between the Scandinavian and liberal nations are seen in their electoral process and their governance form, as well as in the other indicators applied.

National Profiles

A summary profile is provided of each nation along these indicators. The case studies provided earlier detail about how these differences play out in each nation.

The Scandinavian Case

In Finland, Norway, and Sweden, concern with tackling health inequalities is consistent with long-standing public policy traditions that emphasize the provision of citizens with economic and other forms of security and supports. These nations have economic and political structures—and accompanying ideological values—that support the principles associated with health equity and social justice. These values manifest right across a wide range of public policy issues, as amply demonstrated in the indicators provide in Table 9.2.

Sweden seems to best represent the image of the social democratic welfare state in which public policy is focused upon the provision of citizen supports and benefits. It is aided in this task by a central form of governance whose representatives are elected through a proportional representation process. It has experienced the greatest extent of social democratic governance assisted, in part, by its high union density and collective agreement employment coverage. Its greatest provision of benefits and supports through public policy activity is supported by its high rate of taxation, of which the highest marginal rates kick in the earliest. Its social inequalities are the lowest and its health indicators are excellent. Inequalities in life expectancies are the lowest and its somewhat higher ranking in inequalities in children's health have to be seen in relation to the excellent overall health and well-being of Swedish children in general.

Norway and Finland are similar to Sweden with all of its indicators well above those of the liberal welfare state nations. Like Sweden, they benefit from periods of governance by social democratic parties and their proportional representation electoral system. There is some divergence between them in terms of life expectancy and inequalities in life expectancy, where Finland provides not as positive a picture.

The British and Northern Ireland Case

Britain has distinguished itself by its concern with tackling health inequalities, and there is evidence that it has achieved some success in doing so. Its activities, however, are embedded within its liberal political economy, which makes addressing the underlying structures

Table 9.2
Correspondence between Placement on the Action Spectrum for Addressing Health Inequalities and Various Indicators of Societal Structures, Public Policies, Social Inequalities, and Health Inequalities

Placement on Action Spectrum	Sweden[a]	Norway	Finland	UK	Australia	Canada	US
The State							
Welfare state form	SD	SD	SD	Liberal	Liberal	Liberal	Liberal
Electoral process	PR	PR	PR	FPTP	FPTP	FPTP	FPTP
Governance form	central	central	central	mixed	federal	federal	federal
Power Relations							
Electoral behaviour[b]	1	1	3	4	5	6	6
Union density	1	3	2	4	6	4	7
Collective agreement coverage	1	3	2	5	4	6	7
SDOH-Related Policy							
Total public spending	1	3	2	4	7	5	6
Disability policy							
Compensation	1	1	n/a	5	3	6	4
Integration	1	2	n/a	4	3	6	5
Family policy	1	3	2	4	5	6	7
Old age spending	1	3	2	4	6	7	5
Health care policy							
Public spending as % of GDP	2	4	6	2	7	5	1
Public spending as % total health spending	3	1	4	1	6	5	7
Taxation							
Taxes as % of GDP	1	2	3	4	6	5	7
Threshold of highest tax rate	1	2	3	6	4	4	7
Active labour policy	1	3	2	4	5	5	7
Decommodification	1	3	2	5	6	4	7
Social Inequalities							
Family poverty rate	1	3	2	4	5	6	7
Income inequality	1	3	2	6	4	5	7
Developmental inequalities	3	2	1	5	n/a	4	6
Workplace inequalities	3	1	2	6	4	5	7

(continued)

Placement on Action Spectrum	*Sweden*[a]	*Norway*	*Finland*	UK	Australia	Canada	US
Health Outcomes							
Life expectancy	2	3	5	6	1	4	7
Infant mortality	1	3	1	5	4	6	7
Health Inequalities							
Children's health	4	1	5	3	n/a	2	6
Life expectancy	1	2	6	4	3	5	7

SD = social democratic

PR = proportional representation

FPTP = first past the post

NOTES

a. Italicized type indicates equal rankings on placement on the Action Spectrum.

b. Extent of governance by social democratic parties of the left

that drive health inequalities difficult. Public spending is well below that of the Scandinavian nations, and its income tax structures are rather less progressive than theirs.

Income inequality is high and its health indicators are poor. It benefits from periods of governance by a social democratic party of the left, but union strength and collective agreement coverage have significantly deteriorated over the years and employment protection is weak. The election of a Conservative-Liberal Democratic coalition that has promised a 40 percent reduction in public spending does not bode well for the tackling of health inequalities in the future.

Nevertheless, the long period of Labour emphasis on tackling health inequalities has helped place this issue high on the public policy agenda of all the members of the UK. As the authors of the British and Northern Ireland case study note: "A raft of policy measures designed to reduce health inequalities have been announced since 1997 and, although the UK's political system has become increasingly fragmented as a result of political devolution in Northern Ireland, Scotland and Wales, health inequalities have remained consistently high on policy agendas throughout the UK." Continuing to emphasize the importance of tackling health inequalities seems to be one means of controlling the Conservative-Liberal coalition's current attack on the UK welfare state, which only promises to make the health inequalities situation worse than is currently the case.

The Australian Case

Australia, like the UK, is in the middle. Public spending is very low and indicators of social inequalities are closer to those of Canada and the US than to the Scandinavian nations. One interesting aspect of Australia's profile is its relatively high level of collective agreement coverage (60 percent), which historically has led some to argue that Australia (and New Zealand) constitute what Castles (1985) calls "Australasian exceptionalism" or a "wage-earners' welfare state."

This refers to a societal approach to citizen security that reflected the provision of "a fair wage," primarily to the male breadwinner (Murphy, 2006), combined with a general reluctance to build a European-style social democratic welfare state.

Workplace protection in Australia is higher than in Canada and the US and while social spending is low, support for people with disabilities is higher than in the UK, Canada, and the US. In any event, there is evidence that even these distinctive features of the Australian welfare state have been transformed by the onset of neo-liberal ideology (Cox, 2006). Australian indicators for life expectancy (excellent), inequalities in life expectancy (good), and infant mortality (better than the UK, Canada, and the US) support the view of the Australian case study authors that: "Despite some erosion, Australia has a well-developed welfare state that offers support for people in the event of sickness, disability, unemployment, or sole parenthood." There is a need, however, to continue emphasizing the importance of tackling health inequalities. Analysis of the role that the election of parties of the left play in tackling health inequalities seems essential.

The Canadian Case

Canada provides an interesting example of a nation whose conceptual work on health inequalities has achieved some prominence, yet its public policy related to issues of health inequalities is increasingly deteriorating. Public spending is low and the extent of social inequalities is high. The infant mortality health indicator is poor and the life expectancy rank has been slipping in comparison to those of other OECD nations. Increasingly, Canadian indicators (provided in Table 9.2) are approaching those of the US.

The presence of numerous quasi-governmental structures, such as the Health Disparities Task Group of the Federal/Provincial/Territorial Advisory Committee on Population Health and the Canadian Reference Group on the Social Determinants of Health, give the impression that the Canadian government is paying attention to tackling health inequalities. These activities are generally ignored by governmental authorities such that these issues have not made it onto the public policy agendas of the federal or any provincial or territorial government in Canada. There has been no systematic attempt by any political party—including the social democratic New Democratic Party—to raise the issue of tackling health inequalities.

The American Case

The US is distinguished by its very weak welfare state and its lack of any viable social democratic party of the left. The US ranks last on virtually every indicator identified as contributing to the tackling of health inequalities. In addition to structural barriers to dealing with health inequalities, such as its federal system and its manner of electing representatives, corporate dominance of the public policy agenda and its electoral process is almost total. The situation is not assisted by the increasingly strident anti-government attitudes manifested in the US and its deteriorating economic situation. Tackling health inequalities is not on any public policy agenda, and the issues that drive health inequalities—such as income and wealth inequalities and anti-labour union laws—are, in fact, frequently celebrated rather than seen as cause for concern. As stated by Bezruchka in his case study:

Sixty years ago the nation was one of the world's healthiest, but as a consequence of political choices that have increased the wealth of a few, everyone's health has suffered. The US provides many lessons for other countries that want to avoid this health catastrophe.

Conclusion

In Chapter 1 the importance of tackling health inequalities was placed in the context of a human rights perspective that stressed the ethical and moral imperative of reducing unnecessary pain and suffering. A recent report on the presence of "social justice" among members of the Organisation for Economic Co-operation and Development ranked nations based on a number of indicators of degree of (1) poverty prevention; (2) access to education; (3) labour market inclusion; (4) social cohesion and non-discrimination; (5) health; and (6) intergenerational justice, all of which are clearly related to issues of tackling health inequalities (Schraad-Tischler, 2011).

The nations in our present inquiry received the following rankings among the 31 OECD nations in this analysis: Norway (2); Sweden (4); Finland (5); Canada (9); the UK (15); Australia (21); and the US (27). The rather close correspondence between these findings and placement on the Action Spectrum for Addressing Health Inequalities reiterate the view that tackling health inequalities is firmly embedded within a nation's overall approach to social provision. Tackling health inequalities certainly requires information and data related to the presence of health inequalities and evidence as to the most effective means of reducing them. But this enterprise is firmly embedded within a nation's general approach to economic and social security and also in its commitment to the provision of human rights and social justice. Such a conclusion recognizes that tackling health inequalities is not simply a technical exercise relegated to health authorities and experts, but one that requires the engagement of all sectors of society and especially the general public in ongoing discussion of the nature of the society within which they wish to live.

Notes

1. Researchers have suggested that within the conservative regime in which the family is the dominant institution, there is an undeveloped version termed the Latin welfare state (Saint-Arnaud & Bernard, 2003).
2. The most noteworthy effort in public education has been carried out by a local Ontario health unit that created an animation entitled *Let's Start a Conversation about Health ... and Not Talk about Health Care at All* (Sudbury and District Health Unit, 2011). This animation has been picked up and modified for use by at least four other local health units in Ontario (Chatham-Kent Health Unit, 2011; Niagara Region Health Unit, 2011; Timiskaming Health Unit, 2011; Wellington-Dufferin-Guelph Health Unit, 2011).

Critical Thinking Questions

1. What seems to you to be the best way of promoting public policies that tackle health inequalities?
2. What are some of the supports and barriers to tackling health inequalities in Scandinavia versus the liberal nations?
3. What are some of the specific developments in Australia and Britain and Northern Ireland that have assisted in tackling health inequalities there as opposed to the American and Canadian scene?
4. How important are political involvement and public education about these issues in tackling health inequalities? Why?

Recommended Readings

Brady, D. (2009). *Rich democracies, poor people: How politics explain poverty*. New York: Oxford University Press.
> Brady investigates why poverty is so entrenched in some affluent democracies whereas it is a solvable problem in others. Drawing on over 30 years of data from 18 countries, Brady argues that cross-national and historical variations in poverty are principally driven by differences in the generosity of the welfare state.

Esping-Andersen, G. (1990). *The three worlds of welfare capitalism*. Princeton: Princeton University Press.
Esping-Andersen, G. (1999). *Social foundations of postindustrial economies*. Toronto: Oxford University Press.
Esping-Andersen, G. (2009). *The unfinished revolution: Welfare state adaptation to women's new roles*. Cambridge: Polity Press.
> These three books provide a typology of Western welfare states. This typology considers a range of social policies that are linked with variations in the historical development of Western countries. The author describes how profound differences among liberal, conservative, and social democratic political economies translate into widely differing lived experiences among citizens of these nations.

Marmot, M., Atkinson, T., Bell, J., Black, C., Broadfoot, P., Cumberlege, J., et al. (2010). *Fair society, healthy lives: The Marmot Review*. London: UCL Institute of Health Equity.
> In November 2008, Michael Marmot was asked by the then Secretary of State for Health to chair an independent review to propose the most effective, evidence-based strategies for reducing health inequalities in England. This is the final report.

Schraad-Tischler, S. (2011). *Social justice in the OECD: How do the member states compare?* Gutersloh: Bertelmanns Stifung. Retrieved from: http://www.sgi-network.org/.
> The Social Justice Index compares 31 OECD states across six dimensions: (1) poverty prevention, (2) access to education, (3) labour market inclusion, (4) social cohesion/non-discrimination, (5) health, and (6) intergenerational justice. It provides a snapshot related to all the issues subsumed in the problem of tackling health inequalities.

Recommended Websites

European Portal for Action on Health Equity: www.health-inequalities.eu/
The website is a tool to promote health equity among different socio-economic groups in the European Union. It provides information on policies and interventions to promote health equity within and among the countries of Europe by targeting the socio-economic determinants of health.

Institute of Health Equity: www.instituteofhealthequity.org/
The institute was launched in November 2011 to build on previous work to tackle inequalities in health, led by Michael Marmot and his team, including the Commission on Social Determinants of Health and Fair Society Healthy Lives (the Marmot Review). It will seek to increase health equity through action on the social determinants of health, specifically in four areas: (1) influencing global, national, and local policies; (2) advising on and learning from practice; (3) building the evidence base; and (4) capacity building.

Organisation for Economic Co-operation and Development: www.oecd.org/home
This site provides a wealth of reports, publications, and statistics about every aspect of society in modern developed states. Many of its contents are free or available electronically through your local university's library.

World Health Organization's Commission on Social Determinants of Health: www.who.int/social_determinants/en/
The WHO established the Commission on Social Determinants of Health in 2005 to provide advice on how to reduce them. The commission's final report was launched in August 2008, and contained three overarching recommendations: (1) improve daily living conditions; (2) tackle the inequitable distribution of power, money, and resources; and (3) measure and understand the problem and assess the impact of action.

References

Alesina, A., & Glaeser, E.L. (2004). *Fighting poverty in the US and Europe: A world of difference*. Toronto: Oxford University Press.

Armstrong, P., Armstrong, H., & Coburn, D. (Eds.). (2001). *Unhealthy times: The political economy of health and care in Canada*. Toronto: Oxford University Press.

Bambra, C. (2005). Cash versus services: "Worlds of welfare" and the decommodification of cash benefits and health care. *Journal of Social Policy, 34*(2), 195–213.

Bambra, C. (2011a). Health inequalities and welfare state regimes: Theoretical insights on a public health "puzzle." *Journal of Epidemiology and Community Health, 65*, 740–745.

Bambra, C. (2011b). *Work, worklessness, and the political economy of health*. Oxford: Oxford University Press.

Banting, K., & Corbett, A.M. (2002). Health policy and federalism: An introduction. In K. Banting & A.M. Corbett (Eds.), *Health policy and federalism: A comparative perspective on multi-level governance* (pp. 1–39). Kingston: Queen's University Press.

Blas, E., Gilson, L., Kelly, M.P., Labonté, R., Lapitan, J., Muntaner, C., et al. (2008). Addressing social determinants of health inequities: What can the state and civil society do? *The Lancet, 372*(9650), 1684–1689.

Brady, D. (2009). *Rich democracies, poor people: How politics explain poverty*. New York: Oxford University Press.

Brennenstuhl, S., Quesnel-Vallee, A., & McDonough, P. (2012). Welfare regimes, population health, and health inequalities: A research synthesis. *Journal of Epidemiology and Community Health, 66,* 397–409.

Brooks, N., & Hwong, T. (2006). *The social benefits and economic costs of taxation.* Ottawa: Canadian Centre for Policy Alternatives.

Bryant, T. (2005). Towards a new paradigm for research on urban women's health. *Women's Health and Urban Life, 4*(2), 68–95.

Butler-Jones, D. (2008). *Report on the state of public health in Canada 2008.* Ottawa: Public Health Agency of Canada.

Canadian Population Health Initiative. (2004). *Select highlights on public views of the determinants of health.* Ottawa: CPHI.

Castles, F. (1985). *The working class and welfare: Reflections on the political development of the welfare state in Australia and New Zealand, 1890–1980.* Sydney: Allen and Unwin.

Chatham-Kent Health Unit. (2011). *Let's start a conversation about health ... and not talk about health care at all.* Retrieved from: http://www.youtube.com/watch?v=NyTni-vn93Y&feature=related.

Coburn, D. (2004). Beyond the income inequality hypothesis: Globalization, neo-liberalism, and health inequalities. *Social Science & Medicine, 58,* 41–56.

Coburn, D. (2010). Health and health care: A political economy perspective. In T. Bryant, D. Raphael & M. Rioux (Eds.), *Staying alive: Critical perspectives on health, illness, and health care* (2nd ed., pp. 65–92). Toronto: Canadian Scholars' Press Inc.

Cox, L. (2006). The antipodean social laboratory, labour, and the transformation of the welfare state. *Journal of Sociology, 42*(2), 107–124.

Eikemo, T.A., & Bambra, C. (2008). The welfare state: A glossary for public health. *Journal of Epidemiology and Community Health, 62*(1), 3–6.

Epp, J. (1986). *Achieving health for all: A framework for health promotion.* Ottawa: Health and Welfare Canada.

Esping-Andersen, G. (1985). *Politics against markets: The social democratic road to power.* Princeton: Princeton University Press.

Esping-Andersen, G. (1990). *The three worlds of welfare capitalism.* Princeton: Princeton University Press.

Esping-Andersen, G. (2002). A child-centred social investment strategy. In G. Esping-Andersen (Ed.), *Why we need a new welfare state* (pp. 26–67). Oxford: Oxford University Press.

Fosse, E. (2011). Different welfare states—different policies? An analysis of the substance of national health promotion policies in three European countries. *International Journal of Health Services, 41*(2), 255–272.

Graham, H. (2004). Tackling health inequalities in health in England: Remedying health disadvantages, narrowing health gaps, or reducing health gradients? *Journal of Social Policy, 33,* 115–131.

Health Council of Canada. (2010). *Stepping it up: Moving the focus from health care in Canada to a healthier Canada.* Toronto: Health Council of Canada.

Health Disparities Task Group of the Federal/Provincial/Territorial Advisory Committee on Population Health and Health Security. (2004). *Reducing health disparities—roles of the health sector: Discussion paper.* Ottawa: Minister of Health.

Hemrijck, A. (2002). The self-tranformation of the European model. In G. Esping-Andersen (Ed.), *Why we need a new welfare state* (pp. 173–214). Oxford: Oxford University Press.

Innocenti Research Centre. (2005). *Child poverty in rich nations, 2005.* Report Card no. 6. Florence: Innocenti Research Centre.

Innocenti Research Centre. (2007). *An overview of child well-being in rich countries: A comprehensive assessment of the lives and well-being of children and adolescents in the economically advanced nations.* Florence: Innocenti Research Centre.

Innocenti Research Centre. (2010). *The children left behind: A league table of inequality in child well-being in the world's rich countries.* Florence: Innocenti Research Centre.

Irwin, A., & Scali, E. (2005). *Action on the social determinants of health: Learning from previous experiences*. Geneva: World Health Organization.

Kenworthy, L., & McCall, L. (2007). *Inequality, public opinion, and redistribution*. Working Paper no. 459. Syracuse: Luxembourg Income Study.

Lalonde, M. (1974). *A new perspective on the health of Canadians: A working document*. Retrieved from: http://www.hc-sc.gc.ca/main/hppb/phdd/resource.htm.

Marmot, M., Atkinson, T., Bell, J., Black, C., Broadfoot, P., Cumberlege, J., et al. (2010). *Fair society, healthy lives: The Marmot Review*. London: UCL Institute of Health Equity.

Menahem, G. (2010). *How can the Decommodified Security Ratio assess social protection systems?* LIS Working Paper No. 529. Syracuse: Luxembourg Income Study.

Mingers, J., & Willcocks, L. (2004). *Social theory and philosophy for information systems*. John Wiley series in information systems. Chichester, West Sussex, England: J. Wiley.

Murphy, J. (2006). The other welfare state. *History Australia, 3*(2), 1–15.

Navarro, V. (Ed.). (2002). *The political economy of social inequalities: Consequences for health and quality of life*. Amityville: Baywood Press.

Navarro, V. (Ed.). (2004). *The political and social contexts of health*. Amityville: Baywood Press.

Navarro, V. (Ed.). (2007). *Neoliberalism, globalization, and inequalities: Consequences for health and quality of life*. Amityville: Baywood Press.

Navarro, V., Borrell, C., Benach, J., Muntaner, C., Quiroga, A., Rodrigues-Sanz, M., et al. (2004). The importance of the political and the social in explaining mortality differentials among the countries of the OECD, 1950–1998. In V. Navarro (Ed.), *The political and social contexts of health* (pp. 11–86). Amityville: Baywood Press.

Navarro, V., & Muntaner, C. (Eds.). (2004). *Political and economic determinants of population health and well-being: Controversies and developments*. Amityville: Baywood Press.

Niagara Region Health Unit. (2011). *Let's start a conversation about health ... and not talk about health care at all*. Retrieved from: http://www.niagararegion.ca/news/publications/hs/health-convo.aspx.

Olsen, G. (2002). *The politics of the welfare state*. Toronto: Oxford University Press.

Olsen, G. (2010). *Power and inequality: A comparative introduction*. Toronto: Oxford University Press.

Organisation for Economic Co-operation and Development. (2003). *Transforming disability into ability: Policies to promote work and income security for people with disabilities*. Paris: Organisation for Economic Co-operation and Development.

Organisation for Economic Co-operation and Development. (2004). *OECD employment outlook 2004*. Paris: Organisation for Economic Co-operation and Development.

Organisation for Economic Co-operation and Development. (2008). *Growing unequal: Income distribution and poverty in OECD nations*. Paris: Organisation for Economic Co-operation and Development.

Organisation for Economic Co-operation and Development. (2010). *Health care systems: Efficiency and policy settings*. Paris: Organisation for Economic Co-operation and Development.

Organisation for Economic Co-operation and Development. (2011a). *Divided we stand: Why inequality keeps rising*. Paris: Organisation for Economic Co-operation and Development.

Organisation for Economic Co-operation and Development. (2011b). *Health at a glance: OECD indicators 2011 Edition*. Paris: Organisation for Economic Co-operation and Development.

Organisation for Economic Co-operation and Development. (2011c). *Strictness of employment protection*. Retrieved from: http://stats.oecd.org/Index.aspx?DataSetCode=EPL_OV.

Organisation for Economic Co-operation and Development. (2012a). *OECD tax database*. Retrieved from: http://www.oecd.org/document/60/0,3746,en_2649_34533_1942460_1_1_1,00.html#A_RevenueStatistics.

Organisation for Economic Co-operation and Development. (2012b). *Taxation of wage income*. Retrieved from: www.oecd.org/dataoecd/46/18/2506453.xls.

Pierson, P. (2000). Three worlds of welfare state research. *Comparative Political Studies, 33*(6/7), 791–821.

Pontusson, J. (2005). *Inequality and prosperity: Social Europe versus liberal America*. Ithaca: Cornell University Press.

Rainwater, L., & Smeeding, T.M. (2003). *Poor kids in a rich country: America's children in comparative perspective.* New York: Russell Sage Foundation.

Raphael, D. (2011a). Mainstream media and the social determinants of health in Canada: Is it time to call it a day? *Health Promotion International, 26*(2), 220–229.

Raphael, D. (2011b). The political economy of health promotion: Part 2, National provision of the prerequisites of health. *Health Promotion International.* doi: 10.1093/heapro/dar058.

Robert Wood Johnson Foundation. (2010). *A new way to talk about the social determinants of health.* Retrieved from: http://www.rwjf.org/vulnerablepopulations/product.jsp?id=66428.

Saint-Arnaud, S., & Bernard, P. (2003). Convergence or resilience? A hierarchical cluster analysis of the welfare regimes in advanced countries. *Current Sociology, 51*(5), 499–527.

Sayer, A. (2000). *Realism and social science.* Thousand Oaks: Sage Publications.

Schraad-Tischler, S. (2011). *Social justice in the OECD: How do the member states compare?* Gutersloh: Bertelmanns Stifung.

Sudbury and District Health Unit. (2011). *Let's start a conversation about health ... and not talk about health care at all.* Retrieved from: http://tinyurl.com/7t8476f.

Swank, D. (2005). Globalisation, domestic politics, and welfare state retrenchment in capitalist democracies. *Social Policy and Society, 4*(2), 183–195.

Timiskaming Health Unit. (2011). *Let's start a conversation about health ... and not talk about health care at all.* Retrieved from: www.youtube.com/watch?v=bDtLPV9nLJw.

Wellington-Dufferin-Guelph Health Unit. (2011). *Let's start a conversation about health ... and not talk about health care at all.* Retrieved from: www.youtube.com/watch?v=jbqKcOqoyoo.

Whitehead, M. (1998). Diffusion of ideas on social inequalities in health: A European perspective. *Millbank Quarterly, 76*(3), 469–492.

Wijkström, F. (2004). *The role of civil society: The case of Sweden in international comparison.* Stockholm: The Stockholm School of Economics.

World Health Organization. (2008). *Closing the gap in a generation: Health equity through action on the social determinants of health.* Geneva: World Health Organization.

Chapter 10

Applying the Lessons from International Experiences

Toba Bryant

Introduction

The evidence presented in this volume describes a continuum of governmental policy activity across nations that tackle inequalities. These range from comprehensive coordinated policy in Scandinavia to an apparent absence of governmental policy concern in Canada and the US. Britain and Northern Ireland and Australia present mid-level responses. The sources of these differences lie in differing aspects of each nation's state, their power relations within the society, and the extent of social determinants of health-related policy. These differences, in turn, lead to differences in social inequalities and health inequalities as well as the willingness to tackle them.

The task for those concerned with tackling health inequalities within each nation is to either maintain (if health inequalities are being addressed) or shift (if they are not) the characteristics of these contributing components in a manner that enhances governmental authorities' ability and willingness to tackle health inequalities. This is basically the task of implementing public policy. In the cases where these desired activities are not occurring, it is one of implementing public policy *change*. What models of public policy change are available for taking on these tasks and which will be most appropriate for each nation's situation?

This chapter examines different models of public policy change and their relevance for tackling health inequalities through governmental activity. *Policy change* is an adjustment to an existing public policy or set of related public policies. It usually refers to a new course of action aimed at addressing a problem or issue identified by government and others as having negative social implications (Howlett, Ramesh & Perl, 2009). One form of policy change is called *incremental* and involves small changes to existing public policy. Some examples of incremental change to existing public policies would be providing additional resources to enable hospitals and community health clinics to offer health services to those who show the worse health outcomes, such as homeless people or victims of domestic violence. Such changes do not usually involve change in the overall goals and objectives of a policy area. Policy change can also be *paradigmatic* in that it involves a significant shift in policy goals and objectives. Some examples of this would be a nation's effort to tackle health inequalities as a significant public policy goal involving a thorough realignment of existing public policy in a range of areas.

In this chapter a variety of existing models of public policy implementation and change are examined for their relevance to the issue of tackling health inequalities through public policy activity. These models include what are called *pluralist models* concerned with democratic processes, *policy paradigms, a learning model of policy change*, and others that involve a *political economy* approach. As examples, pluralism is concerned with how citizens can get involved with groups that advocate for certain public policies (Brooks & Miljan, 2003).

Learning models consider how governmental institutions use knowledge and ideas in the policy change process (Hall, 1993). And political economy approaches consider the role that politics and economics play in public policy development (Armstrong, Armstrong & Coburn, 2001). It is this latter approach that explicitly examines the roles political ideology and power, the market and the state, and civil society play in shaping public policy decisions on health and social issues. It will be argued that the political and economic configuration in each country will determine which of these models—pluralist, learning, or political economy—will be most appropriate to bring about public policy action that tackles health inequalities.

Models of Policy Change

Implementing public policy—either maintaining desired policy or creating desired policy—is critical to tackling health inequalities. International declarations related to health promotion, such as the Ottawa Charter, and more recent ones concerned with tackling health inequalities developed by the World Health Organization and others identify the development of healthy public policy as a cornerstone of the new public health (Equity Action, 2012; World Health Organization, 2008, 2009). Indeed, Margaret Chan, WHO director-general, states: "Health inequities exist because the wrong policies are in place" (Equity Action, 2012).

In nations where health inequalities are not being addressed, the evidence on the importance of developing health-supporting public policy through action on the social determinants of health has not been acknowledged and certainly not acted upon. In Canada and the US, the field of "health promotion" has limited itself to raising issues of changing individuals' health-related behaviours, such as tobacco and alcohol use, lack of physical activity, and unhealthy eating to prevent disease and illness, rather than developing public policies that tackle the primary sources of health inequalities: differing living circumstances (Raphael, 2008). Canadian and American governments have not demonstrated the will to act on the social determinants of health in order to reduce the social inequalities that create health inequalities. The task here is to shift public policy toward addressing these issues.

The opposite situation is seen in the Scandinavian nations of Finland, Norway, and Sweden. The task here is to maintain these public policy initiatives and defend against threats to them. The task in Britain and Northern Ireland and Australia is to maintain the advances undertaken and build further momentum. What models of public policy change are available to guide these activities?

Three general public policy change models, pluralism, policy paradigms (one form of learning models), and political economy are used in the following sections to help identify what may be required to tackle health inequalities within each of the nations examined in this volume. These three have been selected because they represent the scope of such theories. *Pluralism* is a model of democratic participation that focuses on how interest groups influence governments to make specific forms of public policy. It assumes that governments make public policy on the basis of an analysis of costs and benefits, and is a principal approach in the public policy analysis literature. This is especially the case in North America.

The *policy paradigms* model is consistent with historical institutionalism. It is a learning model of policy change concerned with the role that established governmental and other institutions play in the public policy process (Hall, 1993). A key aspect of this model is the importance of ideas and how these are both embedded in institutions and serve as sources of public policy activity. The model conceives these institutions and their ideas as structuring the public policy-making process. The model examines various types of policy change, but focuses on paradigmatic policy change as opposed to processes associated with incremental change.

The *political economy* model of policy change is a structural and materialist approach that conceives politics as flowing from how the economy distributes power and resources. It emphasizes how political ideology and the relative power of the market versus the state shape public policy-making (Armstrong et al., 2001; Bryant, 2005; Coburn, 2000). In contrast to the emphasis on the role of different groups in putting forth ideas to be subjected to cost and benefit analysis (pluralism), and the role played by institutions' accepted ideas (policy paradigms), political economy is concerned with how societal structures produce and distribute economic, political, and social resources. Public policy is a result of particular groups having more control and influence over these processes, thereby shaping public policy-making to meet their, rather than others', needs and desires.

These models will be used to identify the approaches and actions required in different countries to tackle health inequalities. All three models will have insights useful for advancing the tackling health inequalities agenda. In Canada and the United States, where tackling health inequalities are not on the public policy agenda, addressing them will require paradigmatic change in the goals and objectives of public policies as well as forcing the political will to take action. Such activities will be best assisted by the insights provided by a political economy analysis of the situation.

In countries further along in tackling health inequalities, such as the Scandinavian countries of Finland, Norway, and Sweden, where power imbalances are less salient than in Canada and the US, the pluralist and policy paradigms models may provide more immediately useful insights. The British and Northern Ireland and Australian scenes may benefit equally by insights provided by all three models of public policy change.

Pluralism

Pluralism is one of the most widely used approaches for examining the public policy-making process (Howlett et al., 2009). Developed in the US, it continues to be the dominant theoretical approach for studying politics and public policy-making there and in Canada. Corporatism is a similar theory of politics and public policy-making that was developed in Europe around the same time as pluralism (Howlett et al., 2009). Pluralism considers interest groups as key societal influences on the public policy process. This perspective considers that the complexity of governance of modern society and society itself precludes direct political participation of individual citizens in the policy process (Brodie, 2005). Citizens, therefore, join groups to promote their preferences and interests. Politics is seen as the competition among interest groups to influence public policy. Citizens can belong to a number of groups that advance their concerns such that memberships among interest groups frequently overlap (Howlett et al., 2009). The role of the state is to mediate this competition among different groups and the ideas they bring to the political process. Critics argue, however, that pluralism has an underdeveloped understanding of the inequalities—economic, political, and social—that exist in modern capitalist societies, making such objective mediation unlikely.

Pluralists do recognize that not all groups are equal in their ability to influence the political process or to access government (Howlett et al., 2009). These inequalities in influence are attributable to their lack of financial and other resources. Nevertheless, on this point, McLennan argues, "It is impossible to read the standard works [on pluralist theory] without getting the sense that resources, information and the means of political communication are openly available to all citizens, that groups form an array of equivalent power centres in society, and that all legitimate voices can and will be heard" (McLennan, 1989, 32). Indeed, pluralism implies that citizens and citizen groups can present their ideas to government with the assumption that they will receive a fair hearing (Bryant, 2010).

Pluralism is a consensus model of policy change as it assumes that decisions will be based on meeting the common good for most societal members (Bryant, 2009). It emphasizes evidence and ideas, and how experts, lobbyists, and citizen groups can build support for a particular position on public policy-making (Bryant, 2010). It also assumes that regardless of the positions groups may argue to government, these groups will not meet predetermined resistance to their ideas. In terms of trying to influence policy-makers to tackle health inequalities, for example, by having governments ensure that all citizens have access to economic and social resources to promote their health, those favouring health equity will have as much chance of success as those opposing forms of public policy that reduce social and health inequalities.

Clearly, this is not necessarily the case and the Canadian and US scenes provide ample evidence of this. This is apparent in Canada, where despite decades of document and report making containing evidence on the importance of tackling health inequalities by government civil servants and various professional public health associations, governmental authorities have resisted taking on these issues through public policy activity. The US scene is even more obvious in demonstrating how political and economic power comes to shape public policy-making. Here social inequalities in income and wealth and minimal government intervention in the operation of the market economy—the prime sources of health inequalities—are actually celebrated by many governing authorities rather than seen as causes for concern. The British and Northern Irish and Australian experiences are also replete with examples of governments coming to power that are actively opposed to public policy that tackles health inequalities.

In spite of the limitations of pluralism for explaining and addressing the Canadian and US scenes, it does provide some useful insights for those concerned with tackling health inequalities. In Finland, Norway, and Sweden, where concern with strengthening the social determinants of health to tackle health inequalities is most advanced, pluralism can further our understanding of how public policy-makers, governing and opposition parties, and elements of civil society have come together to tackle health inequalities and the social inequalities that spawn them. Pluralism also has insights as to how various societal groups come to influence public policy in Britain and Northern Ireland and Australia when governing parties receptive to such ideas have come to power.

Policy Paradigms

Policy paradigms is related to a school of thought called historical institutionalism that considers how institutions of governments structure politics and public policy outcomes (Hall & Taylor, 1996).

Policy paradigms grew out of an attempt to explain different patterns of policy change (Hall, 1993). The concept of a "policy paradigm" refers to governments' social learning where social learning is defined as "a deliberate attempt to adjust the goals or techniques of policy in response to past experience and new information" (Hall, 1993, 275). According to this definition, policy change is integrally related to learning from previous experiences. Social learning emphasizes the role of ideas and their interpretation in policy-making. This social learning process is dominated by officials and highly placed experts, and this is especially the case when the issues at hand are highly technical policy fields.

A particular aim of the model is to differentiate between the learning processes associated with normal policy change and more radical or paradigmatic policy change (Bourjolly, Hirschman & Zieber, 2004). These processes involve the acceptance or rejection of particular sets of ideas, and these ideas are advanced by both state and non-state actors. But these ideas have to be processed through the larger political system (Baumgartner & Jones, 1993) such that "Policy makers work within a framework of ideas and standards that specify not only the goals of policy and the kind of instruments that can be used to attain them, but also the very nature of the problems" they are intended to address (Hall, 1993, 279). Hall, for example, argues that the framework in which politicians function is grounded in the terminology (or ideas) through which policy-makers understand their scope of activity. Yet much of these ideas "[are] taken for granted and ... unamenable to scrutiny as a whole" (Hall, 1993, 279).

The interpretive framework or policy paradigm involves ideas embedded within existing political, social, and economic institutions. The terms "policy legacies" and "path dependency" refer to how past policies shape policies being made in the present. In terms of the present inquiry, this refers to some of the reasons why some nations find it so difficult to think differently about tackling health inequalities. This is the case because they are following the same approaches that have served them so well in the past—that is, ignoring these issues. In these cases, moving governmental policy-making toward tackling health inequalities—and this is most apparent in Canada and the US—would require rather radical new ways of thinking. It also helps illuminate why the tackling of health inequalities in Britain and Northern Ireland represented significant policy shifts and why these ideas about tackling health inequalities are so easily implemented in Finland, Norway, and Sweden as they are consistent with long-standing policy directions.

The policy paradigms model, therefore, distinguishes between different orders of change, identifying *normal* and *paradigmatic* patterns of policy change. The aim in developing the model was to learn more about the varieties of policy change. The model identifies three levels of policy change:

First-order change: First-order change has elements of incrementalism, "satisficing," and "routinized" decision-making (Hall, 1993). Such alterations can be minor adjustments to policy, such as changes in monthly social assistance and pension payments, or providing additional resources to community health centres or institutions to provide a particular program to serve people who are homeless or victims of domestic violence. The overall goals of policy, its instruments, and the context of policy-making remain the same.

Second-order change: Second-order change generally involves the development of new policy instruments and a move toward strategic action (Hall, 1993). Second-order change may occur at less frequent intervals than first-order changes. Both first- and second-order changes tend to "preserve the broad continuity" (Hall, 1993) in terms of the overall goals of a policy area. In other words, the policy goals and objectives remain the same, but the policy instruments may change. For example, government officials may want to discourage smoking (Howlett et al., 2009). Initially, they may use public education on the risks of smoking in the hopes that people will change their behaviour in response to the information provided. If this does not produce the desired result of encouraging many people to quit smoking and dissuading young people from smoking, then they may opt for increased taxation of tobacco products. This typically entails more government activity than simply distributing information. Taxation involves deliberate efforts to directly influence the preferences and behaviours of citizens to stop or not start smoking. First- and second-order changes, then, are instances of normal policy change because they alter policy without changing the overall goals of a policy paradigm.

Third-order change: In contrast to first- and second-order policy changes, third-order paradigmatic policy change is manifested by a radical shift in the overall terms of policy discourse associated with the "received paradigm" (Hall, 1993). It tends to be a more disruptive process and may involve sporadic yet well-defined activity. One common example is that of the shift from Keynesian welfare state to monetarist models of macroeconomic regulation in Britain. It has been suggested that this shift involved simultaneous changes in all three components of policy: the instrument settings, the instruments themselves, and the hierarchy of goals behind policy (Hall, 1993).

The development of the welfare state in Canada, the UK, and other western European countries after World War II also represented a paradigmatic shift from a residual model of limited or no government involvement to an institutional approach of significant government intervention and activity in social provision (Teeple, 2000). The welfare state involved high government intervention in such social programs as housing, health care, unemployment insurance, and pensions. The experiences of citizens during the Depression of the 1930s and social science knowledge informed this shift.

More recently, governments in Canada, the UK, and elsewhere have undertaken another paradigmatic shift (Leys, 2001; Teeple & McBride, 2010). They have privatized some health care services, deregulated the market in many areas, and reduced governmental supports and benefits to citizens. These changes now signify a paradigmatic shift in the role of government in the opposite direction than was the case after World War II. This new shift is premised on an ideological belief—neo-liberalism—that the market is more appropriate than the state for allocating resources (Coburn, 2000; Teeple, 2000).

These shifts from one paradigm to another—although supposedly based on ideas—may be more politically than scientifically determined. While arguments mounted by competing factions, positional advantages within a broader institutional framework, resources of various competing political actors, and external factors all play a role, their adoption is primarily determined by the politics of the day and the ideology of governing authorities.

In a significant study of the shift from Keynesianism to monetarism in Britain from 1970 to 1989, British politicians intervened when social scientists were unable to resolve the dispute between the Keynesian and the monetarist paradigms (Hall, 1993). The politicians assessed the merits of the paradigms on political terms. Advancing its own political agenda and policy ideas, the government launched a new era in macroeconomic policy-making in Britain, drawing on social science insofar as it supported the shift to monetarist economic policy. Certainly a similar analysis can be provided as to why some governing authorities adopt the tackling of health inequalities as important foci of public policy-making activity while others do not.

The Political Economy of Policy Change

Political economy is a materialist perspective on politics and the political process. It is materialist as it considers ideas and institutions to emanate from the way in which a society organizes the production and distribution of social and economic resources (Armstrong et al., 2001; Coburn, 2010). Politics and economics are considered to be interrelated and as fundamentally shaping public policy outcomes (Armstrong et al., 2001). This perspective directs attention to the relationship between public policy-making and the economic, political, and social lives of different people, geographic areas, or societies. The state, the market, political power, political ideology, and civil society are considered to be constituent parts of the whole (Armstrong et al., 2001). The whole is shaped by the mode of production, which is capitalism. Issues such as social and health inequalities, as well as patriarchy, sexism, and racism, are examined in relation to the operation of the economic and political system. A political economy perspective also focuses on how gender, social class, and race/ethnicity operate as different forms of social stratification that create social and health inequalities (Armstrong, 2004).

Of recent interest in the literature is the role of neo-liberalism, an ideology that advocates unfettered free enterprise as the means to foster economic growth and social well-being (Coburn, 2001, 2004). The political economy perspective is consistent with a focus on the social determinants of health, and how political and economic environments shape the distribution of social and economic resources within a society.

At the heart of the political economy approach to these issues is a commitment to address social and health inequalities. This can best be accomplished by making explicit the role that institutions, especially the state, play in contributing to health inequalities. Societies in which the market is the most important institution tend to have more pronounced social and health inequalities (Grabb, 2007; Leys, 2001). This is so because differences among groups on the basis of social class, gender, race, and other identities are accentuated. Applying a political economy perspective enables consideration of dominant economic interests that influence policy change, often impeding the tackling of health inequalities. Through such an analysis, a political economy perspective can identify means of shifting public policy toward addressing health inequalities.

The Scandinavian countries of Finland, Norway, and Sweden are especially committed to tackling social and health inequalities. They have embraced the social determinants concept and used it to guide the development of public policies that tackle health inequalities. They do so through provision of a comprehensive welfare state that supports health and reduces economic and social insecurity. That this is so easily done is a result of their being social democratic welfare states, where the economic and political systems are oriented toward promoting equality through state intervention in the operation of the market economy (Navarro & Shi, 2002; Saint-Arnaud & Bernard, 2003). The opposite is the case in the liberal nations of Canada and the US, where the market economy is the dominant institution and governmental intervention in its operation is minimized. Australia and Britain and Northern Ireland represent the effects of social democratic parties of the left gaining power nationally in long-established liberal welfare states.

Models of Public Policy Change and Implications for Tackling Health Inequalities

In Chapter 9, Raphael presents Figure 9.2, which locates the nations discussed in this volume on the Action Spectrum for Addressing Health Inequalities.

Finland, Norway, and Sweden as Comprehensive Coordinated Policy

Raphael locates the Scandinavian countries of Finland, Norway, and Sweden at the level of "Comprehensive coordinated policy." This means that the national governments in these countries not only have tackling health inequalities on their public policy agendas, but have implemented systematic activities to address them. As Whitehead (1998) noted, Sweden had health inequalities on its public policy agenda as early as the 1930s. The state is deemed the most important institution and best positioned to distribute these resources to citizens (Saint-Arnaud & Bernard, 2003). While these countries have ratcheted back public spending in some social and health policy areas, they are still well ahead of the other countries examined in this volume (Organisation for Economic Co-operation and Development, 2011). Nevertheless, the Scandinavian countries have also experienced insreased income inequalities in recent years.

A pluralist analysis would suggest that those in favour of these approaches have been able to have them placed on the public policy agenda through well-organized advocacy and lobbying by citizen and other groups. The policy paradigms analysis would explain this as a predictable outcome of well-established policy directions that have their source in the well-developed Scandinavian welfare state, which has apparently served policy-makers and the public well. There is little doubt that by any objective set of indicators, overall health and quality of life is good in Scandinavia, and this is especially the case when compared to liberal welfare states such as Canada and the US.

But even then, these historical developments must be placed within the context of the operation of their economic and political systems. It is here that a political economy analysis provides useful insights into how the organization of the state versus the market, power balances among various groups, and the development of decommodifying public policy help to explain the Scandinavian concern with tackling health inequalities. Further analyses are presented in the following sections.

Canada and the US as Edging toward Measurement

At the other extreme, Figure 9.2 locates Canada as barely at the "Measurement" level. The US is not even there. Governments in these countries are not themselves directly involved in measuring health inequalities. Nor are these activities part of any organized governmental activity concerned with tackling health inequalities. National and state/provincial/territorial governments in both countries generally fail to acknowledge the existence of health inequalities as significant areas of public policy concern.

Moreover, these failures to tackle health inequalities are not raised by opposition parties in Canada and the US, and the general public is woefully unaware of these issues. In Canada, opposition parties highlight how Aboriginal Canadians are disadvantaged in health outcomes, but issues of social disadvantage among Canadian Aboriginals are not placed within a health inequalities framework. For example, much media attention focused on the appalling living conditions in the Aboriginal community of Attawappiscat and how, in an historic first, the International Red Cross delivered emergency supplies to this community, but these issues operate outside of any kind of health inequalities policy framework (Berthiaume, 2012).

All three models of policy change provide insights as to how this has come to be the case. In Canada (less so in the US), a variety of organizations and agencies have raised issues of tackling health inequalities, but these activities are not well organized and have certainly not placed these issues on a public policy agenda in either nation (pluralist perspective). Among Canadian and American policy-makers, health—and policy initiatives related to its promotion—are equated with *health care* and *healthy lifestyles* (policy paradigms perspective).

Shifting public policy concern from a focus on biomedical approaches to health and public education about avoiding health-threatening behaviours will require a paradigmatic shift to one of instituting public policy that addresses the inequalities in living circumstances that spawn health inequalities. The lack of organized advocacy and lobbying efforts will make this difficult.

But even then, such a shift in Canada and the US would be resisted by powerful economic and political forces that favour current policy directions that create social inequalities (Langille, 2009). These interests and their proposed policies drive the growth of income and wealth inequalities and reduce government benefits and supports to citizens (political economy perspective). Clearly, these analyses help explain both the present situation in these nations and the formidable barriers to having governing authorities adopt a tackling health inequalities agenda.

Australia: Midway between Isolated Initiatives and More Structured Developments

Australia is located midway between the "Isolated initiatives" and "More structured developments" levels. Tackling health inequalities has made it onto the public policy agenda in Australia and this is in large part a result of the Community Health Program (CHP) introduced by the Whitlam Labor government in 1971. A primary purpose of the CHP was to address health inequalities by developing multidisciplinary approaches to address health in a specific geographic area. The CHP—while a single initiative—nonetheless provided a foundation for further action to reduce health inequalities. There has been a systematic national approach to addressing Indigenous health.

Concern with tackling health inequalities has ebbed and waned, it appears, alongside the election and defeat of Labor governments at the national and state levels. Again, these developments can be explained through recourse to the policy change models. Australians have a tradition of supporting the "fair go," which makes governments at least somewhat receptive to a tackling health inequalities agenda (pluralist perspective). Its governing authorities have experiences with a variety of health policy agendas, making these governments less rigid than might be the case in Canada and the US (policy paradigms perspective). But all of these activities are embedded within a liberal welfare state that generally reverts to a preference for less rather than more state intervention in the operation of the market economy (political economy perspective). When Labor governments are elected, there is a move toward tackling a health inequalities agenda, but even then these efforts are modest as compared to the cases of Finland, Norway, and Sweden.

Britain and Northern Ireland: More Structured Developments
Britain and Northern Ireland have had tackling health inequalities on their public policy agendas for some time now. The devolution of power to Scotland, Wales, and Northern Ireland has led to some divergence in addressing health inequalities in the three regions. For example, Scotland covers prescription fees, abolished university tuition fees, and expanded home care provision to seniors. Prior to devolution, however, the United Kingdom underwent a paradigmatic shift toward tackling health inequalities, which began with the commissioning by the newly elected Labour government of the Acheson Review (Acheson, 1998). Health inequalities became a cornerstone of its health policy and a wide range of intersectoral governmental initiatives were undertaken. Opinion is mixed as to the success of these initiatives (Hills, Sefton & Stewart, 2009; Hills & Stewart, 2005).

By the time of the election of the Labour government in 1997, the growth of social and health inequalities had become a widespread public concern and tackling these were a part of Labour's election platform (pluralist perspective). The newly elected government undertook a variety of initiatives, but these were embedded with the ongoing operation of the UK's political and economic system, which is associated with rather higher income and wealth inequalities. There was also a general reluctance to undertake governmental interventions in the marketplace associated with the UK's liberal welfare state (policy paradigms perspective). Critiques of the government's approach toward tackling health inequalities have focused on the unwillingness to address broad issues of income and wealth inequality by concentrating on the needs of the most disadvantaged (political economy perspective).

Even these developments are now threatened by the election of a Conservative-Liberal Democratic Coalition government, which has vowed to cut government expenditures by 40 percent (Bryant et al., 2011). Moving toward the approaches of the Scandinavian nations requires consideration of the many barriers to such action in the UK. Even so, the tackling health inequalities situation in the UK should be cause for envy among those in Canada and the US concerned with these issues.

Implications

This analysis identified some of the features of nations' situations and how these shape governmental approaches toward tackling health inequalities. The 2008 economic crisis has been associated with varying degrees of reduced public spending on health and social programs, but it appears that these declines are most apparent in the nations that have to date resisted tackling health inequalities. While even Finland, Norway, and Sweden have controlled growth in expenditures and, to some extent, reduced them, the extent of this retrenchment is less than is the case in other nations in this inquiry. Again we see the role played by established societal approaches to public policy-making as well as the distinct economic and political features of each nation.

The political economy perspective, therefore, offers the most useful explanation for explaining governmental authorities' action or inaction on tackling health inequalities. By integrating politics and economics, the perspective highlights the relationship between tackling health inequalities and the economic, political, and social structures of these societies. It recognizes the role of dominant economic interests, such as the corporate sector, in shaping public policies on health in countries in which the market is the dominant institution as in Canada and the US. Similarly, by bringing together political and economic issues, the political economy perspective helps explain the considerable progress on tackling health inequalities in Finland, Norway, and Sweden and the more modest successes in Australia and Britain and Northern Ireland.

Tackling health inequalities in Finland, Norway, and Sweden has become such a part of their public policy agenda that all major political parties accept the need to address this issue. While there may be some retrenchment and curtailing of the comprehensive range of health and social programs and other supports made available to their populations, their continued existence is probably not under threat. In Australia and Britain and Northern Ireland, tackling health inequalities seems to depend on whether the Labour Party controls national and state governments. Even then, these authorities are embedded within long-existing economic and political structures associated with the liberal welfare state.

In summary, the political economy approach, which highlights the influence of economic and political interests in whether governing authorities tackle health inequalities, provides the most useful insights into why and how nations tackle health inequalities. It points out how, in the case of Canada and the US as well as Britain and Northern Ireland and Australia, the defining features of the liberal welfare state shape the extent of health and social inequalities and limit governmental authorities' willingness to tackle them.

Pluralism also offers some helpful analysis of the current situation, especially in the Scandinavian countries. A pluralist approach highlights the importance of information on health inequalities for governments to take action to tackle inequalities. In short, advocacy groups and others who present these ideas should not experience government resistance to addressing these ideas. This suggests that continuing to advocate for the tackling of health inequalities will help to keep these issues on the public policy agenda in these nations. One means of maintaining state receptivity to these issues is to keep these issues front and centre for governing authorities, the media, and the general public.

Shifting the Components of Governmental Authorities' Willingness to Tackle Health Inequalities

In the previous chapter, nations were also described as to how their characteristics fit into the various components of Figure 9.4. These were the "State," "Power relations," and "SDOH-related public policies." What do each of the public policy change models suggest needs to be understood about these situations, and what needs to be done to have governments tackle health inequalities? For convenience of presentation, three distinct clusters of nations are used to organize this analysis. These are (1) the Scandinavian nations of Finland, Norway, and Sweden; (2) Britain and Northern Ireland, and Australia; and (3) Canada and the US.

The State

Table 10.1 provides some suggestions as to how aspects of the state could be influenced to promote the tackling of health inequalities. Those suggested by a pluralist approach would emphasize the development and strengthening of citizen groups in order to build support for and pressure governing authorities to tackle health inequalities. Clearly, this is more of a task for Canadians and Americans concerned with tackling health inequalities than is the case elsewhere.

The policy paradigms approach suggests taking account of governmental structures and the need to maintain those supportive of a tackling health inequalities approach and change those opposed to such an agenda. In Canada and the US, such a shift will require a paradigmatic change in public policy-making, which is not to be taken lightly. In Australia and Britain and Northern Ireland, those structures that have been established need to be supported and opposition to their weakening opposed. In Finland, Norway, and Sweden, successes need to be recognized and care taken not to have these successes ignored and/or reversed. Table 10.1 identifies the critical importance of proportional representation in the electoral process, which can strengthen the influence of supporters of policies associated with tackling health inequalities. Finally, in federal states such as Australia, Canada, and the US, means must be identified to enhance the ability of the central government to shape public policy-making across all levels of government. In Canada, this was the case when the central government guided policy development during the 1970s and 1980s by making available to the provinces and territories funding for medicare and social assistance.

Power Relations

Table 10.2 provides some suggestions for maintaining or shifting power relations in a manner that would favour the tackling of health inequalities by governmental authorities. A pluralist analysis would identify differences in tackling health inequalities as reflecting differences in public support and group advocacy for such an approach. The clear implication is to strengthen these activities with the goals of influencing public policy-making.

The policy paradigms approach points out how the three clusters differ in their economic and political structures toward a wide range of issues. Such an analysis highlights the barriers to institutional change, and this is especially the case in Canada and the US. Clearly, the model

Table 10.1
State Institutions and Models of Policy Change—Welfare Regime, Electoral Process, Central vs. Federal System

	Finland, Norway, and Sweden	Australia and Britain and Northern Ireland	Canada and the US
Pluralism	Maintain public support for the Nordic welfare state.	Continue to build public support for policy initiatives.	Educate the public as to the social determinants of health inequalities.
Policy Paradigms	Evaluate and communicate the Nordic welfare state paradigm's successes in promoting health and well-being.	Work to maintain state structures and interest in intervening in the operation of the established market economy.	Recognize the profound barriers to paradigmatic shifts among well-established liberal welfare states.
Political Economy	Work to maintain social democratic ideals behind the Nordic welfare state.	Recognize that forward movement will require ongoing vigilance against market forces.	Work to offset corporate and business interests' dominance of the policy agenda.
Proportional Representation	Maintain proportional representation in the electoral process.	All three policy models suggest means of promoting electoral reform toward proportional representation through public education, restructuring government, and balancing political power.	

suggests the need to strengthen political parties of the left by shifting electoral behaviour and strengthening unions' ability to organize the workplace.

Both this model and the political economy approach make clear that tackling health inequalities is a profoundly political activity that requires more than the collection of evidence and advocacy in favour of such an approach. The importance of changing electoral behaviour and strengthening labour unions in order to shift public policy in social determinants of health-related policy areas seems essential.

Social Determinants of Health-Related Public Policy

Finally, Table 10.3 outlines how each model of policy change would make sense of the differing public policy profiles present in the nations of this inquiry. The task in Finland, Norway, and Sweden is to mobilize public opinion to support the structures associated with the social democratic welfare state. Contrasting their situations with those seen in Canada and the US would help meet these objectives.

Table 10.2

Power Relations and Models of Policy Change—Electoral Behaviour, Trade Union Strength, and Civil Society Coalitions

	Finland, Norway, and Sweden	Australia and Britain and Northern Ireland	Canada and the US
Pluralism	Plurality of interests has historically supported public policies that promote health equity.	Plurality of interests that support health equity has varied over time such that policy directions are inconsistent.	Plurality of interests has never coalesced around tackling health inequalities through public policy action.
Policy Paradigms	Long-standing Nordic traditions promote receptivity to tackling health inequalities.	Shifting political fortunes of social democratic parties limit long-standing institutional commitments.	Dominance of corporate and business interests make tackling health inequalities by governments difficult.
Political Economy	Relative balance between business, labour, and civil society promotes progressive public policy.	Shifting political fortunes of social democratic parties provide inconsistent public policy activity.	Dominance of economic interests makes raising issues of health inequalities difficult.

In Australia and Britain and Northern Ireland, these efforts will be more difficult, but successes have to be acknowledged and continuing barriers recognized. In Canada and the US, significant efforts must be undertaken to educate the public in order to shift the economic and political structures that have shaped public policy-making. These are not easy tasks as the chapters on Canada and the US make clear.

Implications

The political contexts in Canada and the United States are similar in many ways. None of the political parties in Canada or in the US has demonstrated willingness to tackle health inequalities. There is support for such an approach in Canada, with think tanks such as the Canadian Centre for Policy Alternatives and various NGOs raising the importance of addressing the social determinants of health in Canada. In the US, the situation is much worse. Few advocacy organizations have addressed the importance of tackling health inequalities. In both Canada and the US, researchers investigate and demonstrate the extent of inequalities, but governments and their political cultures and institutions resist these ideas.

There is much more activity taking place in Australia and Britain and Northern Ireland. Elections of social democratic labour parties at the federal level in Australia, England, and

Table 10.3
SDOH-Related Public Policy and Models of Policy Change

	Finland, Norway, and Sweden	Australia and Britain and Northern Ireland	Canada and the US
Pluralism	Continue to advocate for strong welfare state.	Advocate for continuing strengthening of commitment to address health inequalities.	Educate the public as to the deficiencies of the Canadian and American welfare states.
Policy Paradigms	Maintain strong commitments to provision of economic and social security to citizens.	Strengthen institutional support for provision of economic and social security to citizens.	Confront and lobby for changes to weak and inadequate economic and social security provided to citizens.
Political Economy	Maintain strong commitment to social democratic principles in public policy.	Recognize significant sectors that resist state provision of economic and social security.	Strengthen citizen action that supports public policy in the service of all.

Scotland have contributed to greater receptiveness to policy innovations to reduce health inequalities. Policy paradigms helps make sense of these developments, but the political economy identifies more explicit levers to bring about change. It highlights the role of social democracy in recognizing the unequal distribution of resources leading to growing health inequalities.

There is an increasing literature as to how to bring about these kinds of changes, and these clearly involve building social and political movements in favour of the kinds of policies that are well developed in the Finnish, Norwegian, and Swedish case studies, and less developed in the Australian, and British and Northern Irish case studies.

What Would a Tackling Health Inequalities Governmental Agenda Look Like in Canada?

The Health Council of Canada recently provided an analysis of what is needed to have governments address the "determinants of health" through what is called "a whole-of-government" approach (Health Council of Canada, 2010). The Health Council's emphasis on the determinants of health is rooted in sometimes explicit, other times implicit, concern with promoting "health equity" and reducing "health inequities."

The Health Council report provides a "Checklist for Whole-of-Government or Intersectoral Work." While it was developed to address the determinants of health, it can be taken as specifying what values, information, and government infrastructure would be needed to tackle health inequalities. It specifies the *Values and Commitment, Information and Data, and Governmental Infrastructure* that would be required to undertake these activities, as is presented in Appendix A.

While the Health Council identifies targets for action, it is important to consider that this chapter—and the previous one—have identified the considerable barriers to having these components implemented in Canada. These barriers are generally neglected in most Canadian governmental and institutional reports that address issues of promoting health equity and tackling health inequalities, instead seeing the failure to address these issues as the result of a lack of information on health inequalities and/or a failure of bureaucratic organization.

Toward the Future

The above examination shows that the countries are at different stages in tackling health inequalities. Absolutely essential for the tackling of health inequalities is an engaged citizenry that will place these issues on the public policy agenda. Without this, governing authorities can easily let the tackling of health inequalities give way to other issues that may arise. What are the specific issues that need to be highlighted?

The broad public policy directions required in Canada and the US will expand the welfare state to embrace a broader range of universal social and health programs. This will ensure that all citizens have access to the social determinants of health, including education, unemployment insurance, employment opportunities, and housing security, among others. In the US, similar to Canada, this requires "a commitment to act upon general guidelines" (Bezruchka, this volume). Specifically, Bezruchka recommends: "The overarching aim would be to decrease economic inequality throughout the nation and to use the proceeds from that effort to foster a healthy early life environment for families. An important first step would be putting in place generous supports for antenatal and parental paid leave and community support for families and children, including those *in utero* and young infants." In terms of broad public policy directions, these should include challenging political, social, economic, and education underpinnings of health inequalities.

The national government in Australia must expand its commitment to Aboriginal health to other populations experiencing disadvantage. Baum et al. (this volume) note that Australia has a well-developed welfare state, but health inequities persist. In particular, Baum et al. argue that: "Concerted policy action is required to use progressive taxation and other revenue raising methods to ensure funding for redistributive policies. Political leadership will be required to create the political will to institute a systematic approach to reducing inequities."

The UK has a well-established tradition of research on health inequalities. Moreover, the UK was the first country in Europe to try to reduce health inequalities (Smith & Bambra, this volume). Smith and Bambra call for research collaboration between academics and policymakers to "co-produce research" on health inequalities. They also call for enhanced public health advocacy and work with communities. Similar to Canada and the United States, UK citizens must be made aware of "the actors and forces influencing policies in ways which are likely to be counter-productive for health inequalities" (Navarro, 2009).

The three Scandinavian countries are further along in addressing health inequalities compared to the other countries examined. Finland has a well-developed welfare state, but these programs can be strengthened. Mikkonen recommends greater focus on "the implementation and monitoring of Finnish policy measures and programs" to reduce health inequalities (Mikkonen, this volume). Specifically, Mikkonen calls for a permanent structure sufficiently resourced to monitor health inequalities in Finland. This would include enhancing the health impact assessments of different policy initiatives. Mikkonen adds there is a "need to look at the impacts of these policies on the lowest socio-economic groups and readiness to formulate alternative policy recommendations if required."

In Norway, the emphasis on upstream public policies to reduce health inequalities by focusing on social determinants is relatively new (Fosse, this volume). The new Norwegian Public Health Act has yet to be assessed for its impact on health inequalities. Nonetheless, that country is well on its way to tackling health inequalities. Income redistribution appears to be central to this policy initiative and should go some distance in addressing social and health inequalities. As Fosse notes, the emphasis on upstream policy approaches is radical and one not generally pursued in Canada or the US. Norway's experience illustrates the importance of social democratic principles in bringing about action to reduce health inequalities.

Finally, Sweden has had a long history of concern with reducing health inequalities. Backhans and Burström assert that: "Health equity should be a goal that most Swedish politicians across the left-right spectrum can endorse, particularly in a country with such a strong egalitarian legacy. There is nothing that leads us to believe that the political majority will change anytime soon. Therefore, new strategies are clearly needed by public health advocates to bring politicians on board" (Backhans & Burström, this volume).

What You Can Do

Figure 10.1 provides a model that, while developed to explain the incidence of poverty in wealthy developed nations, can easily be applied to the tackling of health inequalities (Brady, 2009). In it the outcome "Poverty" is replaced with "Tackling health inequalities." The components of the model are (1) ideologies and interests, (2) welfare generosity, (3) leftist politics, and (4) latent coalitions.

Ideologies and Interests

This is similar to the issue of characteristics of the state and its receptivity to problems associated with tackling health inequalities. As noted, willingness to tackle health inequalities is closely related to the form of welfare regime and the economic and political forces that shape existing ideologies and interests. It is important to recognize the dominant and conflicting ideologies and interests in a society and how these determine whether or not health inequalities will be tackled through public policy action.

Welfare Generosity

There are profound differences in the extent to which each nation's welfare state provides supports to its citizens. In Canada and the US, these supports are minimal. In Finland, Norway,

Figure 10.1
Components of Brady's Institutionalized Power Relations Theory
Applied to the Tackling of Health Inequalities

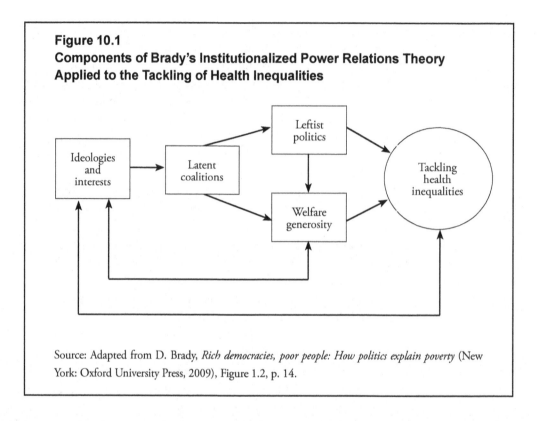

Source: Adapted from D. Brady, *Rich democracies, poor people: How politics explain poverty* (New York: Oxford University Press, 2009), Figure 1.2, p. 14.

and Sweden, they are rather more extensive. Britain and Northern Ireland and Australia provide mid-level portraits. Consistent with the analyses provided in this volume, social welfare expenditures, social security transfers, extent of decommodification of necessary supports and benefits, government expenditures, and public health spending are all related to the tackling of health inequalities. Greater spending and transfers, and greater decommodification are associated with greater public policy activity. Welfare generosity is a key issue that needs to be raised and confronted when resistance to increasing it is encountered.

Leftist Politics

The analysis provided in this volume indicates that the generosity of the welfare state and the tackling of health inequalities are strongly related to the strength of institutionalized leftist political influence; that is, the ability of parties of the left—such as the Social Democrats in Europe, Labour in Australia and the United Kingdom, and the New Democrats in Canada—to gain and hold political power. It also refers to the ability of these left political parties to influence governing parties to implement public policies under the threat of electoral defeat. The tackling of health inequalities is a profoundly political issue and this reality must not be ignored.

Latent Coalitions

Latent coalitions refer to groups of citizens who may come together under differing circumstances to support a more generous welfare state. These would include groups and citizens concerned with the social determinants of health, such as housing, early life, income and income distribution, employment and working conditions, social exclusion, food insecurity, and unemployment and job security, among others. The absence of such a vibrant sector will make the tackling of health inequalities difficult.

Implications

The implications of this analysis for what you can do to promote the tackling of health inequalities seem clear (Raphael, 2011):

Welfare generosity:	→Advocate for more generous supports and benefits
Strengthen left political actors:	→Join/support social democratic parties of the left
Build latent coalitions:	→Join/support an advocacy group
Ideologies and interests:	→Recognize barriers and build support for action

Further examples of what you can do to help move governmental authorities toward tackling health inequalities are available (Bryant, 2009, 2010; Raphael, 2009, 2010).

Conclusion

Public education on the importance of tackling health inequalities is essential. The general public must be made aware of the extent of health inequalities and the means by which they can be tackled. Those working in the health field need to understand how the policy change process brings about social and political change and how they can contribute to educating and mobilizing citizens about health inequalities.

The tackling of health inequalities is strongly influenced by the political ideology of the government of the day. Public spending on health and social programs is a key indicator of government commitment to achieving health equity. A key characteristic of the presence of this commitment is the influence of social democratic principles. All countries, except the US, have an active social democratic party, and most, except Canada, have elected social democratic governments at the national level. This makes a huge difference in whether health inequalities appear on the public policy agenda, and whether the political will exists to take action to reduce health inequalities.

The Scandinavian countries demonstrate that this tends to be the case. The UK has a strong research tradition on health inequalities. Moreover, the Labour government of Tony Blair initiated significant policy action from 1997 to 2009. These activities are now threatened by the election of the Conservative-Liberal Democratic Coalition in 2010. Canada and the US have a number of profound barriers to putting the tackling of health inequalities on the public policy agenda.

By analyzing some of these barriers and providing means of making sense of the differences presented among nations, this volume has attempted to identify the means by which the tackling of health inequalities can be placed on the agenda of those nations where it is being neglected, and strengthened and extended where it is already an issue of governmental concern. This is an ongoing project that requires ongoing citizen engagement in the day-to-day politics of public policy-making. As Frank Fischer (2003) states in his analysis of the future of participatory policy-making:

> The case for democracy derives from its basic normative rationale from the principle that government decisions should reflect the consent of the governed. Citizens in a democracy have the right—even obligation—to participate meaningfully in public decision-making and to be informed about the bases of government policies. (p. 205)

Critical Thinking Questions

1. What do you think are the critical determinants of how a nation goes about tackling health inequalities through public policy activities?
2. Which of the three broad policy change models presented in this chapter best explain how the nations in this inquiry are tackling health inequalities?
3. What would each model suggest as to the reasons why a nation is either tackling or not tackling health inequalities? What would each suggest be done to move this agenda forward?
4. What are some of the things you could do to have your nation's governing authorities tackle health inequalities?

Recommended Readings

Bambra, C., Fox, D., & Scott-Samuel, A. (2003). *Towards a new politics of health.* Liverpool: Politics of Health Group. Retrieved from: http://www.pohg.org.uk/support/downloads/pohg-paper1.pdf.
This volume recognizes that "In a period when the importance of politics and public policy as determinants of health is routinely acknowledged at the highest political levels ... there remains a continuing absence of serious debate about the ways in which political power, relations and ideology influence people's health." This report provides a detailed overview of how politics and public policy shape health.

Bryant, T. (2009). *An introduction to health policy.* Toronto: Canadian Scholars' Press Inc.
With a strong comparative and international element, this volume analyzes the process, implementation, and outcomes of health policy in Canada and elsewhere. It has entire chapters devoted to theories of public policy change and influences upon public policy-making.

Bryant, T., Raphael, D., & Rioux, M. (Eds.). (2010). *Staying alive: Critical perspectives on health, illness, and health care* (2nd ed.). Toronto: Canadian Scholars' Press Inc.
Staying Alive provides various perspectives on the issues regarding health, health care, and illness. In addition to the traditional approaches of health sciences and the sociology of health, this book shows the impact that human rights issues and political economy have on health. This volume takes up these issues as they occur in Canada and the United States within a wider international context.

Signal, L. (1998). The politics of health promotion: Insights from political theory. *Health Promotion International, 13*(3), 257–263.
This article examines three theories of pluralism, the new institutionalism, and political economy and their contributions to understanding and explaining health promotion.

Recommended Websites

European Community Health Policy: tinyurl.com/2s83r9
    The European Community addresses a full scope of health policy, including living conditions and health care. The website identifies health policy priorities for the European Union and links to health policy resources.

International Health Impact Assessment Consortium: http://www.liv.ac.uk/ihia
    Based at the University of Liverpool in the United Kingdom, this excellent website provides a wide range of information and resources on the impact of policies and programs on the health of a population. It provides access to articles, research, and case studies on health policy issues.

Politics of Health Group: www.pohg.org.uk
    The Politics of Health website is based at the University of Liverpool in the United Kingdom. The Politics of Health Group (PoHG) consists of people who believe that power exercised through politics and its impact on public policy are of critical importance for health. PoHG is a UK-based group, but has a clear international perspective and members throughout the world.

Public Policy at the Robert Gordon University: www2.rgu.ac.uk/publicpolicy
    This introduction to social policy examines social welfare and its relationship to politics and society. It focuses on the social services and the welfare state.

References

Acheson, D. (1998). *Independent inquiry into inequalities in health*. Retrieved from: http://www.official-documents.co.uk/document/doh/ih/contents.htm.

Armstrong, P. (2004). Health, social policy, social economies, and the voluntary sector. In D. Raphael (Ed.), *Social determinants of health: Canadian perspectives* (pp. 331–344). Toronto: Canadian Scholars' Press Inc.

Armstrong, P., Armstrong, H., & Coburn, D. (Eds.). (2001). *Unhealthy times: The political economy of health and care in Canada*. Toronto: Oxford University Press.

Baumgartner, F.R., & Jones, B.D. (1993). *Agendas and instability in American politics*. Chicago: University of Chicago Press.

Berthiaume, L. (2012). *UN rights panel disparages Canada*. Retrieved from: http://www.montrealgazette.com/news/rights+panel+disparages+Canada/6195280/story.html.

Bourjolly, J.N., Hirschman, K.B., & Zieber, N.A. (2004). The impact of managed health care in the United States on women with breast cancer and the providers who treat them. *Cancer Nursing, 27*(1), 45–54.

Brady, D. (2009). *Rich democracies, poor people: How politics explain poverty*. New York: Oxford University Press.

Brodie, J. (2005). Power and politics. In J. Brodie & S. Rein (Eds.), *Critical concepts: An introduction to politics* (3rd ed., pp. 2–20). Toronto: Pearson Prentice-Hall.

Brooks, S., & Miljan, L. (2003). Theories of public policy. In S. Brooks & L. Miljan (Eds.), *Public policy in Canada: An introduction* (pp. 22–49). Toronto: Oxford University Press.

Bryant, T. (2005). Towards a new paradigm for research on urban women's health. *Women's Health and Urban Life, 4*(2), 68–95.

Bryant, T. (2009). *An introduction to health policy*. Toronto: Canadian Scholars' Press Inc.

Bryant, T. (2010). Promoting health equity through political action. *Social Alternatives, 29*(2), 57–63.

Bryant, T., Raphael, D., Schrecker, T., & Labonte, R. (2011). Canada: A land of missed opportunities for addressing the social determinants of health. *Health Policy, 101*(1), 44–58.

Coburn, D. (2000). Income inequality, social cohesion, and the health status of populations: The role of neo-liberalism. *Social Science & Medicine, 51*(1), 135–146.

Coburn, D. (2001). Health, health care, and neo-liberalism. In P. Armstrong, H. Armstrong & D. Coburn (Eds.), *Unhealthy times: The political economy of health and care in Canada* (pp. 45–65). Toronto: Oxford University Press.

Coburn, D. (2004). Beyond the income inequality hypothesis: Globalization, neo-liberalism, and health inequalities. *Social Science & Medicine, 58,* 41–56.

Coburn, D. (2010). Health and health care: A political economy perspective. In T. Bryant, D. Raphael & M. Rioux (Eds.), *Staying alive: Critical perspectives on health, illness, and health care* (2nd ed., pp. 41–63). Toronto: Canadian Scholars' Press Inc.

Equity Action. (2012). *European portal for action on health inequalities.* Retrieved from: http://www.health-inequalities.eu/HEALTHEQUITY/EN/home/.

Fischer, F. (2003). *Reframing public policy: Discursive politics and deliberative practices.* New York: Oxford University Press.

Grabb, E. (2007). *Theories of social inequality* (5th ed.). Toronto: Harcourt Canada.

Hall, P. (1993). Policy paradigms, social learning, and the state: The case of economic policymaking in Britain. *Comparative Politics, 25,* 275–296.

Hall, P.A., & Taylor, R.C.R. (1996). Political science and the three institutionalisms. *Political Studies, 44,* 936–957.

Health Council of Canada. (2010). *Stepping it up: Moving the focus from health care in Canada to a healthier Canada.* Toronto: Health Council of Canada.

Hills, J., Sefton, T., & Stewart, K. (Eds.). (2009). *Towards a more equal society? Poverty, inequality, and policy since 1997.* Bristol: Policy Press.

Hills, J., & Stewart, K. (Eds.). (2005). *A more equal society? New Labour, poverty, inequality, and exclusion.* Bristol: Policy Press.

Howlett, M., Ramesh, M., & Perl, A. (2009). *Studying public policy: Policy cycles and policy subsystems* (3rd ed.). Toronto: Oxford University Press.

Langille, D. (2009). Follow the money: How business and politics shape our health. In D. Raphael (Ed.), *Social determinants of health: Canadian perspectives* (2nd ed., pp. 305–317). Toronto: Canadian Scholars' Press Inc.

Leys, C. (2001). *Market-driven politics.* London: Verso.

McLennan, G. (1989). *Marxism, pluralism, and beyond: Classic debates and new departures.* Cambridge: Polity Press.

Navarro, V. (2009). What we mean by social determinants of health. *Global Health Promotion, 16*(1), 5–16.

Navarro, V., & Shi, L. (2002). The political context of social inequalities and health. In V. Navarro (Ed.), *The political economy of social inequalities: Consequences for health and quality of life* (pp. 403–418). Amityville: Baywood.

Organisation for Economic Co-operation and Development. (2011). *Society at a glance 2011, OECD social indicators.* Paris: Organisation for Economic Co-operation and Development.

Raphael, D. (2008). Grasping at straws: A recent history of health promotion in Canada. *Critical Public Health, 18*(4), 483–495.

Raphael, D. (Ed.). (2009). *Social determinants of health: Canadian perspectives* (2nd ed.). Toronto: Canadian Scholars' Press Inc.

Raphael, D. (2010). *About Canada: Health and illness.* Winnipeg: Fernwood Publishing.

Raphael, D. (2011). *Poverty in Canada: Implications for health and quality of life* (2nd ed.). Toronto: Canadian Scholars' Press Inc.

Saint-Arnaud, S., & Bernard, P. (2003). Convergence or resilience? A hierarchical cluster analysis of the welfare regimes in advanced countries. *Current Sociology, 51*(5), 499–527.

Teeple, G. (2000). *Globalization and the decline of social reform: Into the twenty-first century.* Aurora: Garamond Press.

Teeple, G., & McBride, S. (Eds.). (2010). *Relations of global power: Neoliberal order and disorder*. Toronto: University of Toronto Press.

Whitehead, M. (1998). Diffusion of ideas on social inequalities in health: A European perspective. *Millbank Quarterly, 76*(3), 469–492.

World Health Organization. (2008). *Closing the gap in a generation: Health equity through action on the social determinants of health*. Geneva: World Health Organization.

World Health Organization. (2009). *Milestones in health promotion: Statements from global conferences*. Geneva: World Health Organization.

Appendix A

A Checklist for Whole-of-Government or Intersectoral Approach

This checklist synthesizes key information from Canadian and international reports and documents about implementing intersectoral and whole-of-government approaches; our consultants' experience in working with Canadian governments, agencies, and organizations; and the information we gathered from our interviews with officials across Canada.

Values and Commitment

- An overriding philosophy that health initiatives will be viewed through a population health lens
- Leadership at the top from the prime minister, premiers, ministers, Cabinet secretaries, and others
- Recognition and awareness among elected representatives of the importance of the determinants of health for promoting population health and reducing health inequities
- Recognition that it may take years, even decades, for benefits to materialize
- Willingness to name the difficult problems and barriers that exist, and to provide the resources necessary to transcend them
- Commitment of civil servants to undertake a broader approach to addressing population health and reducing health inequities
- Willingness and commitment to ensure a structural approach to placing health projects on the public policy agenda
- Allocation of significant funding that allows for governmental commissioning of research, analysis, and policy implementation

Information and Data

- Decisions should be made and actions taken based on available evidence without necessarily waiting for conclusive evidence
- Information and evidence on the state of population health and the presence of health inequities is presented in a government-instigated integrative report or statement
- Development of clear, identifiable, and measurable goals and targets

- Focusing on explicit concrete objectives and visible results; ensuring transparency in governmental efforts and activities
- Messaging to the public, including media support, about the importance of dealing with population health and reducing health inequities through action on the determinants of health
- Development of practical models, tools, and mechanisms, such as health impact assessments, to support the implementation
- Setting of realistic timelines
- Support for academic and agency researchers who provide data and evaluation
- Provision of ongoing public reports that document successes and challenges

Governmental Infrastructure

- Governments must establish the means for society's participation in the initiatives
- Establishment of an independent authority within government that will be responsible for coordinating activity across ministries and departments
- Cross-ministry structures and processes that provide a basis for these kinds of whole-of-government or intersectoral approaches
- Contacting and drawing support from various external organizations that would be responsive to governmental action on the determinants of health
- Government civil servants' capacity to carry out the task
- Ensuring that leadership, accountability, and rewards are shared among partners
- Provision of adequate resources to sustain activities beyond the tenure of the present governing authority
- Establishment of a balance between central direction and discretion of local authorities to implement goals and objectives
- Establishment of accountability and evaluation frameworks
- Building of stable teams of people who work well together, with appropriate support systems

Source: Health Council of Canada. (2010). *Stepping it up: Moving the focus from health care in Canada to a healthier Canada*. Toronto: Health Council of Canada, 25.

Glossary of Terms

Active labour policy refers to policies and programs developed by governments to create or maintain jobs. These range from sheltered workshops and other job creation measures for workers with disabilities to employment in regular public service and public works projects (i.e., building and highway construction). It also covers subsidies to private business to hire new employees or to extend seasonal work throughout the year, apprenticeship training, on-the-job training and retraining, work-study programs to ease transition from school to employment, and job transition training for workers facing layoffs.

Critical realist perspective explains a phenomenon by analyzing what are called the real, actual, and empirical levels of reality. The *real* involves an explication of the societal structures and powers that have the capacity to create a phenomenon. The *actual* refers to how these societal structures and powers are activated and operate within a specific society. The *empirical* is what can be seen or observed in terms of the activation of the *real* and the *actual.*

Decommodification, in terms of welfare-state issues, refers to the degree to which individuals can live a reasonable life without relying on market wages. Can older people, people with disabilities, or the unemployed (those not earning a market wage) live a reasonable life? Also, to what extent are benefits and services provided on a universal basis to all? Social democratic states have the greatest degree of decommodification and the best health profiles. Canada and other liberal nations have the least degree of decommodification and the worst health profiles.

Disability policy has the goal of ensuring that people with disabilities "are not excluded from society: that they are encouraged and empowered to participate as fully as possible in economic and social life, and in particular to engage in gainful employment, and that they are not ousted from the labour market too easily and too early." Another goal is to "ensure that those who are disabled or who become disabled have income security: that they are not denied the means to live decently because of disabilities which restrict their earning potential" (Organisation for Economic Co-operation and Development, 2003, 3).

Discourse is the manner in which a society chooses to make sense of a phenomenon such as inequality or poverty. The notion of discourse, however, also includes the idea that some frameworks of understanding are more easily acceptable at a given point in history because of how they fit with the dominant politics and economic processes of a society.

Family policy refers to policies and programs designed to provide a secure growing environment for children and to ensure that parents have the material and psychological supports for rearing children. Through these policies, usually involving various forms of financial support and a system of child care, society compensates citizens for some of the costs borne by families with children.

Federalism is a political system in which legislative power is divided between a central government and a number of state or provincial governments. In federations, the powers of the central government to direct policy-making are weaker than is the case in a nation with a centralized government. Canada, Australia, and the US are federations.

Health is usually defined as the absence of disease. When used in this manner, it is best described as health status. The World Health Organization (WHO) has a broader definition: the ability to have and reach goals, meet personal needs, and cope with everyday life. The WHO argues that health requires the following prerequisites: peace, shelter, education, food, income, a sound environment, and social justice. These definitions are primarily focused on the individual, while quality of life is usually focused on the larger community and society.

Health disparity is a purely descriptive term that refers to differences in health among individuals and groups. It is usually used by those who wish to avoid any implication that these differences should be a cause for concern.

Health equity is grounded in the ethical principle of distributive justice and consonant with human rights principles. Equity in health can be defined as the absence of disparities in health (and in its key social determinants) that are systematically associated with social advantage or disadvantage. Health inequities systematically put populations who are already socially disadvantaged by virtue of being poor, female, or members of a disenfranchised racial, ethnic, or religious group at further disadvantage with respect to their health (Braveman & Gruskin, 2003).

Health inequality designates differences and variations in health and risk factors among individuals and groups. It implies that there is cause to be concerned about these differences.

Health inequity takes the concept of health inequalities and adds the moral dimension that these inequalities are avoidable and are therefore unjust and unfair.

Human rights perspective is an approach that ensures the equal dignity and equal effective enjoyment of all human rights by all people. All people have the right to participate and to exercise self-determination as equals in society (adapted from *A Human Rights Approach to Disability*, retrieved from: http://www.yorku.ca/drpi/hRights.html).

Income and wealth inequality refers to the extent to which economic resources are distributed unequally among members of a society. Regarding income, in a perfectly equal society, each 10 percent of the population would receive 10 percent of overall income, and the bottom 10 percent would also receive 10 percent of overall income. Instead, what is more common is that the top 10 percent of the population gains much more than 10 percent of income, and the bottom 10 percent of the population gains much less than 10 percent of income. The same issue applies to wealth. In nations such as Canada, the top 10 percent possesses much more than 10 percent of the wealth, and the bottom 10 percent of the population much less than 10 percent. Income and wealth inequality are important as they are strongly associated with the incidence and depth of poverty within a nation. There are profound differences among nations in degrees of inequality and these differences result from public policies developed and implemented by governments.

Infant mortality rate refers to the incidence of newborns dying during their first year of life. It is frequently seen as providing the single best indicator of overall population health.

Labour policy refers to policies concerned with relations between employers and employees and those concerned with the employment, training, and distribution of workers. This would include policies related to unionization, collective agreement coverage, and provisions for employment security and benefits provision.

Left political parties are political parties that support the redistribution of wealth by way of income support and publicly funded programs for individuals with disabilities, and families and individuals with low income. Strongly aligned with the labour movement, they also advocate for policies to support workers and other policy initiatives that reduce social and health inequalities in a population. The New Democrats in Canada; the Social Democrats in Sweden, Norway, and Finland; and the Labour Party in Australia and the UK are considered left parties. The US does not have a politically relevant left party.

Liberal welfare state is a nation that relies upon the market to distribute goods and resources within the population (Saint-Arnaud & Bernard, 2003). Labour unions are weak, and only a minority of workers are covered by collective employment agreements. Associated with this is rather modest spending on social programs and reliance upon means-tested assistance rather than the provision of universal benefits for all. Means testing refers to benefits being primarily geared to low-income groups.

Life expectancy is the number of years that a person can expect to live upon being born. It is usually seen as one of the best indicators of the overall health of a population.

Low-paid worker is defined in various ways. In Canada, a person can be considered a low-paid worker if he or she earns less than $10 an hour. Internationally, a low-paid or low-wage worker is a full-time worker who earns less than 66 percent of the average median wage.

Morbidity refers to the incidence and prevalence of a disease or illness. It is an epidemiological term that simply refers to the amount of sickness in a society.

Mortality refers to death from a disease or illness. Mortality rates are usually given as a percentage of proportion of a population during a given time period. These rates can be adjusted for the age of the population to allow for comparisons between groups.

Neo-liberalism refers to the dominance of markets and the market model. It has the following tenets: (1) markets are the best and most efficient allocators of resources in production and distribution; (2) societies are composed of autonomous individuals (producers and consumers) motivated chiefly or entirely by material or economic considerations; and (3) competition is the major market vehicle for innovations. The essence of neo-liberalism, in its pure form, is a more or less thoroughgoing adherence, in rhetoric if not in practice, to the virtues of a market economy and, by extension, a market-oriented society (Coburn, 2000).

Policy change refers to a jurisdiction shifting its approach toward addressing a particular issue. There is simple or normal policy change by which a shift is gradual, as well as a paradigm change, which involves a completely new way of approaching an issue.

Political economy perspective is explicitly concerned with the political and economic structures that shape the distribution of power and resources within the population. It is also specifically focused on understanding how the creation and distribution of resources influence the health and quality of life of individuals and communities. This perspective has a strong commitment to identifying how political and economic structures can be changed to promote health and well-being.

Politics refers to how decisions about the organization of society and how it distributes resources are made. Politics is about power and influence, attitudes and values, and the means of shaping society. While politics is usually thought of in terms of what happens during electoral campaigns, politics is a constant ongoing exercise in influencing policy-makers to act in certain ways. Politics in liberal capitalist societies such as Canada are heavily influenced by wealthy economic interests.

Poverty is the condition whereby individuals, families, and groups lack the resources to obtain the type of diet, participate in the activities, and have the living conditions and amenities that are customary, or at least widely encouraged or approved of, in the society to which they belong. Poverty can be considered in terms of absolute poverty, whereby individuals and families do not have enough resources to keep "body and soul together," or relative poverty, whereby they do not have the ability to participate in common activities of daily living (Gordon & Townsend, 2000).

Proportional representation refers to a variety of systems used for electing a legislature in which the number of seats a party wins is more or less proportional to the percentage of popular votes cast. This is in contrast to the first-past-the-post approach in which the party candidate with the most votes in each constituency wins the seat. Proportional representation is the norm in most European nations. It is seen as contributing to the influence of left parties on progressive legislation in many modern welfare states.

Public policy is a course of action or inaction chosen by public authorities to address a given problem or interrelated set of problems. Policy is a course of action that is anchored in a set of values regarding appropriate public goals and a set of beliefs about the best way of achieving those goals. The idea of public policy assumes that an issue is no longer a private affair (Wolf, 2005).

Social democracy is a political ideology that favours stronger labour laws and a strong welfare state. In the modern era, social democrats attempt to reform capitalism to make it more equitable through the creation and maintenance of a strong welfare state. The best examples of where social democratic parties have held power and developed public policies is in Sweden, Norway, Denmark, and Finland. The Labour Party in the UK and Australia and the NDP in Canada are social democratic parties.

Social democratic welfare state emphasizes the role of the state in securing citizens' rights. Emphasis is on reducing inequality. Labour unions are strong, and a large majority of workers are covered by collective employment agreements. These nations have strong universal entitlement programs and strive to achieve full employment. Income and wealth inequalities are minimized by strong redistributive programs that involve progressive income taxes and generous health, social, and other benefits. Employment security and training are well resourced. Families are supported by state benefits when difficulties arise. Strong supports, such as parental benefits and leave, child care, and equity-oriented labour and employment policies, are provided for women.

Social determinants of health are the economic and social conditions that influence the health of individuals, communities, and jurisdictions. Social determinants of health determine whether individuals stay healthy or become ill and the extent to which a person or community possesses the physical, social, and personal resources to identify and achieve personal aspirations, satisfy needs, and cope with the environment. Social determinants of health include conditions of childhood, availability and quality of income, food, housing, employment, and health and social services (Raphael 2009).

Social gradient refers to the finding that socio-economic position is related to health right across the entire spectrum from poor to wealthy. The higher one's position, the better one's health.

Social inequality can refer to any of the differences among people (or the socially defined positions they occupy) that are consequential for the lives they lead, most particularly for the rights or opportunities they exercise and the rewards or privileges they enjoy (Grabb, 2007).

Tax policy is simply a program for setting the level and form of taxes. It is an important means of funding governmental programs as well as redistributing income and wealth from the rich to others.

Union is an organization of wage earners or salaried employees who have come together for mutual support and protection and for dealing collectively with employers over issues of wages, benefits, and employment protection.

Welfare regimes refer to the various ways in which different nations or societies provide for the well-being of their citizens or compensate for the failures of markets to do so. Social democratic welfare regimes tend to provide more resources and on a more universalistic basis than do liberal welfare regimes, which tend to target welfare measures to the poor and to provide less benefits to the fewer who are eligible for them. The conservative regimes provide benefits as an entitlement of working or expect the family to provide support. The Latin regimes are undeveloped versions of the Conservative welfare regimes.

Welfare state is a nation in which organized power is used to modify the play of market forces in at least three directions: first, by guaranteeing individuals and families a minimum income irrespective of the market value of their work or property; second, by narrowing the extent of insecurity by enabling individuals and families to meet certain social contingencies (e.g., sickness, old age, and unemployment) that otherwise lead to individual and family crises; and third, by ensuring that all citizens, regardless of status or class, are offered the best standards available in relation to a certain agreed range of social services (Briggs, 1961).

References

Briggs, A. (1961). The welfare state in historical perspective. *European Journal of Sociology, 2,* 251–259.

Braveman, P., & Gruskin, S. (2003). Defining equity in health. *Journal of Epidemiology and Community Health, 57,* 254–258.

Coburn, D. (2000). Income inequality, social cohesion and the health status of populations: The role of neo-liberalism. *Social Science & Medicine, 51*(1), 135–146.

Gordon, D., & Townsend, P. (Eds.). (2000). *Breadline Europe: The measurement of poverty.* Bristol, UK: The Policy Press.

Grabb, E. (2007). *Theories of social inequality* (5th ed.). Toronto: Harcourt Canada.

Organisation for Economic Co-operation and Development. (2003). *Transforming disability into abil-ity: Policies to promote work and income security for people with disabilities.* Paris: Organisation for Economic Co-operation and Development.

Raphael, D. (Ed.). (2009). *Social determinants of health: Canadian perspectives* (2nd ed.). Toronto: Canadian Scholars' Press Inc.

Saint-Arnaud, S., & Bernard, P. (2003). Convergence or resilience? A hierarchical cluster analysis of the welfare regimes in advanced countries. *Current Sociology, 51*(5), 499–527.

Wolf, R. (2005). *What is public policy?* Retrieved from: http://www.ginsler.com/html/toolbox.htp.

Contributor Biographies

Mona C. Backhans has a PhD in social medicine and a Master's degree in sociology, and is employed at the Department of Public Health Sciences, Karolinska Institutet, Stockholm. Her research has a special focus on gender equality and the health effects of social policy. She has also contributed to international comparisons regarding public health policy and work environments as a determinant of health inequalities.

Clare Bambra is a professor of public health policy, Durham University, and acting director of the Wolfson Research Institute for Health and Wellbeing. She holds Bachelor's and Master's degrees in political science, and a PhD in politics and policy from the University of Manchester. Her principal research interest is the role of work and worklessness as social determinants of health and health inequalities. She has published over 100 research papers, reports, and book chapters in these areas, as well as a sole-authored book, *Work, Worklessness, and the Political Economy of Health* (Oxford University Press, 2011).

Fran Baum is professor of public health and director of the Southgate Institute of Health, Society, and Equity, and the South Australian Community Health Research Unit at Flinders University. She is co-chair of the Global Steering Council of the People's Health Movement. Professor Baum is a fellow of the Academy of the Social Sciences in Australia, and one of Australia's leading researchers on the social and economic determinants of health. In 2008 she was awarded a prestigious Australian Research Council Federation Fellowship focusing on development of effective government and community responses to social determinants of health inequity and social exclusion. She holds several other national competitive grants investigating aspects of health inequity, and has an extensive teaching career in public health. Her textbook, *The New Public Health* (3rd ed., Oxford University Press, 2008) is widely used as a core public health text.

Stephen Bezruchka is senior lecturer in the Departments of Health Services and Global Health at the School of Public Health, University of Washington, where he received the 2002 Outstanding Teacher Award and the 2008 Faculty Community Service Award. He is from Toronto, where he studied mathematics and physics at the University of Toronto, followed by graduate study at Harvard in mathematics before studying medicine at Stanford. He worked clinically as a doctor for 35 years, including three decades as an emergency physician. He spent over 11 years in Nepal, writing the first trekking guide to that country

(8th ed., 2011), running a community health project a week's walk from the road, training Nepali doctors in a remote district hospital, and advancing concepts of population health. His focus is on creating greater public understanding of the determinants of health through teaching, lecturing, and writing at various levels from middle school onward.

Toba Bryant is an assistant professor of health sciences at the University of Ontario Institute of Technology. She is the author of *An Introduction to Health Policy* and co-editor of *Staying Alive: Critical Perspectives on Health, Illness, and Health Care* (2nd ed.), both published by Canadian Scholars' Press. She has published numerous book chapters and articles on public policy change, housing and health policy, and women's health and quality of life. Dr. Bryant has served as a consultant to Health Canada and the Wellesley Central Health Corporation on urban health issues.

Bo Burström is a professor of social medicine at the Department of Public Health Sciences, Karolinska Institutet, Stockholm, where he has worked for the last 15 years on studies on inequalities in health and health care and on comparative studies on the impact of health and social policies on the health of disadvantaged groups in different countries. He has both an MD and PhD degree.

Matt Fisher is a research officer at the Southgate Institute for Health, Society, and Equity in the School of Medicine at Flinders University in Adelaide. His main research interests are in social determinants of chronic stress and mental illness, health and social policy, and political philosophy. Matt completed a PhD in political philosophy at Adelaide University in 2010. He is currently researching ways in which Australian mental health policy does or does not take account of evidence on social determinants of mental health. Previously, he has worked as a policy and research officer in the non-government community housing sector. He has a long-standing commitment to values of social and environmental sustainability, and has strong interests in the development of urban communities and environments to be both health promoting and environmentally sustainable.

Elisabeth Fosse is professor of health promotion at the Department of Health Promotion and Development, University of Bergen, Norway. She is a political scientist and her area of specialization is in the formation and implementation of health promotion policies in European countries. Over the last few years, she has focused on European policies to reduce social inequalities in health. From 2009 through 2012 she has participated in the EU-funded project, GRADIENT (Applying Public Health Policies to Effectively Reduce Health Inequalities among Families and Children). She has been leading a project studying policies in four European countries representing different welfare state regimes.

Angela Lawless is deputy director of the South Australian Community Health Research Unit (SACHRU) at Flinders University. SACHRU undertakes research, evaluation, and training in the primary health care and community services sector. Angela has extensive experience in evaluation of community and primary health care projects and services and in workforce capacity building. She has a long-standing research interest in health equity and models of health care. Her current research includes use of program logic frameworks to evaluate the effectiveness of comprehensive primary health care services, and health in all policies as a means to embed health and equity considerations into policies and programs across government.

Juha Mikkonen has 10 years of professional experience in the public policy arena and has worked with numerous non-governmental organizations in Europe. Currently he is a Vanier Canada Graduate Scholar (2012) specializing in health policy and equity in his PhD studies at York University in Canada. Previously he studied social sciences at the University of Helsinki (M.Soc.Sci 2011; B.Soc.Sci 2009). Mikkonen was one of the organizers of an inspirational writing contest which collected 850 autobiographical writings from people living in low-income situations in Finland. He is the editor of the books *Arkipäivän kokemuksia köyhyydestä*, 2007 [Everyday Experiences of Poverty] and *Rikas runo*, 2009 [Rich/Wealthy Poems; an anthology of poems about poverty]. As a visiting scholar at York University, Mikkonen co-authored the report *Social Determinants of Health: The Canadian Facts* (2010) with Dennis Raphael.

Dennis Raphael is a professor of health policy and management at York University in Toronto. His research focuses on the health effects of social inequality and poverty, the quality of life of communities and individuals, and the impact of government decisions on Canadians' health and well-being. He is editor of *Social Determinants of Health: Canadian Perspectives* (2nd ed.), co-editor of *Staying Alive: Critical Perspectives on Health, Illness, and Health Care* (2nd ed.), and author of *Poverty in Canada: Implications for Health and Quality of Life* and *About Canada: Health and Illness.* He was co-author (with Juha Mikkonen) of *Social Determinants of Health: The Canadian Facts*, which was prepared as a primer for the Canadian public and has been downloaded 75,000 times from http://thecanadianfacts.org.

Katherine E. Smith is a tenured lecturer in the Global Public Health Unit at the University of Edinburgh, Scotland. Her PhD, awarded in 2008, explored the relationship between health inequalities research and policy in Scotland and England. She is currently building on this research to explore the relationship across the whole of the UK and writing a book summarizing the findings. Her other research interests include corporate influences on public policies impacting on health, the role of think tanks in public health research and policy, and theories of policy change and lobbying in the European Union.

Copyright Acknowledgements

Figure 2.8: V. Shkolnikov, E. Andreev et al., "Trajectories of Life Expectancy at Birth (e0) and Dispersion in Age of Death (e†) (Inter-individual Differences in Age of Death or Average Life Expectancy Losses Attributable to Death) for England and Wales, Japan, Sweden, and the United States," from *Demography* 48(1). © Springer, 2011. Reprinted with permission of the publisher.

Box 3.1: "VicHealth's Commitment to Action on Health Inequalities," from *VicHealth strategy and business plan 2009–2013*. © Victorian Health Promotion Foundation, 2009. Reprinted with permission of the publisher.

Figure 6.1: T. Valkonen, H. Ahonen et al., "Life Expectancy of Men and Women Aged 35 by Social Group in 1983–2005 (Three-Year Moving Averages)," from *Health Inequalities in Finland: Trends in Socioeconomic Health Differences 1980–2005*. © Finnish Ministry of Social Affairs and Health Publications, 2009. Reprinted with permission of the publisher.

Figure 9.2: M. Whitehead, "Placement of Nations' Governmental Authorities on the Action Spectrum on Inequalities in Health," from *Milbank Quarterly* 76(3). © Milbank Memorial Fund, 1998. Reprinted with permission of the publisher.

Appendix A: "A Checklist for Whole-of-Government or Intersectoral Work," from *Stepping it Up: Moving the Focus from Health Care in Canada to a Healthier Canada*. Toronto: Health Council of Canada, 2010. Reprinted by permission of the publisher.

Index